PRAISE FOR 'SCOUTS OUT!'

"I have never read a book that has taken me on a ride like this one did..."

SGT Brad Keller, U.S. Marine Corps

•

"Evermore poignant in these raw-post war days, Robicheaux's Scouts Out! *regales the journey of a modern soldier. From driven student pilot to contemplative veteran, we ride aloft as our eyes are opened to what was Afghanistan's ever present yet out-of-mind warzone..."*

Captain Ian Norris

•

"The battle accounts were both descriptive and gripping. The interactions with the locals and the descriptions of the scenery made it easy to imagine how difficult the situation became ... I highly recommend the book."

PO2 Michael Mooney, U.S. Navy Security Specialist

SCOUTS OUT!

CONTAINS **70** IMAGES & MAPS

*A **Kiowa Warrior** Pilot's Perspective of War in Afghanistan*

RYAN ROBICHEAUX

SCOUTSOUTBOOK.COM

Library of Congress Control Number: 2021919270
Preassigned Control Number (PCN): 9781737243809

For inquiries, bulk order discounts, or information about this and other works, please visit:
www.ScoutsOutBook.com
www.RotorheadPublishing.com

Published by Rotorhead Publishing, LLC in North Port, Florida, United States of America.
First Edition.

ISBN: 978-1-7372438-1-6 (hardcover)
ISBN: 978-1-7372438-0-9 (softcover)
ISBN: 978-1-7372438-2-3 (ebook)

Editor: Leigh Corbell / NeutralGroundCreative.com
Proofreader / Editor: Jackie Dawn / LiteraryJacks@gmail.com
Maps illustrations: Brooke Stefanelli / BrookeIllustrations.com
Cover design & interior formatting: Mark Thomas / Coverness.com

This work is dedicated to my grandmother,
Virginia Robicheaux.
Without her dying wish and my word to have it published,
this book would have never existed.

TABLE OF CONTENTS

STATEMENT OF INTENT AND PURPOSE

To understand exactly what this work is, and how it came about, a quick explanation is in order. I have adapted the bulk of what this book contains from hundreds of pages of journal entries that I had written and made available to select family and friends back home and in real time. I later transposed those entries from the present tense and dates in which I wrote them. The attempt was to weave the full and overall accounts into one large and all-encompassing story. This took me years, as I had to move from sentence to sentence, page by page, to change every single thought and account from present to past tense. The references to the people, organizations, enemy, and any other instance or subject involved have been kept as original and true to form as possible. This includes terminology and humor that may offend some; however, my hope is for the reader to appreciate historical context, as I am unwilling to change what really happened at the time in order to be less offensive at present. Like many generations of soldiers before us, our military bestowed a simple, and overtly offensive moniker to our enemy. Much like in World War II, with "Krauts" for Germans, or "Japs" for the Japanese, or the enemy being known as "Charlie" in Vietnam, we in the Operation Enduring Freedom and Operation Iraqi Freedom wars usually referred to our enemy and the surrounding population as "Hadji." This is both singular and plural. It was as common and simply used as saying, "The sky is blue."

Some dialogue, names, callsigns, missions, dates, and locations have been changed in the interest of operational security and protecting the identity of military members and units involved. Everything that I had recorded in my original journals was written with the non-military reader in mind, and I have done my best to keep that approachability here. A glossary has also been included to assist with the various military and aviation acronyms.

I wanted to limit what writing I did in retrospect, especially as it concerns the deployments. My biggest goal was to not let 20/20 hindsight interfere with the real story, so I was driven to ensure that there was no distortion of what I believed to be the truth or my feelings at the time. During my first few months of deployment, I was overly cautious about not recording events in great detail. When writing this book and encountering parts where I lacked further notes or information, I simply refused to make up elaborate fantasy battle narratives. My promise was to present the full story, and this includes many points often not spoken about outside of military circles that occasionally made life suck. For years, I fought the urge to omit these things and was encouraged by numerous squadron-mates to keep everything as authentic as possible. I recognize that this will make me personally vulnerable and sound less-than-stellar at times, but I refuse to alter what really happened in order to make myself feel or sound better.

For brevity's sake, I still removed hundreds of pages of mundane or unimportant aspects of my journals. For the reader's sake, I'll allow you this sole bit of reflective insight:

Since enduring everything described, I have grown and matured, even taking different stances on some subjects. The deployments, sights, and experiences of war have changed me and many of those I knew. We used to screw around, laugh, and have fun in large groups as young and just as idealistically innocent peers back at Fort Rucker. Those of us without deployments under our belts really did not understand what we were getting into or what would come.

War is romanticized, but I assure you that there is nothing romantic or wonderful about people engaging in combat and ripping each other apart. Be it close combat, or with small and impossibly fast-traveling projectiles, war is always horrific. I believed that we were on the defensive, seeing ourselves locked into the classic role of good fighting evil. Despite anything and everything that is written here, I want to clarify that I still believe that. We fought and continue to fight with an enemy so evil that there is nothing else that can be done, other than pursue their absolute destruction. Our biggest folly is in our method, not in the true tenacity and drive within those front line combatants who wish to tip the battles in our favor.

Everyone had volunteered to serve, and each did it how they saw best for their ideals, situation, and their families. While we may have all had minor or even major differences of opinion, those that had collectively answered America's call had something in common. We all loved our country, and we were trying to do what we thought was right. Our individual methods, beliefs, or tactics notwithstanding, there is still something to be said for what every military member out there volunteered to do or continues to do today.

What follows is the condensed account of one U.S. Army OH-58D Kiowa Warrior pilot assigned to the 3-17 Cavalry Squadron, spanning from induction into the squadron in 2008, all the way to the bitter end of the Kiowa Warrior program. I did my absolute best due diligence in reaching out to trusted friends and fellow pilots to scrub the work and ensure that I wasn't missing the mark.

This is the story as seen from the vantage point of one man, but my goal is to shed light on what happened to all of us, so it may not just simply be revealed, but also understood.

'FIDDLER'S GREEN'

(Author Unknown)

Halfway down the trail to Hell,
In a shady meadow green
Are the Souls of all dead Troopers camped,
Near a good old-time canteen.
And this eternal resting place
Is known as Fiddler's Green.

Marching past, straight through to Hell
The Infantry are seen.
Accompanied by the Engineers,
Artillery and Marines,
For none but the shades of Cavalrymen
Dismount at Fiddler's Green.

Though some go curving down the trail
To seek a warmer scene.
No Trooper ever gets to Hell
Ere he's emptied his canteen.
And so rides back to drink again
With friends at Fiddler's Green.

And so when man and horse go down
Beneath a saber keen,
Or in a roaring charge of fierce melee
You stop a bullet clean,
And the hostiles come to get your scalp,
Just empty your canteen,
And put your pistol to your head
And go to Fiddler's Green.

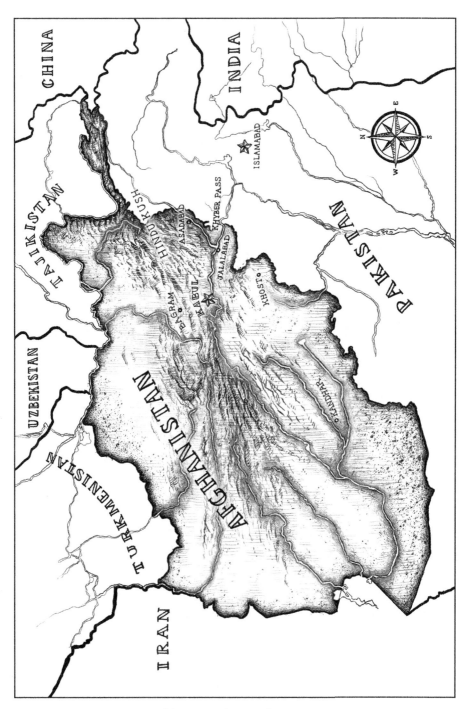

Afghanistan and surrounding nations
(rotate to view)

TAGAB VALLEY, AFGHANISTAN

September, 2010

"Wildwood, this is Eagle 26! Taking fire from the tree line, over!"

Ice water shot through my veins; our ground guys and their small convoy were taking heavy fire, and we could see the fight intensify close below and to our left. We turned in a hard bank, with our wingman in the Lead aircraft's position quickly exclaiming, "I see them, I see them! They're moving down the ditch near the riverbed!"

The sound of the radio crackled unintelligibly, and I knew the cacophony of the noises that I was hearing consisted of both incoming and outgoing rounds.

The radio operator came back on suddenly and much more clearly. "Request you lay fire on muzzle flashes to our west, south of the river, gun runs east to west, immediate suppressive fire, you're clear to engage, over!"

The enemy gave us an opening—we were seeing the dirt kick up from a shooter wedged in between some rocks and the low ruins of a wall.

"Confirm location of enemy is to your west, no friendlies in that area, clear to engage?"

"Affirmative, clear to engage!" The radioman and his convoy were desperate for some cover, and we could hear it in the urgency of his voice. The visceral feeling of combat—the anger, rage, frustration, fear for their safety, adrenaline, and feeling of responsibility to save the ground guys—overtook me.

"Inbound from east to west, engaging," Lead called back. We followed close behind as .50 caliber bullets kicked up dirt and destroyed everything in their path. Our wingman made a breaking hard turn, "Breaking right!"

We responded with, "Engaging!"

Our aircraft bumped slightly up towards the sky, momentarily pausing in our arc and taking in the bright sun. As we began to angle our nose back downward, the snow-capped mountains blurred up the windscreen and the terrain began to return into full view along the craggy, brown and green river bank. Just up the side, we saw the dust still swirling from the previous gun run.

My teeth chattered in my skull as the .50 caliber barrel that sat only a few feet away from me began to roar. With no doors between me and the concussion of the muzzle, I was one with every shot. Brass rained down and lead met the dusty earth. Our tracers and rounds created bright red ricochets off of the rocks.

"Breaking right!" We called out and followed our Lead ship once again. I spotted a puff of smoke just before an RPG flew in the direction of the convoy's foremost vehicle, slamming into a nearby wall along the road. The enemy had missed, but we were livid.

"Request immediate re-attack, RPG shooter vicinity of graveyard near last run!" The radioman called out.

This time, Lead had preceded the gun run with rockets. They nosed over and let fly two Hydra rockets, followed immediately by a spray of .50 cal.

We followed suit. The rockets flew into the target area with a satisfying "Ca-chunk! Ca-chunk! Boom, boom!"

We broke right once again, my head swiveled back and forth, each of my senses firing on all cylinders. I swung our optical Mast Mounted Sight (MMS), the large ball that was affixed to the top of our rotor disk, to focus into our target area. The MMS optics acted as the Kiowa's set of binoculars, and I quickly instructed the system to lock on and observe, no matter our helicopter orientation, so that we could continue to see movements in the area. There was a series of old destroyed structures and ruins, perfect for those wishing to stay masked and conduct a solid ambush. The dense foliage in the area was a real problem for us, forcing us to rely on more thermal imaging.

The radios again came to life, the ground element and the Lead aircraft yelling, "taking fire!" This situation was getting worse.

A few enemy rounds had just snapped past my wingman, barely missing him, and soon after, I heard the telltale snapping of rounds whizzing by our aircraft. "Shit, taking fire!" I yelled as we began to maneuver up and away, while still trying to maintain cover and eyes on our wingman.

Along with our guys on the ground, we were having a hard time locating the source. We flew around, keenly fixed on the hunt. Our fuel and munitions were running low just as we were zoning in. We got a break once we spotted a few individuals and flashes near a busted up, abandoned structure right near the graveyard. These insurgents had shot at U.S. forces from here just a few days prior, and now, we had them in sight.

The Lead aircraft made another gun run and got lit up once again. Fortunately, the insurgents were terrible at shooting today. We followed close behind and laid down more covering fire into the area. I witnessed a huge cloud of smoke and realized that our ground guys were lying down larger munitions.

Our AH-64 Apache gunship brothers back at Bagram (BAF) were getting ready and reported that they'd be arriving soon. The ground forces were working up further coordination with anything available in the higher altitude stack of aerial combat support assets to see who else could help. Fighter jets and Unmanned Aerial Vehicles (UAV) began to race to move overhead.

"Break, break, break! Wildwoo- (rat-tat-tat-tat-tat-tat-tat)!" There was a pause. My heart sank a bit. Had another RPG been fired? Had the radioman gotten hit? Had anyone else gotten hit? Was there anything else that we could do? How much longer could we possibly stay on this low amount of fuel, and with this diminishing number of rounds? Was I doing everything that I could to save them? Were we able to do more?!

"Trail, this is Lead, I got more muzzle flashes. We're turning inbound!" Lead put more .50 cal down, followed by a short burst from us. We didn't have much more left to give. The fuel gauge was showing an unsettling number which would force us to retreat to the French-controlled base Morales-Frasier to rearm and refuel.

The requests for gun runs continued, and we made shorter and shorter runs, trying to conserve what little we had left. Suddenly, after our last run, the fire stopped.

"Wildwood, confirm you're no longer making runs and that you no longer see activity," Eagle 26 asked anxiously.

"Roger, we are complete with our runs and no longer see movement or fires from that area, nor are we experiencing any more fire on us, over," Lead reported.

The relief in the radioman's voice was obvious. "Copy Wildwood, great job, please continue to scan that area as long as you can. We've gotten our disabled vehicle moving again back towards Kutschbach, confirm you're about to have to leave station for refuel?"

As we began discussing logistics, we were re-engaged as quickly as it had stopped.

Five, maybe ten minutes tops. That was all we would be able to squeeze out before going past the point-of-no-return and be walking home. Effective small arms fire began to descend again on our convoy and the ground forces, now confident on the location of the enemy, let loose larger munitions.

I called ahead to Morales-Frasier and let them know that we would need a NASCAR-quick turn out of the Fuel and Rearm Point (FARP). I informed them that each aircraft would dispatch the left-seated pilot to jump out and aid in ammo and rocket loading, so long as they could pump the gas quicker than they'd ever done before.

Our team agreed to one final gun run on the enemy positions before breaking our coverage for the FARP. We closely followed Lead's engagement, letting go of the last remnants of our .50 cal ammo into the area before our weapon went dry. We broke out and let them know that we would be back as quickly as possible, and that the Troops in Contact (TIC) call should already have the Apaches queued up and on the way to relieve us ASAP.

Our FARP turn was conducted in near-record time while our engines and rotors still turned at 100 percent. I got the .50 cal loaded and was assisting with the rockets when even more people rushed out to help. I jumped back into the cockpit just as the last of the fuel was being dumped in. We waved them off at our cutoff point and I was still buckling my harness as we pulled back up into the sky. We made our way back, seething like anxious hockey players sitting in the penalty box, ready to get back in and fight.

Meanwhile our counterparts, the Apaches, co-located with us back at Bagram, were in the air flying at max speed towards the battle. Callsign "Angry," we had been living and working so closely together that we felt as though we were in the same troop, or "company." They were our brothers, and I was happy to have them assist.

As we neared the ground forces, we saw that they were still taking and returning sporadic fire. We remarked internally that we had the utmost respect for the ground unit; they were intent to stay and keep up the fight with the enemy instead of breaking contact. They were pissed off.

Angry had arrived on station and were briefed. As we conducted our Battle Handover (BHO), the ground forces were engaged by an even more emboldened enemy descending upon them. The enemy had moved from a structure 100 meters out to now less than 50 meters away, along an entrenched and highly foliage-dense position. Eagle 26 yelled on the radio once more that they were taking even heavier and increasingly effective small arms fire now, much closer than before.

There was no time. We were now working on a situation in which our engagements would be considered "danger close." We could no longer rely on the rockets aboard, only very precise and expertly laid .50 cal between our forces and the embedded enemy. Lead moved in with a perfect string of fire and broke out, followed by our Trail aircraft. We were immediately engaged as we made our run, and to make matters worse, our gun spit out only ten rounds before jamming. I swore as we broke out, attempting to run the emergency procedure to get our weapon back online. I tried to shrink behind the tiny, bulletproof side-door panel.

"Well, this blows," I said, as I stuck my head out into the wind stream to check the gun and attempt to re-cock it. As we moved away to regroup, we tried to untangle our now-convoluted communication situation. With five radios in use and an active battle raging, properly utilizing our communications could be one of the most critical situations that we, as Kiowa pilots, could not afford to mess up. It was a medley of confusion, noise, and adrenaline.

The last thing we heard was that Angry now had control of the situation. Our mission to protect any of the ground elements from harm had been successful, and now, Angry would begin to work up some Hellfire missile shooting to put a bit more ordnance on the area. We headed north to clear the way, and I slumped back in my seat. Looking at my watch, I realized that the entire incident had lasted under an hour. It certainly felt several times that.

We landed back at Bagram and did our final refuel before putting the aircraft to bed. As the blades coasted down, the other pilot and I sat in quiet reflection, exhausted.

I also realized a few things all at once: The windscreen was filthy; the aircraft was filthy; and I was filthy. My face felt caked in grit, my stomach ravenous, and my body drained after that final capstone event in an over six hour flight. The troop we were in was like a tightly knit, small family, and our crew chiefs could see that this had been an exceptionally pain-in-the-ass day for us. They didn't pry, but began to help, securing the aircraft, tying down blades, and installing the coverings. They silently helped us with our gear, pulled mission data cards for us, and gathered the things we left behind.

Inside our Command Post (CP), we sat down and debriefed as a team. We were heavy and spent, yet keenly aware of the next steps. An important aspect of our job was not quitting, even when the bird had been shut down. We submitted grids, sightings, findings, descriptions, and accounts, all typed up and forwarded for those who deal in the farming of such information to ponder and sort. Finally, we spoke of what we had done right, what we had done wrong, and what we could learn from and improve on. This final ritual was important, especially after such a day as this.

Afterward, we would each claim a piece of furniture on which to unwind, eat, chug water, and doze off here and there until it was time for the next shift to show up and replace us. This happened every 12 hours, so that we would continue to maintain coverage 24 hours a day, seven days a week, for the entire year.

INTRODUCTION:
BECOMING AN AVIATOR

Like many I served with, my intentions for joining our United States armed forces were simple: I wanted to do something good and wanted to serve my great country. The 9/11 attacks happened during my senior year of high school, and it had really stuck with me. I was called to join the military. It was in my blood.

My father had been a Marine A-6 Intruder pilot. My brother was initially a Marine infantryman, then transferred over to the Army. He became an infantry officer, and upon graduating from Airborne and Ranger school, he went on to command a platoon in one of the worst neighborhoods in Baghdad at the height of insanity there. Both grandfathers had served in World War II; my paternal grandfather was an Army infantryman, a fierce warrior NCO fighting with his men from island to island in the Pacific. My maternal grandfather was an Army Air Corps pilot, flying the P-40 Warhawk in the Pacific, where he survived an unreal ordeal as a POW, escaping into the jungle to wage guerrilla war on his Japanese captors and embark on a long journey to find his way home.

I was in awe of these men, and all the other men and women in our military who had come before me. There was no way that I could see my life moving forward without joining their ranks and doing my part.

I joined the Louisiana Army National Guard in the summer of 2003. I was to report to Basic Training, followed immediately by 91W Medic School. Once a medic in the LA Guard, I continued college at Louisiana Tech University with the goal of transitioning to active duty as soon as I graduated. I almost left college a few times; I wanted to get into the fight so badly, I could hardly stand it. Medics were needed, and bad things were happening in the sandbox. My brother, Marc, was fighting door to door in nasty back alleyways in the Al-Adhamiyah district in Baghdad, and I was drinking beer and living it up on campus, going to Army drill once a month.

A few times, Marc called me in the middle of the night with an urgent need to know what we were seeing on the news, both online and on television. Most of the time, the story in no way reflected reality. My professors had been briefed so that if I suddenly gathered my things and left class, they knew it was because I had received a call from an Iraqi cell number.

One day, I received a call from Marc during class and as I sprinted out, I could hear the urgency in his voice. I ran to the student center and began reading aloud all the breaking war news on a computer from CNN, FOX, and Al Jazeera. Some Al Jazeera reporters were suspiciously "lucky" to be in the area to get footage of attacks on U.S. troops. I'd given him all that he needed to know, he told me that they were all mostly okay, and had to go.

The summer before I was supposed to begin my senior year, I moved to Arkansas and transferred to the 39th Infantry with the Arkansas Army National Guard and was accepted for transfer into Henderson State University. I would get the same bachelor's degree in professional aviation that I was pursuing at LA Tech, but their path to completion for me was quicker since they'd accept my Army credits from Medic School. It was here that I developed a dream to not fly fighters, but stay in the Army and fly helicopters.

The path to Warrant Officer Candidate School (WOCS), followed by Flight Training, was incorporated into one entire application program known as WOFT. The candidate pool at the time was very saturated, and the WOFT program proved to be very competitive. There were many, many months of paperwork shuffling and talks with recruiters.

In Oklahoma City, once I completed the flight physical, I donned my dress green uniform and addressed a board made up of several selection officers. Interestingly enough, there were no warrant officers, or even aviators, present on the selection board. The Army major in charge of the process noted that I had a college degree in professional aviation, and she asked me why I was trying to become a warrant officer instead of a commissioned officer.

I did not expect this question. She further explained that with the current state of the war, they desperately needed more commissioned officers. I was qualified to be either a warrant officer or a commissioned officer, the latter being because I possessed a degree. She wanted to adjust my application process and convince me I was making a bad mistake. I fought back, trying to explain that there was no intention on my part of being a regular officer. The members of the board quickly met my response with indignation. *Oh no,* I thought. Here I was, a sergeant of the Arkansas Army National Guard, standing on the carpet of an active duty selection board and telling these officers I wanted to make a better decision and become a warrant!

My explanation of my desire to fly, not to command, seemed to settle in. The major sighed and told me to go wait outside while they discussed. I endured what seemed like an hour of sweaty and anxious waiting. I was called back in, checking my watch quickly and realizing that my perceived hour was less than five minutes. I was to report to a Military Entry Processing Station in Little Rock and be transferred into the active duty component of the Army. I would soon be reporting to WOCS with flight school immediately following.

I was over the moon. My dreams of becoming an Army aviator were finally being realized. I would be a helicopter pilot! Not only that, I would most likely be going immediately to fight the enemy. It was on.

*

I arrived at Fort Rucker, Alabama, about a week before my official WOCS date. They placed me in a temporary holding barracks, where I became a "Snowbird." I removed my sergeant rank and placed the W.O.C.S. rank patch in its place. They quickly gave me the rundown: when accountability formations were held, when Physical Training (PT) times were, where chow was, etc. I was informed that I was to stencil my name on every piece of clothing, to include every single sock, and each stencil must be done in a very specific way, size, orientation, and prescribed location per garment. Clothing would have to be rolled and tucked away to precise measurements in the drawers.

My WOCS class began, and what followed was six weeks of ever-increasing silliness. Intensive PT, studying, lectures, reduced free time, and purposefully built time crunch drills were all dished out to make us masters of time management. I was in "purple class," so we had to wear purple shoelaces and hats. We looked stupid as hell, every single one of us. After weeks in and out of additional drills, training exercises, classrooms, and final evaluations, we all graduated and got our "dot."

A warrant officer's rank is a silver vertical bar, with between one and four black enameled squares on the interior, to signal what rank the individual holds. The top rank, a CW5, is the same silver vertical bar; however, instead has one solid black enameled vertical bar running up and down the middle. The squares on warrant rank are generally referred to as dots, and a brand new warrant is sometimes also referred to as a "spot," depending on what salty person is giving the officer grief. Now that we were all newly minted spots, we began to await our respective turns for Initial Entry Rotary Wing (IERW) training to start.

I moved less than half a mile down the road from the WOCS barracks to just outside the Fort Rucker gates. The very first thing on the left when exiting the gate was the Daleville Trailer Park. The wooden fence line of the park had a mural depicting an epic Vietnam helicopter battle scene, which opened up to my new Shangri-La. A fully furnished, single-wide trailer was $400 per month, which was perfect for a single warrant officer like me. Many of my peers migrated here, and we soon found that we had made a wise decision. The park was at least 90 percent occupied by Army flight school students and with soldiers constantly coming and going at all hours, it was the safest trailer park ever. The man who owned and operated the park was an old retired Army major who had flown in Vietnam. I could occasionally see him at random moving about the park in his robe, a .22 caliber derringer pistol tucked into the top of his boot. A small pool sat in the middle of the park, and several grills were scattered about. We would grill, drink beer, and stress and study until it was time to graduate, all the while banking our living allowance checks.

Once a pilot candidate received their slot to begin, it was off to Aeromedical training, Night Vision Goggle (NVG) training, and a water survival and escape course called "Dunker." This is where you're dumped upside down into the water while strapped into a large helicopter mock-up and must escape without drowning. In the initial stage of Dunker, you're given a tiny scuba bottle with around five minutes of air in it. As you learn how to escape, the drills become more challenging. Eventually, you no longer get the scuba bottle. Divers at the bottom of the pool would watch and test each candidate as they free themselves from the back of a simulated UH-60 Blackhawk utility aircraft. The final test is done alone and upside down in a closed canopy resembling an Apache cockpit. I sat in the seat, heart beating fast as I waited to fall. Suddenly, I felt the weightless sensation as the contraption was released and then a jolt as I slammed into the water. I swung and bubbles swarmed. I held my breath and awaited everything to settle, then reached up to my chest to unbuckle the five-point harness that held me tightly in the underwater trap. I rotated the buckle as I was trained to do, but the belts held tight. I stopped a moment and then tried again. It didn't work, and I was beginning to wish that I could breathe. Up top, my buddies watched on a video screen as I sat trapped, and were alarmed when I stopped moving and closed my eyes. I calmed myself, knowing that to rush and become frantic would only quicken my pulse and use up my remaining oxygen in my circulation. I finally slowly rotated the buckle, this time freeing myself and opening the canopy door. I made my way to the surface, followed closely by a scuba diver who had waited to see if I would start to drown. I broke the surface and a few of my pals laughed, saying they thought I wouldn't make it. For a minute there, neither had I!

After completing all the initial training, it was finally time to get the keys and take our first real helicopter flight, traditionally known as a "nickel ride." We were randomly paired up with another flight school student as our partner, known as our "stick buddy," and shuttled out to the training fields.

Shaking with anticipation and excitement, we strapped in and cranked up our Bell TH-67 training helicopters. Once out in the training clearings of Fort Rucker, it was our turn to fly. There, we bobbed, weaved, and violently spun in ascents and descents, drifting all over and trying not to kill ourselves while attempting to learn to hover. A crusty old Instructor Pilot (IP), mostly prior Army servicemen themselves, sat in the left seat and kept us alive.

The IP would let us get right to the brink of danger or a crash, then with a lightning-fast correction, our aircraft would be perfectly still. In the beginning, they'd just laugh at you and say, "try again." If you listened to their words and fought the urge to overcorrect and overreact, then the art of a helicopter hover only took a few flights to have down. If a guy panicked or tuned the IP out, then the IPs would get angry and start chewing their ass out. It was all about exercising finesse—we had to become experts in anticipating what would be required next and make the small coordinated corrections necessary. Once the IP was ready to sign us off, my stick buddy and I took the helicopter up into the traffic pattern without him on our first solo. A few IPs stood in the grass below the control tower, chain-smoking and watching their fledgling bird-men take flight from the nest all by themselves.

After the solo ride, we continued through the rest of that portion of IERW. We then moved into Instruments, followed by Basic Warfighting Skills. Each phase had its extreme challenges and hardships. After I had finished all the initial portions of flight training, they ordered me up to our main collection point, Bravo Company.

The night before selection, I once again spoke to Marc, trying to weigh the pros and cons of each aircraft that may be available to me. After hearing some of his stories about combat in the streets of Baghdad, my answer became simple. I would make my very first choice the hard-to-get OH-58D Kiowa Warrior. The Kiowa had accounted for an amazing amount of cover and close air support for my brother and his guys. Essentially, the Kiowa was the least known aircraft to anyone other than those directly supported and assisted by one, usually in combat roles.

Marc told me a story about an enemy sniper that had been playing cat and mouse for quite some time in Baghdad. They had a general idea where he would usually shoot from, but the problem was, they couldn't figure out how he made it to and from his shooting position. Marc's platoon relayed their problem to a Scout Weapons Team (SWT), the official name for a pair of Kiowas giving support to any good-guy elements on the battlefield. The SWT looked atop a few roofs from the air and quickly set about snapping photos and gathering information.

Within a few minutes, the pilot had gathered his photographs and notes. After the mission, these pieces of information and drawings were emailed to Marc and his platoon. The infantry platoon reviewed the intel and saw that the insurgent had been jumping into this position from a nearby roof, and he had covered his ingress and egress routes well. The next time that it happened turned out to be that sniper's last jump.

Shortly after that experience, a senior Kiowa pilot contacted the platoon with a request. He showed up at their doorstep ready to go out on a dismounted foot patrol with them. The pilot accompanied the platoon all night through the streets of Al-Adhamiyah in an effort to get the experience and see the vantage point that the men witnessed from the ground. His intent was to return to his troop and share his experiences and notes with the others so that they'd provide better close air support within the city. My brother and his guys respected the hell out of the Air Cavalry troop for this, and in turn, the Air Cavalry guys respected them even more.

What Marc told me about the character and bravery of the Kiowa pilots had me hooked. It was exactly the level of involvement that I wanted to have in the fight. The next morning was selection day. Fortunately, my academic standing enabled me to snap up one of only six available Kiowa slots offered. My adrenaline pumped and my heart raced, as I knew that I had just chosen a very elite and dangerous path.

*

The Kiowa training turned out to be incredibly intense and stressful. We flew days, nights, and some weekends, too. Learning to fly the aircraft turned out to be the easiest part; it was learning how to operate the surveillance and weapons systems, manage its five radios, and rapidly gather and pass intel that was the real challenge. We had innumerable tests, both written and oral evaluations.

Midway through the course, we were shown footage from a helmet camera. The pilots in their Kiowa were flying very low over Iraqi rooftops. Suddenly, the taps from AK-47 fire grew audible, and one of the pilots started screaming out in pain. Wounded and pissed, he pulled his rifle off the dash and began pumping rounds out the left door opening. The helicopter maneuvered aggressively as more rounds could be heard and radio calls for emergency medical aid were being placed by the pilot flying. The helicopter set down roughly on a dirt road as a few soldiers and presumably a medic rushed up to the helicopter, and then, the screen went dark. Our senior instructor said solemnly, "he made it, but unfortunately, not everyone will. This is the reality of our job. What we do is dangerous, and you all need to be very damn good at your job in order to have the highest probability of surviving." The point was crystal clear.

We sweated and banded together for months as a small, but strong, tightly knit class. By the time each of our final evaluations (known as "checkrides" in aviation) came, we were all exhausted, but had held it together and knew what we needed to know.

My Kiowa checkride was one of the hardest events I had ever encountered in my life. Toward the end, I was at a high hover in the left seat of a lurching Kiowa, soaked by the blowing rain and wind, dazzled by the lightning flashes of a fast-approaching storm. I sat in my seat in a cold sweat, frantically setting up a Hellfire shot while my instructor shouted at me, "hurry up! We need this missile, people...are...DYING!"

I set up the shot before the storm hit and shut down the airfield. With shaky legs and a fatigued brain, I sat down for the checkride debrief. The instructor had a few quibbles like all checkrides, but then he slapped my folder shut. He looked at me hard, then smiled wide.

"Congratulations, Ryan. You made it. You're a Kiowa pilot now." He then clapped me on the back and shook my hand with an iron grip. Our whole class had made it, and we celebrated hard.

After successful completion of the checkride and a few follow-up courses, we finally had our graduation ceremony at the Army Aviation Museum on Fort Rucker. Me and one of my Kiowa classmates, CW2 Dede Murawsky, had elected to stay a little longer and attend a special school that was available to us before showing up to our respective troops in Savannah. Dede was in her early-20s and had already spent a few years enlisted in the Air Force as an avionics technician. She was a tall, skinny Florida girl with auburn hair, an infectious smile, and a friendly disposition. I still nicknamed her "Copperhead" however, because if she was agitated enough, her sudden strike could be surprisingly quick and fierce.

We attended the Aviation Life Support and Equipment (ALSE) school, where we spent several weeks learning how to outfit, repair, and refurbish aviation gear such as pilot helmets, make basic stitch repairs to equipment, and put together survival and medical kits for downed aircrews to use while they evaded and awaited rescue. Becoming ALSE officers would make us immediate assets to our new units right upon our arrival.

I showed up in Savannah and was assigned to one of the three "line" troops that made up the front line elements of the 3-17 Cavalry Squadron on Hunter Army Airfield. Upon signing in, I became the newest member of Bravo Troop and I was informed that if I didn't already have one, then I better go buy a Cavalry Stetson hat right away. I was also assigned my first official duty: Fridge Bitch. Since I was a Warrant Officer Junior Grade, I was known classically as the WOJG, pronounced "Whoa-Juh." I would be the one to go to and from Sam's Club and get all the snacks and sodas to sell from our fridge, so that we could have a side fund to use for troop needs.

The age-old practice of having a junior pilot as Fridge Bitch is one of those constants that bespeaks the genius of the Warrant Officer Corps. Without this, there's no way that we could have ever had the funds to send a member of a troop away with a gift of gratitude for their service or to buy flowers and cards for a troop-mate's family member in need of support. A Cavalry troop is an incredibly tight-knit family, and I figured out that hierarchy and closeness of the members very quickly. As a WOJG, you were untested and had a long road ahead to prove yourself worthy of holding a spot in the troop. This was not given away, but instead, a hard-earned right to join such an elite family of professionals.

Unluckily for me, I was the only one there the night that they came to "break in" my Stetson. A "break in" is pretty gross. Down on River Street in Savannah, my Stetson was filled with every liquor and beer that Kevin & Barry's Irish Pub had to offer. It was also doused with food ingredients and hot sauces that were liberated from the kitchen by some enthusiastic troopers that couldn't be stopped by the staff.

I did push-ups and listened to the history of the Stetson break in, some Cavalry lore, and the recitation of the poem, "Fiddler's Green." I then chugged out of my Stetson until my sponsor stepped in and shoved the hat atop my head. My eyes burned, but I laughed and hugged everyone that I could catch, smearing them with the sludge. The guys cheered and passersby stopped to watch and chuckle at the curious scene they were witnessing. I was now an official member of the Cavalry, and soon, we would go to war.

An Alpha Troop bird readies for a practice engagement, Fort Stewart, GA.

My brother, Marc and I enjoying a scotch the night before my graduation.

PART ONE

OPERATION ENDURING FREEDOM X

Area of Operations, Bagram, Afghanistan, 2010
(rotate to view)

CHAPTER 1

During our train up for deployment, we had a shift in our command structure. What follows may sound complex, but the formidable information here is, at its core, simply an orientation. We were the 3-17 Cavalry serving under the 3rd Combat Aviation Brigade of the 3rd Infantry Division. The powers that be had decided that the coming deployment needed another front line troop in addition to our normal Alpha, Bravo, and Charlie. I was informed that I would be a member of this new group: Fox Troop. The last time 3-17 Cavalry had utilized their Fox Troop was during Vietnam, so out of respect, we naturally retook their name: The Centaurs. Our new Fox Troop was hastily assembled and attached to the 2-3 General Support Aviation Battalion (GSAB). Instead of going to Jalalabad, like Alpha and Charlie Troop, or Solerno, like Bravo Troop, my unit would be going to Bagram Airbase north of the Afghan capital of Kabul.

In addition to our small, half-sized Cavalry Fox Troop, 2-3 GSAB received Apaches by way of absorbing Bravo Company from the 1-3 Attack Battalion. This was done so that 2-3 GSAB would have its own Apache support in addition to our small band of Kiowas. Bagram Airbase had also highlighted a need for a troop such as ours due to increased attacks and threats to the base and surrounding area. Our whole group of aforementioned-units going to Bagram encompassed what was known as a Task Force, in this case, we were Task Force Knighthawk.

Fox Troop was made up of some new guys and some Iraq veterans, but none had served in Afghanistan. Given how we had been assembled and what attention (or lack thereof) that we were afforded, we soon had an alternate reference for ourselves. A few of us secretly re-designated ourselves "The Red-Headed Black Sheep," and we made our official unofficial patch and logo. The patch would be worn in lieu of our Fox Troop 3-17 Centaurs or the Bravo Company 1-3 Warlords colors whenever we saw it was fit and safe.

In regards to how our troop itself was composed and operated, here's the general idea. Within the troop, we had two main platoons, each consisting of around eight pilots, and roughly the same amount of crew chiefs taking care of the helicopters. Each platoon was led by a lieutenant, and the commander over them and everyone else in the troop was a captain.

As far as pilots go, we had a basic organizational structure. In Army aviation, a pilot progresses with more responsibilities as they gain experience. A new guy starts out as a "PI," which is short for pilot. Eventually, with dedication and a demonstration of sound technical and tactical decision making, a PI is offered a chance to upgrade to "PC." The Pilot-in-Command (PC) role is what everyone is expected to strive for and attain. This status puts the responsibility for the aircraft, its munitions, conduct in the course of a mission, all of it, on the PC. It is a very hard-earned right of passage. In a mission conducted with more than one aircraft, a PC who has also demonstrated the highest level of trustworthiness and confidence will be designated as an Air Mission Commander (AMC). They have the final say in how a team conducts business, and the overall success or failure of a mission falls ultimately on the AMC. That may all seem like quite a lot, but all of this jargon will fall into place.

Right off the bat, our troop had a shortage of experienced PCs, and we new guys needed to step up to help our understaffing issues. Soon after Fox Troop was created, we were all integrated and moved around for a few months, training in different locations across the U.S. and getting ready to deploy.

Finally, we were given the deployment date and told to start preparing to head out. This was the moment that we'd trained so hard for, and everyone seemed eager to go and bring the fight to the enemy.

★

Deployment was set for Sunday evening, November 15, 2009. I was excited for this new journey in my life. I was young, naïve, bold, and ready. I thought I should record the events transpiring around me and began to keep a journal on that day. The intent was to share it all in real-time throughout my deployment so that my family and close friends could keep tabs on me. I knew what I could not talk about, and my initial goal was to keep it light-hearted to assure those concerned that I would be okay.

On the morning of November 15th, I was joined by my girlfriend, Sally, and my family to spend a fun-filled day enjoying my favorites that America had to offer. I had a massive seafood lunch on Tybee Island, then jumped into the frigid ocean in all of my clothes so that I could have one last swim. After finishing some last-minute packing, we pulled out of my driveway and I watched my home fade away in the rearview mirror. We had a steak dinner on the way to the airfield, talking and trying to remain upbeat and positive. We then proceeded that evening to what, unknown to us, was the chaos unfolding on Hunter Army Airfield.

As we drove onto the airfield, the lights from the hangars illuminated the scene. There were hundreds of camouflage bodies hurriedly moving about, family members crying around their loved ones. Loud speakers played triumphant Army band songs, and the music echoed strangely off of the buildings.

We pulled up to the Kiowa hangar, and the back of our vehicle was immediately raided by many enlisted soldiers grabbing my bags.

"Sir, plane one or two!?" They were hurriedly asking. "Sir, main body eight or nine!?"

My loved ones tried very hard to remain strong and positive. My father fought to hold back tears as he engulfed me in a giant bear hug.

"You be careful, stay safe, and fly smart. I love you." He said, quietly and closely to my ear. I began to choke up myself and fought it off. "Don't worry, I will. I love you, too."

My girlfriend, Sally, was next, and we embraced as she cried. I heard announcements over the loudspeakers, ordering us to assemble in the hangar and say our last goodbyes. I held Sally at arm's length.

"So, this is it?" She asked through a sob.

"Yes, sweetheart, this is it," I replied.

I did my best to hold it together and could feel a knot in my chest. I felt that it was important for me to be strong for them, and I promised that I would be careful and do everything I could to come home safe. We then parted ways on the tarmac between the Cavalry and Blackhawk hangars.

Soon after our goodbyes to our families, we played the hurry up and wait game until we finally boarded our plane, a civilian chartered airliner, to Germany. There, we deplaned and sat around forever... only to be told that our plane was broken as hell and that there were bunks available for us to sleep in. It was anticlimactic. About eight hours later, we finally departed for our next stop in Manas, Kyrgyzstan on a flight that seemingly took forever. As we flew in the night, the lights on the ground grew more and more faint, until finally, it was impossible to distinguish the sky from the horizon or sparse settlements below.

When we deplaned in Manas, I was instantly glad that I had good cold-weather gear because I figured that Siberia must not be too far away. Many of our bags were laid out in a wet, slushy mess. We picked our bags out of the muck and did a long bag-drag walk to some tents that we would call home for about 24 hours. Everyone was jet-lagged and out of whack, so much of that time would be spent sleeping. We were quite literally situated in the middle of nowhere.

The following morning was already Wednesday the 18th, and I took a glorious shower in what was arguably lukewarm water. A few of us ventured from our tents and managed to find a few positive sides to Manas. The chow hall was open 24 hours and was very good, and so was the Morale, Wellness, and Recreation (MWR) center. I admired that they had gone a long way to make an uncomfortable place somewhat bearable. Time flew by quickly and once again, we found ourselves on a plane, this time an Air Force C-17, bound for our final destination of Bagram Airbase, Kapisa Province, Afghanistan.

Sub-zero conditions in Manas, Kyrgyzstan.

CAV/Attack flight line on Bagram Airbase, located only a few hundred yards from our living quarters on the east side.

B Huts, our home on the flight line for the full year.

*

Upon landing in Bagram, we were herded into a tent and given the standard new-guy brief by a soldier who had given the spiel way too many times. We were then placed in temporary quarters on the east side of the airfield. For the next several days, we sat through a lot of briefings and pilot classes: Some were boring and repetitive, but some fascinating, like the improvised explosive device (IED) recognition and avoidance training.

Afghanistan's profound wilderness and beauty fascinated me. The sunrise and sunset over the 15,000-foot mountain peaks were an impressive and memorable sight. *It really is a shame that this populace has so many psychos*, I mused to myself.

I was awestruck by the sheer number of Afghan nationals, Department of Defense civilians, and contractors on the base, who seemed to far outnumber actual military personnel. The Afghan nationals worried me, and for good reason. We had to squeeze our water bottles before drinking them to make sure that they had not been tampered with. We stayed in groups to thwart kidnapping or assault attempts, which was a recurring and credible threat.

Luckily, our troop lived in a sparsely populated and less-traveled area on the faraway "east side," that included a guarded gate. For the next year, we would be living in B Huts, which were essentially small plywood shacks with partitioned rooms inside. Our rooms were only about 6'x8', but by lofting the bed over a desk, some guys were really living comfortably. Our B Huts were also only a few hundred meters from our aircraft parking, which would be a huge plus for our ability to get right to our birds without any transportation requirements. We went in as a group and bought private internet equipment and a satellite hookup, which we hoped would arrive by Thanksgiving. I bought an Afghan Roshan Telecom cell phone and a prepaid minutes card at a steep $55 for 200 minutes so that I could reconnect with the world and also for our own inter-troop needs.

About a week after arrival, I moved into a shared transient B Hut to await swapping one-for-one into our built-up B Hut rooms as we replaced the outgoing pilots. A few hundred meters from the B Huts was our main building from which we'd be working. Pilot gear lockers lined the hallways and there was a nice lounge room outfitted with a pool table, darts, foosball, and commercial refrigerator. Our CP marked the end of the hall by our flight lockers, while a gym was also available on the opposite end.

The flight line with our helicopter pads was situated right next to the main building. Out there, we had every bit of munitions we wanted. Green metal ammo cans with 100 rounds each of .50 caliber ammunition were plentiful and stacked high. Additional ammo cans with 5.56 ammunition for our rifles and piles of differently colored smoke grenades were also readily available. Containers of 2.75 Hydra rockets sat open on their sides, the rear of each rocket facing us and ready to pull in a second. The most common rockets featured 10lb, high-explosive warheads, while other specialty variants were also available—phosphorus for marking, flechettes which acted like a giant, thousand steel dart slinging shotgun shell, illumination rockets to light an area up, etc.

Hellfire missiles were also available, but they were not as quick of a grab as the .50 cal or rockets were. Many of us liked Hellfires for their more-precise targeting and different capabilities. Some punched through walls to explode within the interior of a structure, while others created for caves or bunkers created an over-pressure thermobaric explosion—almost like a depth charge used to crush submarines. If a target was in the open, a high explosive model was set with an additional blast fragmentation sleeve that would send out thousands of shards, like a massive hand grenade.

At the discretion of the troop's maintenance and munitions availability, pilots could consider what our perceived mission needs may be, and each aircraft's weapon loadout could be modified. Whenever we opted to use the .50 cal M3P machine gun in any configuration (majority of the time), the gun and its magazine were always installed on the left side of the aircraft. We would then additionally install either a rocket pod or a Hellfire launcher on the right side. Alternatively, we could also elect to do a combination of a Hellfire and rocket pod, while other times we opted to set the bird up with the "Rocket-Rocket" loadout, having one rocket pod installed on each side instead of anything else. This last configuration was also known as "the crowd pleaser" due to the impressive racket it made when up to 14 rockets, seven from each pod, were fired in rapid succession. Never in any of my time did we do "Hellfire-Hellfire," since in our conflict it was simply not as practical as the other options.

*

Our troop was almost completely through with transferring in to replace our predecessors. Everyone was preparing, discussing missions, unpacking, and finally settling into a groove. Our full-blown takeover of all missions was set to begin very soon. What I so desperately wanted was to get off the ground and into the sky. I gazed longingly at the teams coming and going, just barely able to take it any longer. I was ready for my turn.

On December 1, it happened. I was finally asked the best question I had heard since leaving home: "Hey dude, you wanna go fly?"

"*Hell yes*, I wanna go fly!" I exclaimed, literally jumping out of my seat to go get my gear. Some guys chuckled and congratulated me, finding it funny how pumped I was about finally getting to fly. I shook with anticipation as I dug through my locker in the hallway. I had my helmet and body armor ready and began to piece together what information I would need on my kneeboard.

CW2 Nick Payne, a senior PC who had become a great mentor and friend to me, looked on in amusement. Nick was a stocky man of normal height and always appeared to wear a smile. He sported an obligatory Cavalry mustache and was a great counterbalance to poor attitudes, always able to add positivity to impossibly difficult situations. As I passed Nick in the hallway, he grinned widely at me.

"Look at you! Holy smokes, we're finally letting you fly," he laughed. I high-fived him and continued my quick march towards the door leading out to the flight line. Near the aircraft, I met up with my instructor, who was also the troop Standardization Pilot (SP). Usually, the SP is the most senior of the instructors and the lead warrant officer in a troop, charged with unofficially keeping the pilots in line. He smirked at me as he could see my zeal for getting to go out, and it seemed to rub off on him a bit.

I entered the cockpit to strap in. Since I hadn't flown in a while, I was deliberate and thorough as I hit each checklist item. Once I was ready, I flipped on the aircraft battery switch. The Kiowa Warrior came to life, and the screens welcomed our mission waypoints and radio frequency inputs. Before I knew it, we were ready to start. The SP looked at me.

"Alright brother, you ready?" Indeed I was, so I nodded and prepared to start. Our crew chiefs stood outside of the rotor disk, nodding and giving a thumbs up to confirm to us that no one was too close to our rotor disk or standing by the tail rotor. I placed my finger on the start switch and wrapped my other hand around the throttle. The SP stuck his head outside of the aircraft door, yelling, "Clear!"

I pressed the start switch and heard the clicking, sparking sound of the igniters rapidly firing. A mechanical whine began. A few seconds later, I cracked open the throttle to introduce a rush of JP-8 jet fuel into the engine. The fuel hit the fire from the igniters and exploded into action. The low-pitched rumble and vibration from the reaction gave me an adrenaline rush, and I watched the engine instruments and turbine temperature begin to rise. The rotor blade tips began to swing in front of our windscreen, spinning above us faster and faster. The engine sound intensified into a beautiful hum of turbine and spinning blades. She was alive, and it felt great to be back on the controls.

Soon, the aircraft was running at 100 percent and our SWT was ready to go. I was in the Lead position of our pair of Kiowas for the day, and Trail said, "Alright, Lead, we're all set. Following you, Robo."

I pulled up with my left hand on the collective control lever, lifting our aircraft into the standard three-foot hover. I was joined by my wingman as we hover taxied down the line to our departure area. We spoke briefly with the control tower, and obtained our clearance to depart the ramp and split off towards the east. With my right hand, I pushed the cyclic control stick forward, causing the Kiowa's nose to dip downwards, and we began to pick up speed. Slowly and methodically, I pulled the collective flight control lever upward. This changed the pitch of the rotor blades so that they would bite into more air and cause us to lift into the sky.

Forward, faster and faster! Upward, faster and faster! The ground was rushing by now, and we flew directly toward the control tower. I broke off to the right at an altitude just level with the glass that the air traffic controllers stood behind, while our Trail ship split the tower by doing the same thing on the left. We knew that most of them liked it when we buzzed the tower like that.

The perimeter fence line was ahead, and we streaked over the final guard tower. We had left Bagram Airfield and were now in Afghan airspace. The surrounding mountains were huge; I didn't get a sense of how big they really were until airborne. Although it was a scenic area, we remembered that it was still a combat zone.

We readied to test fire our weapons at a range set up off of the airfield to the east. I found Hadji, the blanket term used for locals (most especially hostile ones), hanging out below. They worked hard to collect the brass that fell from the sky. Our spent brass casings from fired rounds provided enough scrap value for them to make a living. I heard that they would get around 50 cents per casing, which was big money for them. The competition below appeared to be fierce, and we nicknamed these individuals "the Jawas" after *Star Wars* creatures. We'd shout quotes from the movie at them.

After not having flown or shot in over three months, it surprised me at how quickly I picked it all right back up. This was the fun part; shooting stuff with a Kiowa never got old. I lined up with the intended target on the ground, set my speed, and bumped the aircraft's nose skyward. The windscreen filled with blue and featured big, white, puffy clouds. I pushed the nose back over into a slight dive and then brought the M3P .50 caliber machine gun to life. The SP shook and shuddered with the violent concussions to his left, and then, I released the fire switch and called, "Cold, breaking right."

I was more on target than I had ever been and was super-pleased with myself. After shooting, we flew around the area close to Bagram, practicing combat maneuvering flight, as well as approaches to pinnacles and ridgelines while reading and dealing with the winds. Mountain flying was something I had limited experience with, and these mountains were exponentially larger than anything I had ever been amongst. Once we had done the remaining tasks discussed in the earlier briefing, I got a surprise change of plans.

We landed out in the middle of nowhere and were told we were going to do extraction training. I jumped out of the helicopter and ran over to the other Kiowa to strap myself onto the rocket pod, in order to simulate being rescued by my wingman. As good as this impromptu training was, I later learned that the area was not officially cleared of landmines leftover from the Soviet-Afghan War. I had landed in and ran through a probable Soviet minefield. I had mixed feelings, no doubt, but chief among them was the thankful resolve that none of us had been blown up.

CHAPTER 2

To understand how we operated, here's the nitty-gritty of how a mission would usually work. In the right seat of the Kiowa sat the primary pilot, who was tasked with flying for the day. His flight controls were set up specifically to control the aircraft, while also being able to switch between reference pages on his display and change between radio frequencies. This was all possible at the touch of buttons without removing either the right or left hand from the controls for even a second. The right seater also had the trigger for whatever weapon systems were mounted.

The commonly referred to "left seater" job was to operate the navigation system, set up the weapons systems, radios and other communications, and use the optics in the Mast Mounted Sight (MMS) atop our rotor system to look for things. The left seater may also be holding a pair of binoculars, a high-end digital camera, and even an M4 rifle in some cases, when necessary. Furthermore, the left seater also utilized a kneeboard on their thigh with notes, frequencies, times, and location grids scrawled all over it.

The left seater would also monitor up to five separate radios, at the same time. Sitting amongst all the equipment on the dash was also a mission packet. The packet contained page after page of secret documents, frequencies, locations, etc. that the left seater frequently needed to pull down to reference and input into the aircraft systems. A set of backup flight controls was also present in the event that he needed to take control of the aircraft for any reason.

Each Kiowa pilot was rated in both seats, and where one sat would be negotiated by the crew each flight. Since we Kiowas operated so independently by nature, we were by far the most flexible mission aircraft that the regular Army had, and we did not often require hours upon hours of planning. At the end of every flight, we completed a process known as an After Action Review (AAR) which was also the standard practice for any job and any task across the whole Army. The AAR was conducted in order to try to learn something, whether good or bad, and develop ourselves to be better at our jobs. Since I was new, each AAR yielded a vast amount of commentary and points of improvement, so I took everything carefully and closely to heart.

During the downtime, I worked to complete my training to become fully mission qualified. I wanted to learn how to best do my job and be taken under the auspices of those seasoned pilots who had operated and fought in the real-world circumstances. I knew that there had to be more to fighting the war than acronyms, reporting, and manuals. To my chagrin, I was still not on the mission schedule yet. The surplus of free time could be its own battle, and the boredom could make one stir-crazy. I tried to find odd tasks and help when I was able.

*

In mid-December, it relieved me to be almost done with training. For the last two days of the training phase, I was to adjust my sleep schedule and daily routine in order to become nocturnal. I had been looking forward to joining the night schedule team, so this was a welcome surprise. In my off time, I climbed into a Kiowa and practiced with the MMS. There was an art to adjusting the sight to attain the best and clear display picture that could only come from experience. The thermal capabilities proved to be a fantastic tool in catching the enemy laying IEDs and moving around when they believed they were otherwise concealed by darkness. When night hunting, we also flew "blacked out" so people on the ground could not see us. They may hear us, but a Kiowa is a pretty quiet helicopter and could be sneaky.

My body clock adjusted reasonably well to the night shift and just in time: December 18th marked my first official mission. It was a "deliberate" mission, which was the phrase that meant we had a purpose that we knew about beforehand and a list of tasks to complete. The mission was on a moonless, starless, and very dark night. Even with NVGs, the visibility and haze coupled with the lack of moonlight pushed our crews to the limits. We all agreed that it was what we referred to as "asshole dark" out and even our seasoned guys were less than thrilled about the visual challenges it presented. We flew around some areas I had just seen during my area orientation in the daylight, and it now looked like another planet. We checked houses and compounds (known as "qalats"), vehicles, patterns of life, and everything else of note that we'd been tasked to give details about. My saddle was breaking in a bit, and I was finding my operational groove. Although we found nothing of note that night, the following evening that I flew was very different.

The calm had already ended. My second real-world mission briefing was cut short by a phone call to our CP. There had been a few skirmishes earlier in the day, and some ground forces nearby were about to get into another fight. They requested air support, as it was their belief that the enemy were maneuvering close by. We hurried through the rest of our preparations and made it out to the aircraft. As we started up and tuned in the radios, I could hear the urgency of our need to be overhead growing. My pulse quickened, and I tried to move faster. My PC understood that I was new and would make mistakes, as every one of us had at that point before. But time was critical, so he still added to the pressure by telling me, "Dude, I get that you're just out of training, I really do. But, this is real-world shit and we gotta hurry the fuck up here!"

My pride and my ego hurt a little, but he was right. I had to learn to prioritize what to set up first and what could wait. The pressing issue was that our forces expected to be in enemy contact any minute. Some of what they had trained us to input, calibrate, and check within our helicopter systems was not always immediately important. The PC looked at me and said, "Remember: Grid. Freq. Callsign. Most of that other shit can wait to get done en route." That nugget of veteran wisdom of a seasoned Kiowa pilot stuck into my brain and catapulted my consciousness forward. I punched in the grid coordinates of the troubled ground unit. I placed their FM radio frequency at the top of our priority list. I confirmed with our TOC who I should talk to once we arrived.

I imprinted into my memory: *Grid. Freq. Callsign. All the other shit can wait.* Got it.

On our way to them, the Troops in Contact (or "TIC," for short) call sounded. The AK-47 fire erupted from concealed enemy positions and was met by ready U.S. forces. I was in the left seat working the MMS like crazy. The practice that I had taken using and adjusting the MMS a few days prior was paying off. I was now sweating and furiously talking the ground guys onto their objectives while spotting anything and everything detrimental to their safety. I enjoyed the hell out of it and the adrenaline rush became an instant addiction. The satisfaction of finally getting to be part of a real battle and make a difference suddenly hit me. All the training—the endless recitations and memorization of countless subjects, acronyms, lists, limitations, criteria—all of it became instantly worth it as I watched the United States Army Infantry kick the enemy's asses, all while being critically depended upon in my perch close above.

After breaking station with our ground guys and with no further support required, we headed towards the FARP on Bagram. When in remote areas, and especially when in a hurry, we would send an advance radio request. Our call would inform the support personnel how many minutes we were out and give them a chance to get ready. They then took our ammo order, kind of like going through a drive-through and saying, "About three hundred rounds of .50 cal, and five high-explosive 10lb rockets, please." We did not require a rapid FARP turn luckily, as our mission needs had shifted from supporting the ground guys into an intel-gathering mission. That's how it always was for us, and we lived by the phrase "Semper Gumby" which meant "always flexible and changing."

We were given coordinates and directed to gather intel in an area none of us had ever flown into and, honestly, had never even considered flying into. The lights of Bagram and its border towns disappeared behind us as we ventured to the dark side of the moon, passing very high over mountains and continuing to climb higher still. The lights denoting any semblance of civilization completely ceased, and no fires, or even candles, illuminated the few remaining sparse and abandoned clusters of qalats below. There appeared to be no one else for miles, although we knew better. We flew over a plateau and the surface of the ground atop it looked otherworldly, with smooth hills and evidence of erosion sloping down into crevasses and mini canyons. Many craters were present, some probably from Soviet bombs dropped long ago. It was still dark out, and I tilted my head back and tried to identify something outside of the cockpit without the aid of my NVGs. I saw only inky blackness. I looked over to my buddy flying.

"Dude, this place is eerie. I have a bad feeling about this," I said.

"Yeah man, this is nuts. I feel it, too."

We continued onwards, "alone and unafraid," as we used to say. Our wingman assured us that their crew was equally alert about this creepy place. I was relieved when my right seater and the PC of the other aircraft agreed that we finally had enough and had gotten what we needed. We descended out of the alien place, turning a few corners and cresting more mountains. Then, through the haze, down in the distance, we could finally make out the lights of Bagram. We descended into the bowl and upon leveling out on a course to the airfield, both of us let out a big long "whew!"

I called to our Trail ship on the radio, and they chuckled and explained that they had done the same thing. I really don't know how to describe the feeling or why it was so spooky, but I think there is something to be said when all four crew members feel the same bad ju-ju at the same time. The tension finally subsided when we were on the ground at the refuel pad.

*

The next several nights gained in action. On December 22, we got to help some ground guys in a convoy by giving them a warm and fuzzy while flying overhead and checking for signs of enemy fighters or IEDs along their route. There were essentially two main types of IEDs, being delineated by their detonation mechanisms—pressure plate and remote detonation. A pressure plate is used much like a landmine: Once something steps on or rolls over the top of the plate, it triggers a mechanism to create the explosion. Remote detonation refers to an individual initiating the explosion, whether it be by a command wire linked to a remote or via a more advanced wireless means, such as a cell phone. The explosive itself could be a military munition such as a rocket or mortar round, a land mine, or a homegrown package of destruction containing metal objects like nails and shards. Also, coins, as in murder through pocket change. That was one reason we never gave Hadji any coins, and luckily, all of their own national currency was paper notes. Marbles were dangerous, too.

We had stumbled upon a convoy while doing our own flying patterns out in the area looking for work, and it took a bit for us to figure out who they were or how to talk to them. All we knew was that they were obviously broken down in a bad neighborhood, so we stuck around. I made a very low and slow pass by them and flashed my infrared spectrum (IR) lights, knowing that they would see us with their NVGs, but anyone without the aid of night vision would not. One of the gunners in his turret atop a truck known as an MRAP excitedly started waving an IR light back at me, then pointed and circled his light beam on the temperamental vehicle in front of him with it. This act of creating a "lasso" with an IR light beam was the best way to quickly gain the attention of anyone in the area and point something out.

On the next pass, I put my aircraft's IR spotlight briefly on the indicated vehicle and rocked the aircraft. The rocking of wings is a general sign in aviation for hello, goodbye, or acknowledgment. We ended up sticking with them for quite some time, escorting their limping convoy all the way back towards Bagram and checking the route, fore and aft, for any kind of movement by Hadji. Typically, when people heard helicopters, many of them decided to quickly duck indoors. Most of the civilians in the villages (whether they liked us or not) rarely wanted any trouble or to be perceived as a threat. Spooking us up in the sky was usually bad for all parties involved.

It felt good to do another worthwhile mission. The hours upon hours of circling and doing figure-eights above a convoy could get boring, but one had to keep it in perspective. The soldiers on the ground undoubtedly breathed a little sigh of relief when we were overhead, and I always tried to remember that.

We supported the battered convoy for another four hours before it finally and successfully drove into the gates of Bagram. My butt was numb from all the aggressive steep turns over the convy and their route, and I was mostly at fault for inducing it.

The next morning, I was off duty and heard the crew chiefs outside loudly nailing boards to construct a walkway over the rocky, muddy ground. They'd unfortunately woken up a night crew guy who wasn't happy about it. My sleep schedule was askew, so they didn't wake me, at least. Sleep/wake cycles were one of the biggest but understated difficulties with 24-hour Quick Reaction Force (QRF) operations.

One of our Maintenance Test Pilots (MTP), CW3 Erik Newhouse, additionally served as our troop's de facto personal trainer. Bald and sporting the obligatory Cavalry mustache, Erik was a fitness freak and the closest to a bodybuilder that we had. He had been in the Army for a long time and had the most experience in our troop. He was, by far, one of the best pilots a new guy could hope to fly with, as he possessed the patience, skill, and mentorship abilities to help us better ourselves. We would work out at 0000-0130, four to five days a week. He was especially talented at finding exercises that targeted new muscles we didn't know about. I was eating healthy, and that, coupled with getting back into the gym, helped me feel better and less fatigued. I ate jerky, trail mix, and dried fruit like a machine and even skipped dinner for it occasionally. I had vowed not to get fat while I was deployed and began to realize the dedication necessary to uphold such a promise.

Another of our other many mission hats was that of escorting UH-60 Blackhawk and CH-47 Chinook transport and utility aircraft around the various, more kinetic areas, which was the word adopted by the military to denote something potentially or actually dangerous. Our team would fly ahead of the other helicopters, conducting recon to check out the sites they considered for landing. This was where we would decide if we felt as though it were safe and clear of the enemy or obstacles. We would then radio back to those whom we escorted to inform them of the perceived status of their intended Landing Zone (LZ), or Pickup Zone (PZ). We would do this by relaying our Cherry/Ice call. The words were an obsolete holdover from when a more-advanced enemy could be reasonably suspected to have hacked into our communications and could listen in. Cherry meant "The LZ (or PZ) is hot; danger exists from enemy presence and fire," while Ice signaled "LZ (or PZ) is cold; there is a reasonable certainty or belief that no immediate dangers are present."

Sometimes, there was an emergent reason for us to choose a landing area for them, like in those cases where someone was wounded and a MEDEVAC aircraft needed to plant down right next to where an IED went off. We also had to be cognizant if there was a threat to the MEDEVAC, because sometimes the wounded were used as a decoy by insurgents to kill a bigger target, such as an American helicopter responding to the carnage. Our enemy may not have been as classically educated as their western adversaries, but they were certainly effective masters in the creative art of imparting violence.

CHAPTER 3

I had just recently read a quote from Ernest Hemingway that I found profoundly fit my situation. In 1936, he wrote: "Certainly there is no hunting like the hunting of man and those who have hunted armed men long enough and liked it, never really care for anything else thereafter." I relayed it over the radio and we all chuckled, as many in our troop fell into this category. I didn't realize it then, but this notion would forever stick with me and prove to be an integral part of who I would become.

On Christmas Eve, I walked to my locker, gathered my things, and began preparing for another flight. I had all but forgotten about the holiday, and it wasn't until I was going about my routine that I even realized what evening it was. The only hint of Christmas was the crew chief walking by in a Santa hat and the freezing temperatures. I shrugged, put on a Santa hat that was passed over to me, and conducted my preflight. I spent my Christmas Eve with a low-key flight and a crude movie name game over the radio that kept us laughing and awake. After post-flight and debriefing, we settled into the Operations room and aired the last few years of *South Park*'s Christmas specials. It was juvenile sick humor and had us all in side-splitting laughter. The comedy was just what we all needed. After a while, things calmed again, and I finally fell asleep.

I awoke from the couch in the TV room to an Apache pilot kicking my boot and being told: "Merry Christmas, Sunshine!" I sleepily began walking back to my room and checked my available cell phone minutes. I had just enough to make about eight minutes of Christmas calls before getting back into my room to sit by my two-foot tree and open the few presents I had received from Sally and my loved ones stacked under it.

After opening my last present, I slept the entire day and only woke up after hearing people moving around. I remembered something about a special chow delivery to our gym for Christmas dinner. Walking in, I was dismayed to find that I had slept through most of it but got a few cold turkey scraps and some sweet potatoes and egg nog. The Apache unit's commander burst out of a hallway suddenly, dressed in a Santa outfit with a captured enemy AK-47 rifle draped over his shoulder, ho-ho-ho-ing while everyone laughed and cheered. He passed out presents to each one of his guys, every pilot and crew chief having to briefly sit in his lap for a photo.

It was awesome and helped take away that feeling that only a Christmas spent far away from home can make you feel. The remaining duration of the deployment was becoming more and more real to all of us. The next Christmas I would have would mark around a month of being home from Afghanistan, and that was a mildly depressing thought.

A few days after Christmas, I was finally on a normalized flying schedule. Both QRF and scheduled missions increased in frequency, and I got 10 hours of flying over the course of only two nights. I began to settle into my role as a scout pilot; the rapidly accumulating flight time helped me feel more seasoned and useful. We knew the information most valuable to the guys on the ground, and developed effective strategies to keep convoys and patrols safer and the enemy more at bay. IEDs were still an issue, just as they had been from the very beginning of our conflicts in the Middle East with the dishonorable savages who fought like cowards.

I tried hard not to walk down the path of hating my enemy, as history has shown that hating the enemy often leads to less effective outcomes than those occurring from carefully studying and exploiting the enemy. Strong emotions, like hatred, lead to rash decisions. It was still hard to place that wise knowledge into personal practice.

The time seemed to go by rather quickly and weeks began to feel like only days. The private gym set up just for our area allowed us to work out like prison inmates and thus, cut down on stress. Another WOJG alongside me was CW2 Justin "Chico" Chacon, and like myself, he possessed an equally warped sense of humor. He was Latino, a California-born man who had also joined as a teenager and had experienced a long life in the Army since he was previously enlisted on active duty. He was famous for some of his one-liners and his unique way of speaking to our lieutenants. He would be told something like, "Chico, I need you to get this supply paperwork done and sent up the chain." Chico would respond literally, "I understand, sir...comma. Pause for effect. I'll get to it as soon as I can."

We developed into good friends, and he also proved to be a great workout partner. Treating the deployment like a prison and working out or reading often initially aided in curtailing any depression due to sitting idle for lengths of time. I was enjoying flying the Kiowa and loved supporting our ground forces. The senior guys in my troop told me that I would eventually get sick of flying and my zeal would be beaten out of me. I'd had a pilot's license since high school and had been flying around with my father since grade school. My grandfather had flown P-40 Warhawks during WWII. Even my brother and uncle were pilots. The love of aviation was ingrained in me, so I shrugged the comments off and figured that perhaps I was different. Flying didn't feel like a job to me, yet. I really hoped that this would not change—that the love of flight would not be stripped from me by the Army and war. I was still young and naïve, however.

*

Operations in January continued to pick up speed. On the night of the 7th, our guys were spread out in the building, all sitting on QRF. I walked alone down the hallway from our gym towards our CP, and then I heard a sound. The distinct "whoosh-whoosh-whoosh" and whine of incoming rockets resounded, and I barely had a second to respond or process it. The earth shook and insanely loud explosions echoed just outside the building. The concussion and force from the 107mm rockets rocked the building hard, and dirt, dust, and debris from the ceiling and lockers immediately saturated the air. The electricity flickered. I stumbled and almost fell against the lockers, instantly enraged. I heard a few people coughing back towards the gym as I raced to open my locker. I yelled over my shoulder, asking if everyone was alright, as I grabbed some gear. I heard a positive response from the gym, and one of our crew chiefs did a quick look around to make sure no one inside the gym was hit. The phone in the CP began ringing, and I heard someone pick it up as I ran outside toward the helicopters.

The hangar had taken damage, and I rounded a corner just in time to see a door fly open and a few coughing and gagging soldiers stumbling out in a cloud of dust.

"Is everyone in there alright?!" I asked. "Was anyone hit?"

"We're okay, sir, that was fucking close!" One soldier yelled back. "Go get 'em!" The crew chief was right, we had to launch as quickly as possible. I ran past a large, deep crater in the ground, shrapnel shards having torn a path of destruction back towards our building. An Apache sat with obvious damage. I continued running to my helicopter and threw on my gear. Reaching into the cockpit from outside, I flipped on the battery switch to start the system sequence to get us airborne at record speed.

Nick came sprinting up with notes he'd just hurriedly written. We didn't even need to talk, as we both ran through the QRF launch drill. Others were rushing outside to help and get our team airborne. I stopped one man and asked him if anyone was reported hurt or killed yet. "Not sure, sir. It nailed an Apache good and damaged a rack of Chinook blades. Everyone I've seen so far somehow managed to not get hit."

I thanked him and promised that whoever had done it had little time remaining to their life span if we found them. The engine began to whine, and the low rumble of the turbine light off happened almost in perfect timing with our wingman. In just four minutes, our team was taking off and hauling ass towards the fence line and reported direction of origin for the attack. We searched long and hard, and The Rocket Man had played his cards right. The enemy was a ghost already, and we cursed his luck. That volley had been a successful one for the enemy in terms of damage caused and nerves rattled. Fortunately for us, not a single injury had occurred, at least this time around.

We returned to the airfield, and one of the Apache guys slapped me on the ass. "Good game."

I nodded back. "How's your bird out there?" I asked.

"Man, that's gonna take a while to fix. It's pretty banged up from that last rocket that hit," he replied. "One of the crew chiefs was out back smoking when it happened and a piece of shrapnel that had slowed down just enough bounced off of his boot. Says it scared the shit out of him and he lit another cigarette to celebrate being alive."

In the 48 hours of the 7th and 8th, I had spent 28 of those hours on duty, with nearly 12 of them actually in the air. The increase in activity was surprising, and we began to hope that the tempo would slow back down.

*

I was set to start "reversing out" back to the day schedule and had mixed feelings about it. I had to stay awake the entire first day, which by my current body clock was my sleep time. I would then attempt to sleep that evening and stay up the whole next day and sleep that evening. I had no choice but to be successful in my reverse out. We had a small group of pilots to work our mission load, and I began a shift at 0600 the following morning. I knew it would take a bit longer than two days for my body to fully recover from weeks upon weeks of nocturnal living, but we all had to deal with it the best we could. Snapping the body back and forth between nocturnal and standard living too many times in succession without adequate adjustment could be devastating to an individual's mental and physical health. Even though we did a good job of remaining within the legal limits of these switches, it definitely created a hard existence at times for those who were switched most often. As a junior pilot, I was in just a proportionate enough pool to supplant our operations with adequate coverage. Our PCs, however, being at a less-than-ideal staffing level, forced them to bear the worst brunt of these demands.

The recent flying and busy schedule left me tired and a bit complacent. I made a bonehead move and, although it was essentially chalked up as a rookie mistake resulting from fatigue, I was still hard on myself about it. Missing steps on a checklist, especially steps like ensuring that there is enough ammunition on board in a combat zone, was inexcusable, and I missed it. Once this was discovered by my PC, he was so mad at me that he couldn't even speak to me for a while. I felt terrible and instead of moving on, I dwelled on it, and got into the aircraft before realizing that my rifle was still inside the building. It was all a serious wake-up call. I was counseled informally by Nick and Erik, being two of our senior mentors, and having them disappointed in me was greater than any official punishment. The hit to my ego didn't matter—guys on the ground needed me to be at the top of my game at all times. I revisited manuals, procedures, and other material in a promise to get my head back on straight. The mistake had fortunately been caught, and the resulting kick in the ass had made me better.

I requested to stay in the left seat on my next several flights. A few nights' consistency for hours on end with the MMS allowed you to become more proficient in its adjustments and usage. A thermal imaging system takes a lot of minute adjustments, and I was continuing to improve with it. The left seat also incorporated other duties in the cockpit to aid the pilot, who was primarily on the controls, and it was good to equalize my competency in both seats. This was especially true for a newbie like me, and I could tell my confidence was rising proportionately to my experience level, which was a good sign.

After two days, I completed my reverse out of nocturnal living. On the last day, I made it through the entire span of sunrise to sunset without sleeping, partly thanks to a visit from the French. They flew in two of their Tiger attack helicopters, which is the French version of the Apache. Accompanying the Tigers were about 20 pilots and crew chiefs to our CAV/Attack island, and we pilots immediately started talking shop. The French soldiers climbed in and out of the Kiowa and Apache, and we opened doors and climbed in and out of their Tigers. Their commanding officer noted my last name, Robicheaux, and we subsequently discussed fine Cajun cuisine. We were all very interested in the kind of equipment and machinery the other nation had and how they used it. The French guys were cool, and this was a good opportunity for us to communicate face to face, voice concerns, and come together as allies.

After eating lunch with them, I got on our little bus that we called the Panda Express due to the transit maps inside and obvious former life it had lived as a small town transport somewhere in Japan. We headed to the west side to resupply the basic essentials (soap, phone minutes, pens/pencils, etc.) at the Post Exchange (PX), which is essentially Army Walmart. While I was on the west side, I decided to call my brother Marc's old pal from the 20th Special Forces (SF) Group out of Mississippi. Sure enough, the man answered and our several weeks-long game of phone tag ended. I showed up at the separate SF compound within the Bagram perimeter and was escorted into their world. My brother had ended his time in the military as a part of their unit, and they talked trash about him leaving, wishing that he had come with them. Naturally, we decided to call Marc. It was not even 0500 back in the states, so he answered a bit sleepily, but instantly perked up and was glad to hear from everyone. I ended up hanging out for a few hours with the SF guys, and we exchanged a lot of information about what we each did and how we may work together. I was sad to hear that they'd be leaving in the next few weeks and hoped that we'd be able to keep a rapport with their replacements.

The 20th SF Group allegedly ran "Pirate Radio," 96.5 FM. It was an unauthorized, privately-operated radio station and was hated by higher commands. No one had been successful in shutting them down, and they had quite a cult following on Bagram. They played music 24/7 and had their own set of no rules. I was given a bumper sticker with the illicit radio station's logo and info on it, and I promised to take a picture next to the Kiowa with it. It was good to meet some friendly people who knew my brother, so although I had never met them before, I was treated like one of the family. After my recent bungles, it was a great pool of motivation to draw from.

My flight the following day would be a big change of pace for me. I would see more clearly and be able to pick things out in more detail while scouting. I fell asleep to the distant sounds of gunfire and explosions, hoping for a flight where all hell doesn't break loose. We awoke to an early set of chow, mission briefs, coffee, and preflight. The plan was to fly at least four hours doing convoy escorts and looking for IEDs. There was some miscommunication about one of our convoys, so we had the opportunity to free fly around a little and practice some maneuvering and terrain flight while we waited. We crested mountains at high speeds and dove over the backsides, flying low level over qalats and fields (mindful of wires). The whole thing made our team downright jovial, and I desperately hoped to have days like that more often.

I groped through my flight suit pocket, finding the packet of caffeine paste that I needed to keep my rush. Finally feeling happy, I thought about the little things that I would appreciate so much when I returned home. Affection from loved ones, being able to stay indoors and walk just steps to the bathroom in the middle of the night, peace if I so desired, and no more damn rocket attacks. I could walk downstairs and have the ability to cook literally whatever I wanted in my kitchen, even enjoy a late-night glass of scotch or wine at my bar if I chose.

I sighed and snapped back to reality just as we rolled hard into another maximum degree dive and hard bank. The roller coaster ride of adrenaline and caffeine brought me out of my daydream state, punching me straight back into the present. I hollered a wild yell and we laughed hard. For now, this would suffice and so long as we survived, all of that other stuff could wait.

*

We were increasingly flying many more hours per day and being assigned some great missions. My skills as a scout were ever improving and a few days later, I was able to find something small and of potentially significant importance to report up for the first time all on my own. This resulted in a solid and genuine kudos from the others in our debrief. The intelligence folks were very happy, and I finally swelled with pride again. I was back. My slump had subsided and the enemy suffered as well for it.

It wasn't long before my mood came crashing down from happiness to rage in an instant. An IED suddenly blew up a truck in our convoy below. The MRAP truck billowed black smoke and burned as the wounded came stumbling out of the vehicle and fell hard into the dirt. Others from nearby MRAPs raced over, guiding the dazed and screaming soldiers away as a few more jumped into the burning wreckage to save those still inside. A few bodies were pulled out and laid in the dirt. One of them was very badly burned and bloody, and I couldn't tell if he was still alive. The unit below didn't have a medic with them and was on the radio calling for help, desperate to save their comrade. My gut wrenched, my heart pounded. I'd been a medic. I had the basic knowledge and medical gear that I needed to try to stabilize the patient. We needed to establish an airway. We needed to stop the bleeding. We needed to land so I could get out and help!

No. My comrades told me no and brought me back to the present. This could be a trap, and I was not a medic anymore. I needed to toughen up, stay in the air, and do my job to the best of my ability. We had to protect the MEDEVAC helicopter and their medics scrambling to come to assist. I needed to check for the safest and closest place that the MEDEVAC bird could land.

I saw red. Not just the red of the man's blood, but the red of my hatred and rage for the enemy who had hit them. The wisdom of not hating the enemy didn't seem to apply. I hated them with full passion; and while they were warriors, I didn't see them as such. They had hit the guys we were protecting, and although irrational, the guilt and responsibility sat heavy on our shoulders. Shaking with anger, I set about clearing my head. I told myself, *Help where you can, listen to your team. Find a landing zone for the Blackhawk. Ensure there is nothing near the zone you pick, no hazards to create more dead or dying. That's your job now.*

The Air Force Pararescue Jumpers (PJs) from right next door on CAV/ Attack Island were in their Blackhawk, minutes away with a team of field medics whose sole job in life was to rescue wounded and desperate isolated personnel on the battlefield. If anyone could arrive right there and now, it was them. We talked with the PJs, callsign Gonzo on the radio, relaying our position and the condition of the wounded, as best we could gather. Gonzo assured us that their aircraft was mere minutes out, as they were much closer than the Blackhawk assigned from our task force still on the ground at Bagram.

I was relieved; our Gonzo boys would come and save the man. We had the landing zone picked out and provided cover for Gonzo in case some opportunistic enemy was getting the shot that they had been waiting for. As Gonzo was on their approach, we watched as the wounded on the ground were getting patched and covered up as best as possible. Then, Gonzo suddenly broke off their approach and departed the area.

"What the fuck?!" One of our guys shouted. "Where are they going?!" I couldn't believe what I was seeing, my brain wouldn't allow the translation. We transmitted our alarmed query to Gonzo, and their response sent an icy shiver down my spine: They'd been ordered to not respond to the casualty.

They were just as upset about it as we were. This was an Army affair and was under the jurisdiction and responsibility of our task force, so we were launching our own assets. Americans lay bleeding in that dirty Afghan road, but incongruent procedures of inter-service military cooperation prevented what was common sense and a proper response.

I didn't have time to cater to the anger inside. We all just set our jaws, having to watch what happened with no power to change a thing. I had never been more ready to kill anyone in my entire life than I was at that moment. A seed of doubt was planted from that experience, and I just couldn't shake it. Our own procedures became an enemy to our collective survival. Would it be possible that some crazy procedural doctrine could leave me or one of my comrades to a similar fate one day?

CHAPTER 4

W e received two senior pilots from our Charlie Troop down in Jalalabad to assist us with our flight schedule and to take some of the load off of our PC shortage issues. One of them was an MTP with a wealth of knowledge and experience. In a very short time, I learned a ton of tips, tricks, rules of thumb, and overall finesse in the operation of our helicopter. He also began to steer our troop into implementing more advanced combat flight and attack tactics, techniques, and procedures, which were impressive and welcome. It was all dangerous stuff when you got down to it. These maneuvers required a lot of skill and coordination, as well as trust in the other helicopter and crew to do their part of the dance.

We continued along on our typical QRF Day Shift, which usually went something like this:

Around 0500, I woke up, got ready, then went over to the troop. I figured out what bird I was in, then proceeded to preflight in the very dark and chilly air, climbing atop and knocking around in an ice-cold aircraft. Following that small ritual, everyone would then conduct a crew change and sit down for the early morning weather and intelligence brief. Now and then, I was reminded of the words of Mel Gibson in the movie *Air America*: "Guys, I really wish that you wouldn't use the word 'intelligence' to describe what you do..."

From there, aside from being the at-a-moment's-notice, on-call QRF asset, we would decide where to go, what was most important to do, when to go, etc. Shortly after this, we would launch at whatever time our crew needed to complete any deliberate or other mission requirements. Many times, we would be additionally tasked with things while in the air. Upon landing, we'd refuel and hope for some lunch to be waiting for us. Hopefully, we'd even have time to eat it. Later, we flew again. Before we knew it, we had come to dinner time, and hopefully, someone had gotten it for us. I would then finally be able to return to my room after our shift change by about 2000-ish, maybe slightly earlier, more often than not slightly later. At that point, I was usually ready for nothing more than sleep. Around 0500, we would repeat the cycle.

I was fortunate to have the following day off. My equally junior Kiowa and workout pal, Chico, was covering my flight so I could attend a 20th Special Forces Group BBQ. They had invited me after my visit to their compound, and Chico knew that I wasn't only going for chow. Any dealings behind the scenes with SF folks could be potentially beneficial for us receiving more interesting mission opportunities. The SF guys, whom I had come to affectionately blanket nickname "the bearded ones," were leaving soon and would be introducing me to their replacements (some of whom had already arrived). I hoped to get a good working relationship started outside of the normal official channels. My most sincere hope was to coordinate accidental meetups in the field so that by circumstance and coincidence, we might function on "impromptu" missions together.

On the morning of January 17th, I hitchhiked over to the west side and met up for the BBQ. Hitchhiking on BAF was strongly frowned upon, as it could be dangerous and get someone potentially kidnapped and whisked off the base to never be seen again. However, sometimes there were no other alternatives, and I would be picky about which stranger's car I would climb into. Naturally, I preferred contractor vehicles with American-looking folks behind the wheel, and even better, some company logo on it rather than a beat-up, murder mobile-looking ride. I kept my Beretta close and chambered just in case I got into a car with a contractor who had a higher-paying bidder. Paranoid perhaps, but better safe than sorry.

The SF guys ended up cooking hundreds of hot dogs (which ran out quickly), and an incalculable amount of burgers, steaks, and even Louisiana-style boudin! It was a beautiful sunny day with a comfortable, cool temperature. Most of the guys I had met and knew were busy at the grill, so I sat on a picnic table for hours relaxing and soaking it all in. I probably drank five or six Beck's non-alcoholic near-beers just to feel like I was at home. They'd forgotten to tell me to wear civilian clothes, but I didn't really mind. Being a warrant officer with unit patches and such on my uniform did get me some curious glances. Most of the guys did not wear unit insignia, and everyone on the compound was pretty squared away and professional, so no one bothered me aside from welcomes and short pleasantries. One or two even figured out that I was a pilot just by my rank, and when they asked what I flew and I replied with my position as a Kiowa pilot, they just grinned and shook my hand hard. It was gratifying, as nothing else needed to be said and I was in turn honored to meet and support them.

In my opinion, the men that surrounded me were quintessential warriors, much unlike several of the Pizza Hut-frequenting, latté-sipping people throughout Bagram.

Once the SF guys drove me home and we said our farewells, I had to mentally readjust back to my reality that was the east side of the airfield and my mission at hand. I had an earlier-than-normal showtime the following morning, so I needed to wind down. It was a good thing that I had turned in early, for my morning flight was a solid, non-split up rollercoaster that was much different from our previously uneventful norm. The area had suddenly come to life, with both sides deciding that it was a good day for some skirmishes. Our radios were a-buzz, and the missions coming across to us were legitimate and continued to splinter into different primary and secondary objectives. Bullets from AK-47s and larger were answered by bullets from M4s and much larger. Luckily, none of our side experienced any casualties, but I could not say the same about the other side.

The skirmishes escalated to battles, and the danger continued to rapidly increase. At one point, I experienced pure suspense and adrenaline, a high I wasn't sure I'd ever felt before. My world had erupted into the biggest and craziest blend of chaos that I had never even known existed. My body tingled, my senses were heightened, and my mind raced. I felt as though I was burning a few thousand calories per minute as we fought like mad. The previous experience with Hadji shedding the blood of our protected ground unit was being avenged. In the earlier days of my writing, I kept details even out of my own journals so unfortunately I cannot recall the specifics of this day and refuse to just make something up. It was a good, but exhausting, day helping our ground units.

Once that conflict had cooled, and we were no longer required, we made our way up a valley to the north of a large Soviet compound we'd discovered. Suddenly, we flew right by a Russian ZSU-23/4 radar-guided, four-barreled, anti-aircraft killing tank. If we were on a conventional battlefield with an organized enemy, that's where I would have died. Luckily for us, although it was remarkably preserved, it was noticeably damaged and had been discarded by its operators long ago. Of all the abandoned vehicles littered around the area, this particular one was the scariest to us because it was in the best condition of any other wreckage I'd seen.

I had a lot going on that I wished that I could write home about, but because of the sensitive nature of what we were getting into and the fact that it was all an ongoing operation, we could only talk about it amongst ourselves. My day flights had pushed the envelope even further than I had ever experienced. Despite the ridiculous responses and ineptitude of our higher orders, I remained in reasonably fine spirits and our team did our best to take it all in stride.

The following day on the 19th, the sky fell, and I flew to the maximum legal window of my duty day, logging right at seven hours of mixed day and NVG flying. It was one of those days that one small occurrence could get blown way out of proportion and vastly shift the focus in the wrong direction. Overreaction, drama, and war was a terrible cocktail mix, and I could go without evenings like that again and be just fine, but no matter what, I knew that the circus we'd just dealt with would undoubtedly happen again. And again.

After we refueled for the last time, we set the aircraft down on our parking pad and slowly moved through the last of our checklist items and shutting down. The crew chiefs could see that we were beyond exhausted. I slumped back and closed my eyes as the rotor blades slowly coasted down. Both aircraft crews sat silently in our Kiowas, all of us seemingly in a half daze. Once the blades stopped, we practically melted out of the cockpit and were assisted by our awesome crew chiefs patiently standing by. They helped gather our things after literally helping us from the cockpit to the ground, then carrying almost all of our gear inside for us. Erik and I looked at each other and shook our heads. Many in our troop were *Star Wars* geeks, so we decided that our flying was a lot like Mos Eisley back home on planet Tatooine. From that point forward, we used *Star Wars* nomenclature to designate areas and add them to our personal maps. When we would reference things like "Kessel Run," the Apache pilots just stared blankly at us until we showed them why an area was named.

A few shifts later, we discovered a new flight route, replete with amazing canyons to fly down. This new favorite started above 8,000 feet and wound all the way down past a few dug-in terraced villages and eventually emptied into a river valley. It was a blast to fly down while hauling ass and practicing terrain flight. We dubbed the route "Beggar's Canyon." There was an unfriendly village down towards the end of Beggar's Canyon, so we put the route in our back pocket as a secret ingress option, should we ever need to sneak up on the village without alerting their usual spotters. All over our area were locals who would pass along to the enemy that American helicopters were in the area and which way we seemed to be headed.

Our Beggar's Canyon route ended with emptying over a final canyon at around 20 feet over a river. We continued down low, noting all the built-up positions along the banks. We began to refer to the many three-sided, low rock-walled curiosities scattered about as "duck blinds." There were also large rocks in the river that jutted up out of the water, much like what someone might do to make the crudest decoy possible. Besides the duck blinds, we also found and mapped out a few crossing sites. The ones most interesting to us were those with a wire going across, which we knew were used to swap supplies between sides of the river, including weapons.

Following that fun and despite my being off the next day, there was no opportunity to sleep in because we all needed to do our part and make the breakfast run for the guys who were on shift. I wished we could find a better system than the guy who was off waking up early as hell to go fetch breakfast, however, our group was small and it was just how it had to be. In my downtime, I watched a documentary called *The Gem Hunter in Afghanistan*. It was like a modern-day, real-life *Indiana Jones*. The documentary followed a man on one of his many trips to Afghanistan in search of rare and precious gemstones. I recognized some names and places that were visited. Of greatest interest to me was the history and trading of the lapis lazuli stone. The rich blue stone was mostly unique to the region and had been found in Egyptian burial sites over 5,000 years old. The masks of pharaohs and golden statues used lapis stone in some form. Evidence showed that the stone had been mined and traded for at least 6,000 years along the Silk Road in the ancient world. There were many lapis lazuli artifacts and sculptures for sale in the bazaar and other "Hadji-marts," as we called them. I have always liked Egyptian and other ancient cultural history, architecture, and artwork. To see that key elements of some of this came from a mine just north of where I sat gave me a profound respect for the mountains I frequently flew among. We used to say all the time, "This place is so beautiful, it's really a shame that so many assholes live here..."

As I pondered antiquity, my piece-o-crap cell phone died. It was used, torn up, and I had to use duct tape in order to get the charger just right. This time, it really had died, so off I went to the Hadji-mart cell phone shop. Upon entering the small shop, I encountered what I had expected: pure madness. Many contractors and military personnel crowded into the cramped store, and the salesmen bargained and remained as animated as ever. The difference between the cell shop and the bazaar was that they actually had a commodity which was highly sought after, and they were also the only cell phone shop around. I'd take waiting in line at the AT&T store for two hours any day over having to barter for an overpriced, cheaply made cell phone. I knew it was necessary so that I could keep in touch with my troop and family, but forking over money to a cell shop that probably paid quiet taxes to the enemy made me feel less than proud. But, hey, at least it had a flashlight which helped me unlock my room in the always-dark B Hut! Little trivial pleasures were everything to me then.

I traveled back to the east side after a phone call, understanding that we were going to have an interesting day beginning early the next morning. My PC, Nick, tried to convey that we needed to link up and pre-brief a bit. He was cryptic, but that was out of necessity. We didn't discuss sensitive info over our cell phones, but I got the basic understanding that we would have some real stuff to do and I anticipated that there would not be a dull moment. I stopped messing around and made it back to my room to ensure that I could be well-rested, well-fed, and properly hydrated. I would need to be in the best shape that I could be. A recon for a sniper team insertion needed to be conducted, and we had to ensure they were dropped in the best location for their mission.

The next morning, we mapped grids and flew along ridgelines deep in our main and large hotbed of bad guy activity called the Tagab Valley. The valley was vast, with many smaller offshoots holding ever-increasing danger the deeper in you traveled. The Tagab was populated by many locals and featured a large river system and tons of farmland and foliage-dense areas, surrounded by tall and steep mountains. It was controlled by French forces and some other U.S. and multinational special forces. The south end of the vast valley featured Lake Surobi. From the eastern edge of the lake, a series of valleys and canyons led out to Jalalabad and Asadabad, situated along a dangerous border region with Pakistan and where most of our 3-17 Cavalry people were located. A narrow mountain pass extended far from the southwestern tip of the lake and gave passage all the way through the tall mountains into the eastern outskirts of Afghanistan's capital city, Kabul.

We finally located a few suitable landing zones that would be devoid of enemy influence. They were high up and almost inaccessible to anything other than goats, and after hearing the target and mission of the sniper team, I was absolutely astonished at how far away they intended to shoot from. We took our pictures and submitted our grids, being confident in our work. The ground force receiving the intel was surprised and applauded the movie and presentation that we'd made for them. It was very gratifying.

*

The flying continued to be anything but boring. I was gaining a healthy respect for the fact that the enemy was dangerous and would act offensively if given the chance. We weren't screwing around doing "idiot circles," as we called them, very much anymore. The enemy had been allowed to become very emboldened over the past mild winter. We did an exercise where I was to get low, set the aircraft at a certain power setting, and was not allowed to make any further adjustments unless absolutely necessary (i.e., about to run into a mountainside). We were practicing low-level masking and maneuvering over open plains, while also ensuring that no power lines or man-made obstacles, such as towers, would get us. I had become familiar with many of the areas around our Area of Operations (AO) and was comfortable whipping through canyons and riverbeds and sneaking up on villages and clusters of people at high speeds. This sneak-attack flying caught them off guard, and was a wild and old-fashioned fun way to fly. Low and fast had a purpose, too—our flight path didn't give them a chance to "get a bead on us" (which is military-speak for aiming well enough to effectively shoot something) should someone take a shot as a target of opportunity. This element of surprise also allowed us to catch them in the act of whatever they were doing before their few seconds of frozen shock wore off—much like how a hunter will make a deliberate noise, freezing their prey momentarily to take advantage of the pause.

There were many schools of thought on this kind of flying. Some said that it was more dangerous because of such low altitudes and high speeds. These nay-sayers usually would prefer to remain high, with the argument that they were out of weapons range. Although still relatively new to the game, I had begun to formulate my own opinions on the matter. From what I had experienced, both schools of thought were correct in certain situations and a blanket statement that one way was right or wrong was a senseless endeavor. In areas that were historically (and through personal experience) known to be undoubtedly hostile, remaining high was a reasonable plan. Small arms had a limited range, and as long as you knew and understood that, your tactics for the area of interest could be formulated around that coupled with other factors.

When flying into an area, a lot of planning and calculation was quickly performed by the pilot to ensure the best odds of survival and offensive effectiveness. In some situations, remaining low and fast were advantageous for the same reasons listed previously in respect to the element of surprise. If doing this, however, you can't plan on sticking around too long or doing it again too often. We'd get an unfiltered look, seeing if anything was suspicious or if we took fire, and then, we'd move on before anyone could organize or hide. Some teenagers would throw rocks at us and were pretty good at it. Some had rock chuckers that could sling the rocks at what felt like the speed of a bullet.

Increasing violence and combat losses in our and neighboring regions forced our higher-ups to finally make wise decisions and speak the only language that the locals understood: punishment. The bazaar on our base was suddenly shut down until further notice. Bagram was almost entirely closed to outsiders after Hadji's idea of a fun evening was to continuously lob a lot of explosives over the fence.

Our team flew overhead one of the main entrance gates to Bagram. Sketchy local workers were massing in a mob, pissed off and yelling because they were being denied entry into the base, where they likely made ten times a normal Afghan's wage. Most of them saw us as invaders and they sympathized with our enemies, but we paid well. More began to gather until they were outside most of the gates, throwing rocks, chanting, and acting like savages. We flew low over their heads several times to disperse the crowds. When that didn't work, we began dropping smoke grenades amongst them. They were all starting to really piss us off, and I wanted them to lose their minds and keep being stupid. If their display could get any more out of hand, then maybe Bagram officials would permanently disable the troublesome locals from entering our base. I thought of all the violence that I had witnessed thus far—most importantly, those Americans I'd watched bleeding who had been sent to help stabilize their country. The beauty was that the protests got them nowhere, and in fact, validated the collective leaderships' decision. The strategy seemed to be simple—make the idiots go home and oust the insurgents from their safe houses and/or turn them in so that the merchants could keep getting their relatively nice paychecks. It was all above my pay grade, but the rumor and deduction on that point made sense.

Some may have seen myself or those I served with as "racially insensitive" and/or offensive in our views towards Hadji. I would have invited the offended party to hang out for only a few days with some locals. My advice would be to keep your wits about you, and I would also suggest being armed, and especially, not be alone. It was impossible to ever know where their individual allegiances may lie. Between their religious belief that we were lesser humans than they, and the reported ability that they were also easy to buy allegiances from, it was foolish to not keep your guard up. Even worse were the insurgents and Taliban, being the Islamic hard-liners and taking their extremist beliefs to make war. I hated what they stood for. Unlike wars in the past between nations, where the enemies were soldiers and warriors doing what they felt was best for their country, and some rules of war existed, none of that felt like the case with those whom we fought. Insurgents in Iraq had recently strangled a captured American soldier with his own intestines. They would cut living people's heads off on camera and broadcast the brutal acts to the world. They lit a man on fire in a cage and laughed as he burned.

There was a reason we often referred to the enemies we faced as "the savages," as they were evil scum and not classified as people.

*

The weather was once again becoming a problem. Several freezing, rainy, and dreary days began cutting some of our flights short again. I welcomed the early return to base one day since I was in the aircraft that had a maintenance issue preventing us from flying with doors installed. The Kiowa community was usually adamant about no doors ever being installed, that is, until it was absolutely freezing and wet outside and then we changed our tune a bit.

Our troop had adopted a simple code word structure, the best and most useful being the terms "yellow duck" and "brown duck." If a team of two Kiowas were in flight, and one pilot got on the radio and said either term, it was a code amongst ourselves that at our earliest convenience we must find that person somewhere to use the restroom.

My favorite phrase may have just been special to our troop, which was "Purple Rain." Having five radios in each Kiowa, things could get busy in a hurry. Sometimes, it wasn't busy at all and we had a few radios free. We would always talk between our two aircraft on our private FM radio frequency known as Team Internal. The actual frequency could be listened to if we didn't have it set up secretly, which was sometimes the case. Now and then, we would be locked into an inappropriate conversation or saying things that we really, really didn't want anyone else to hear. We knew that sometimes our TOC would be bored or feeling a bit too nosy and would try to snoop in on our chats. If we even came close to suspecting this, or just wanted to talk in private, our solution was simple. Someone would suddenly and randomly begin singing a Prince song, clearly and smoothly transmitting, "Purple rain, puhhh-rrrrple raaaain…"

We would then disappear. We had alternate frequencies and radios, including cypher and encryption means, an ability allowing us to effectively scramble our existence from the world. The aircraft could all but vanish from TOC laptop tracking software with the flip of a circuit breaker as an added measure of privacy if we so chose, in addition to our team transmissions going dark. One day, a Chinook pilot who had gotten injured and thus screwed into working in the TOC admitted to me that what we suspected about them listening in was true. He also laughed his ass off and knew that I wouldn't admit it, but told me he admired our ballsy endeavors to be left the hell alone.

The expansive, ruggedly beautiful, and dangerous Tagab Valley.

Local village cluster of structures known as "Qalats."

Soviet gun emplacement, destroyed long ago. Western Tagab Valley rim.

Armored U.S. "MATV" vehicle built to thrive in Afghanistan's rough terrain.

CHAPTER 5

Thanks to the newest weather breaks, the end of January afforded us some great flying. We got to go to my favorite place, the Panjshir Valley, which extended north of Bagram and way up into the endless mountains. Having no directive or mission for the day, we opted to scout deep back into the pass and offshoots. No friendly forces were even close to being nearby. Recent snowfall left the area breathtakingly beautiful. The air was crisp and cold, and uncharacteristically clear. We played no radio games and engaged in no banter, opting instead to quietly enjoy the rare calm and peace while we were able.

I ended up less than calm and quite frustrated flying in the Tagab Valley the next day to support the French and their radioman, callsign Jiffy. I had gotten used to talking to Jiffy, and the many radio operator voices that encompassed Jiffy's callsign and operations. Sometimes Jiffy spoke well and without too much difficulty in our conveyance of information to each other. Jiffy even would occasionally lighten up and do or give us anything we wanted when our female pilot would get on the radio and tease and flirt with him a little. There were other times that I got the Jiffy who must've learned English from an online crash course. This would become dangerous. The confusion of sending a map grid location for "friendlies" vs. "bad guys" could end very poorly, and it happened more than it should have. Luckily for us, we had no direct incidents of fratricide (that I know of), but occasionally, we got way, way too close for comfort.

An example that sticks out the most was when I repeatedly asked Jiffy where his guys were located. Jiffy confused the map grids a few times, and I knew that he was struggling. An RPG slammed into a structure near the French dismounted soldiers close to one of their vehicles. The problems and firefight quickly escalated, and Jiffy became more and more flustered. I attempted to eliminate all the military code/buzzwords and ground to air communications protocol. I'd found that in a firefight sometimes talking very simple, plain English with someone was most effective.

"Jiffy. Please confirm that you have no French soldiers west of the following grid," which I read off slowly. Jiffy replied with, "Yes."

"Jiffy, I understand no French soldiers are west of that grid. The bad guys, you say they are at the grid," where I slowly read off our target grid. Again, Jiffy replied with, "Yes."

The battle raging on was obviously dicey and keeping my composure and calm was very difficult. A French soldier lay bleeding on the ground and his buddies dragged him through the dirt to cover, as mini-eruptions of dust and rock kicked up and AK-47 rounds whizzed by them. I explained our planned route of attack against the enemy. I then asked if he understood and if we had clearance from the French to engage. I got a simple, "Yes."

I cautiously explained that I'd need more of an answer than that and somehow got what passed as a reasonable enough confirmation to proceed. I called our wingman and conferred with my PC, and everyone agreed that from what they were seeing, it sounded like Jiffy had finally unscrewed himself and his report coincided with what we were witnessing below.

We moved into position and began our gun run, where two things immediately went wrong. First was the RPG that was fired obviously at us this time, which thankfully missed as it was fired in haste. The grenade still burst uncomfortably close and I felt the concussion of the blast. The usual shockwave of a grenade sends a ripple through your thorax and rattles your brain a bit, but fortunately we were spared that discomfort from this particular one. Secondly, as we laid down a nice string of .50 cal right into the target area we'd talked to Jiffy over and over about, I saw strange movement and then my jaw dropped.

I could only describe the movement as a cartoon scene of two bushes leaping up and hauling ass towards the French position. Their apparent scout or sniper team was sprinting to get away from where we were shooting.

I couldn't believe it, and got on the radio with Jiffy again, now angrily asking, "Jiffy, we almost killed some of your guys who were nowhere near where you said all the French people were. So let me ask again, will you please check to make sure you know where your people are before you have us do something like that again?!"

Operations in the Tagab continued on as the French ramped up their offensives in the various offshoot valleys. Our TOC assured us we had plenty more fun to come. As we departed the valley, I saw an impossible amount of French armor—personnel carriers, vehicles, and tanks. I couldn't believe what I was seeing, and also didn't fathom how in the hell they even got it all over there and down into the valley without us seeing it. For once, our TOC was right. The French were positioning themselves to disprove a stereotype and do some serious war fighting.

We landed at the FARP in Morales-Frazier, and I was halfway outside the helicopter when a thunderous concussion rocked my brain. I stumbled and fell against my aircraft, and still plugged into our communications system, I heard the other pilot yell, "Owww, seriously dude?!" The French weren't the most courteous at warning bystanders when their artillery may unleash hell, and I shouted every broken French insult I knew in their direction. I should've known better than to expect a sympathetic response.

*

Back on our island, Erik and I assisted the Air Force PJs at their request with some extraction training. I became their training dummy, and it surprised me at how quickly and efficiently they could pull me from the cockpit and onto a stretcher. It was a great use of our idle time while the weather was being temperamental, thus making us and our QRF shift otherwise worthless. I had set up the training with one of the PJs after a few trips over to their team room and shooting the breeze. Once they found out I was a prior medic and learned more about what Kiowas did as a mission, they were on board with getting more dialogue and training going with us.

I returned to the troop area and found that a sensitive items inventory had been passed off to me. This inventory was a great example of one of the cons of being an Army officer. The packet contained long lists of every weapon and expensive thing that the commander had signed for and was currently issued throughout the troop. Every single rifle, pistol, night vision goggle set, aircraft rocket pod, .50 cal, radio, and anything else deemed valuable and/or with a serial number had to be actually seen and checked off by a designated officer each month. Given the state and tempo of our operations, flexing schedules with crews and aircraft in and out of missions and maintenance, I'd have to devote two full days to realistically get it all finished.

Early February was finally starting to get busy again after the rash of weather cancellations. The 3-17 Squadron Commander and SP were arriving any day. As a new guy, I would especially have to be on my game. To make matters more stressful outside of combat, we also had an internal Arms Inspection going on. Essentially, an Arms Inspection was an inspection like our sensitive items inventory I'd just finished, but on a much larger scale. It was done to ensure that a unit was organized and functioning properly, that all equipment was present and accounted for, all regulations and procedures were documented and being followed, and many other factors were examined, as well, from the lowest individual all the way to the top guy.

Doing this inspection in a combat zone was very taxing on everyone and difficult to accomplish. Someone in a swivel chair or cubicle somewhere believed that it was a good idea and wanted to know our status on things, so we had to complete the arduous task despite a great deal of bitching and moaning. Arms Inspections also taught us that some of the craziest additional duties and jobs could suddenly be made up. Sometimes, red tape seemed to be a nearly equal adversary to the enemy that we encountered on the battlefield.

Besides flying combat operations in a hostile country, helping with the big level inspection, a visit from important people to evaluate us, and my tasked troop internal sensitive items inspection, I also had my Officer Evaluation

Report (OER) brief with the boss in charge of our whole task force.

This special affair was essentially when an officer and their boss's boss sat down with a piece of paper detailing everything having to do with that officer's professional status within the Army. The OER is like an Army resume for the purpose of getting promoted, desired career advancements, or to receive any special training or other requests. It lists every job someone has and how they have satisfactorily or unsatisfactorily accomplished it, includes lists of recommendations from their supervisory platoon leader and commander, and so forth. Basically, it's staff work done once a year.

Paperwork headaches were usually a rarity for warrant officers who were aviators as compared to regular commissioned officers (who chose that path mind you), but when it rains, it pours. I couldn't wait for all of the sudden circuses to be over and done with so we could just get back to flying some damn missions and fighting the enemy. I really despised the regular Army non-combat life with a passion. I understood it and the necessity for some of it, but man, did I still loathe most of it.

*

I began to passionately argue and convince others that some psychological operations were in order while out flying for the next week. We needed to let a particular village know that we were angry at them for continuing to support IED emplacers, since credible intel pointed to a recent attack originating from there. A small French convoy had been traveling on a road just north of them, which closely hugged the terrain and had a steep drop off to a river below. An IED was placed on a curve in the road, and it exploded as one of the French personnel carriers had passed. The blast obliterated a section of the road, sending rocks, debris, and a French vehicle down the steep terrain and into the river. We understood that there had been fatalities and terrible casualties as a result. The message to the village was simple: "Harbor the enemy or give them aid, and U.S. helicopters will continue to harass you day and night. You will not sleep well, and you will not feel safe. We'll be on you, always watching, always poking and spying on you. Kick the insurgents out of your village, or you'll never sleep again."

Soon afterward, French legionnaires moved into a small compound in the middle of the night near the IED location that had taken out one of their countrymen's vehicles. We stumbled upon the operation, knowing that legionnaires rotated in and out Forward Operating Base (FOB) Morales-Frasier, but I'd never seen them in action. We kept our distance, orbiting high and out of the way while locals were lined up along a wall outside the compound. One of the detainees in flex cuffs was obviously shouting and antagonizing the raiding party, perhaps erroneously believing that they were a conventional force and mistook them for U.S. soldiers. A legionnaire stopped talking with his men momentarily and walked casually towards the man. I watched in shock through the MMS while the legionnaire, without breaking his stride, punched the man so hard in the face that his head snapped back, slamming into the compound wall behind him. The man crumpled and lay still in the dirt, and those around him bowed their heads while the legionnaire lit a cigarette and resumed talking to his buddies. I'd never seen someone get hit so hard in my entire life; I seriously wondered if brain damage had just occurred. I stopped recording, rewound, and hit record again while focusing the MMS on the surrounding mountains in the distance. There was no way I would let anyone get in trouble for what I had just witnessed, and I happily kept it to myself. The Hindu Kush mountains, which had borne witness to multiple millennia of human violence, silently watched the continued cycle while keeping their ever-present beauty and neutrality.

Perhaps we were not in line with the "winning hearts and minds" approach, but that just doesn't always work for some people. We aggressively saturated the area, and the local populace took note. I finally wrote home what I passionately believed:

"As much as it may seem that I talk trash about Hadji or even as it may seem that I hate him, I don't really wish for that to be the full takeaway view. Hating your enemy has never worked well, whether referring to modern-day history or Sun Tzu's era. Getting close to and understanding the enemy is a far better and more successful solution. I respect the everyday civilian here in limited and certain capacities. The way that the people of Afghanistan live and survive is amazing. Truly, it is. Their lives are like a minimalist never-ending camping/survival trip. Despite knowing that I shouldn't hate our enemies so much, it's a very hard thing to actually put into practice. I am trying, but frankly, these bastards can really get to us with their savage brutality."

I was young and I felt as though I was a hard-charging soldier, like we were all supposed to be. When I looked at our society, where public concern centered more around celebrity scandals, what's on TV, and other frivolous debate, I struggled to wrap my head around it. I'd been reprogrammed. Only recently had there even been the occasional mention of what was going on in Afghanistan, and that was only due to the added military personnel surge into the region. Many of us recognized that the only mention of our involvement in the war was regarding budgetary concerns, and not because our general public seemed to be all that concerned as a collective whole. I believed that in many people's cases, the war was all but forgotten, and would stay that way until they were directly affected by it in some capacity.

On the other hand, the Afghan civilian was very aware of hardship and war. They had endured struggle for centuries. The Afghan civilian worked hard in their field, gathered food, and lived day to day seemingly with only one key motivator: survival. They ate what they could, wore whatever was available, and occupied whatever ground or qalats they could get.

From what I saw, several owned only a tarp and lay claim to a cave or even a hole in the ground. When I flew over almost every village, the scene was almost medieval. The literacy rate during the time was reported to be 20 to 25 percent. There was a total lack of any kind of technology outside of the few major civilization centers, save the occasional busted up car here and there. Women were hanging clothes on clotheslines in small walled courtyards and squatting by water jugs washing their dishes. Children scurried about in groups playing with sticks. Buildings were clustered together in no architecturally motivated way, as function was far superior to form. In the more turbulent areas, some people would stand watch on rooftops with weapons, not to engage foreign military forces, but to protect their village and properties from aggressors in neighboring areas and tribes.

It was all fascinating and something that I had not expected to appreciate, but here it was before me. No training that we'd had mentioned much about the relevant tasks we'd encounter when having to study the patterns of life and ascertaining what was not the norm. Intel gathering on the local populace seemed to be overshadowed by a lot of bureaucratic and big Army nonsense. I felt that we, the forward observers to the fight in terms of recon, intel gathering, and ground support, were getting a much better feel for the area and conflict than I could have ever possibly imagined.

I respected the Afghans in our area for what they endured and could survive with.

Did I agree with many of the fundamentalist religious, or even cultural beliefs? Absolutely not.

Did I come to believe that we were locked into an ideological and religiously centered conflict that could fundamentally never be truly resolved? Yes.

Did I believe that, most times, the hardships of tribal and civil war are self-induced? In a complex sense, mostly yes.

The Taliban ensured that the public remained uneducated and ignorant. Outside of Kabul, it was said that most people knew little to nothing about the current government. Tribal law and local governors were all that they knew. Coalition forces were there attempting to build schools and roads, in hopes to modernize the country and attempt to bring it into at least the middle 20th century. This still seemed to be the only real way to get the casual attention of the average civilian.

Throughout our troop, we had differences in our views and fundamental beliefs for what we were doing, why we were there, and if or why we should leave. The question was also if any of our efforts were even worth it in the end. During each flight, we would see or learn something new to think or talk about, even if it was something small. The whole thing was an impossibly complex struggle we dealt with, and it was constantly in our faces. The tired, canned answers from our leadership or government about our noble cause were of no comfort. Those in power did not watch dead and dying bodies get loaded onto MEDEVAC helicopters and ambulances, and those soldiers who still fought in their place no doubt found little solace in sacrificing themselves or their recently departed so that the Government of the Islamic Republic of Afghanistan (GIRoA) could properly function. Afghanistan's chief exports were drugs, rugs, nuts, fruits, and raw materials. Corrupt Afghan leaders and officials stole from our taxpayers to fund their own tribal conflicts and struggles for regional and national power. It was hard to defend what was going on, even for the most bright-eyed and idealistic of those amongst us.

CHAPTER 6

The conversation on the chow bus one morning concerned our newest OH-58D pilot: a female. A debate had broken out regarding how many goats that she may be worth in trade to Hadji. The argument centered on the knowledge that the Afghan people were very practical, and a goat is highly valuable. It was concluded that one goat was her trade value because she could just do hut chores, fetch water, and do whatever else Hadji wanted. She was there the whole time; she was a good sport.

I knew that it had to be difficult to be the only female, as I had often witnessed with my friend, Dede, during flight school and our normal life back in our squadron. It appeared they needed to put even more effort in to be accepted by their troops, whether that was even a reality depended upon the particular dynamic of those pilots they flew with. Usually though, fair or not, a female faced more scrutiny than their male counterparts. Even more difficult would be the distrust leveled towards them by squadron wives and girlfriends of those whom they fought alongside. There were always bullshit rumors that would begin out of jealousy and petty drama that a female soldier had to ignore in the course of doing her job. There is no room for that extra layer of stress in combat. The simple fact is that we all had to have thick skin. We were often terrible to each other, and everyone always tried to find what would set a certain individual off. We called it the red button, and everyone had to keep their pet peeves a secret, lest the troop discover that weakness and relentlessly exploit it.

When we got back from chow, terrible news was delivered. On February 21, 2010, an OH-58D went down near Tikrit, Iraq with neither of the crew members surviving. The cause of the crash was not because of enemy fire, but a mechanical failure. We learned the names of the pilots a few days later. One of them was going through the Kiowa course around the time that I was, and it was sobering to hear that someone I knew and had thrown beers back with at Fort Rucker had departed. The other pilot had been one of our troop SP's students early in his time at Fort Rucker, and the news hit him hard. It seemed surreal and strange to see a photograph of someone I knew in a news article that has just been killed. It further reinforced the seriousness of what we were involved in, and I began to understand what people had told me about being slightly changed when you return home.

We were experiencing some discouragement and frustration because we felt we were not being used to our full potential. We hoped that, as time went by on the deployment, our missions would make more sense—we wanted to be used in a more efficient and effective manner. Mind-blowing and stupid chains of events compounding over time began to force my first real discouragement that my brother warned me would happen. There was a feeling of helplessness when you knew that you could make a positive impact on the war effort, but weren't allowed due to factors and regulations outside of your control. Like the time when Gonzo had to leave wounded on the battlefield, for instance. The war was fast becoming even more political, risk-averse, and convoluted. Our appetite for risk as a military was waning, which forced us counterintuitively into more danger. Having to wait until an aggressive act was actually committed by an enemy could be maddening and frustrating. It was as if we were a team in a sport, allowing the other team to calmly and casually set themselves in their positions and ensure that they were ready before the match would begin. And they always had the whistle to signal the start.

I tried desperately to not have a defeatist attitude. I resolved to continue to do my best, be myself, and strive to be good at what I did. We would continue to fly our asses off and hunt down insurgents. Serious consequences had recently come to those who spoke the truth. I had just read in *The Army Times* about a crackdown on blogs and soldiers speaking their minds (many times at odds with their command's wishes). I thought the article hit the nail on the head, citing the idea that soldiers who fight to protect their country and the freedom of speech are not allowed to exercise those rights themselves. My writing to my family was a grey area, being taboo, and could be threatened to be shut down at the worst. I wasn't writing anything sensitive; I was just provocative. Still, I had encrypted and password protected everything, just in case. I felt as though a secret blog-style format was more efficient and much safer than social media or emails which could be easily shared, copied, forwarded, or otherwise exploited. Something about the word "blog," however, was a trigger for military madness and censorship. I felt bad for those who had received disciplinary action for saying bad words and antagonizing our system, but I also planned to sail under the radar myself while exercising my first amendment rights.

The following evening I saw the first evidence of the impending "troop surge" that we kept hearing about. Upon landing and post-flighting the aircraft, a column of Polish vehicles drove slowly down our pad, and in tow was a giant, Russian-built Mi-24 Hind attack helicopter. The thing was an impressively massive beast, and I'd always been curious about them. It looked even bigger than a Blackhawk, but was a primary attack helicopter that could additionally still transport up to eight passengers. It filled two roles in one, just like the efficient utilitarian commie bastards who created it intended it to do. We were laughing because of how poor of a decision to have Hinds in the skies over Afghanistan again might be. Our new agenda in the war was to "win the hearts and minds." When the Russians were occupying the country and at war in Afghanistan, the Hind was liberally used as a relentless killer. We mused that having them fly around again in the area would understandably cause Hadji to have flashbacks and freak the hell out. The Polish brought the Hinds along with some larger Mi-17 transports (also a Soviet staple aircraft, being their dedicated equivalent of the Blackhawk mission). The Polish ended up moving in right alongside us. I talked to some of their pilots and maintainers and they were really cool guys. I certainly looked forward to crawling around the Hinds once they got them all set up.

*

The dog and pony show back off the battlefield was progressively, and unfortunately, getting worse. Since we were scheduled to be deployed for a year or longer, everyone must be given a "mid-tour leave." This policy dictated we must go elsewhere for an allotted two weeks. You could go home, or you could go to Sri Lanka for all the Army cared—you just couldn't stay in Afghanistan when your leave slot arrived. I opted not to return to the United States because I didn't want to experience a cruel taste of home which would too soon be taken away again. Instead, I would backpack in Germany and Scotland, with airfare being fortunately on the Army's dime. For my leave to begin, I was informed at the last minute that I must exchange a pair of my ACUs (the regular Army uniform I never wore) for a brand new set. I also had to exchange a pair of my boots for a new pair. The next humorous occurrence was that, despite turning in my weapons to my unit armorer, I'd also have to wear my Kevlar helmet and big bulletproof vest to Kuwait. I was being dolled up with new clothes, then disarmed, yet armored up, to ride on a plane to a relatively safe desert town. Upon my arrival, I would go through a complex process to tag, annotate, and store my Kevlar and vest in a giant facility there.

I also only knew the day, but not time, when I would be getting on the plane. I expected that I'd get to the terminal to report early in the morning, not to leave until around midnight. I was also having trouble telling my dad and Sally when I would be getting to Germany because no one could really know for sure; there was no way to plan for it. I didn't even know what German airport I'd arrive at.

I had gone to the PX and west side for my final packing of incidentals. I realized how undesirable it would be to travel with my military ACU camo backpack. I was lucky to find a decent black, nondescript 72-hour pack for a carry-on bag. When I got to Kuwait, I could change into civilian clothes since I would be traveling overseas. The first decision that I'd heard that made sense was not to have us unduly stay in our uniforms. With khaki jeans and black fleece, and a very out-of-regulation haircut, I would blend in almost anywhere. I had a guidebook on Germany, but I still didn't have hotel reservations or any itinerary. I would lean on internet cafes and advice from locals. Wherever I ended up during my two weeks of leave and however I got there, I was certain that it would be fun. Especially compared to what was going on in Afghanistan.

Beginning the second week of March, I boarded my plane to finally, yet temporarily, leave Afghanistan. I arrived in Kuwait, and it was just as much of a debacle as I'd imagined. Finally getting my Kevlar and armor turned into the huge warehouse (a taxpayer-funded black hole), I made it over to some tents that looked unoccupied. I found an empty bunk with an air conditioner running nearby and a bunch of strangers, so I got some sleep. I changed out of my uniform into civilian clothes as soon as possible. Since I walked around alone and not in uniform, it was assumed that I must be a contractor, so I wasn't bothered a bit. With my plane ticket to Germany finally being secured, I boarded my bus to the airport.

My transportation super-special-security-tactical-awesome detail was my most favorite sight that I'd ever seen. We were transported by Air Force personnel, doing what they thought was a great job of blending in while also looking cool doing it. Wearing the latest and greatest in tactical apparel and sunglasses, they were seriously dedicated to ensuring we safely arrived at Kuwait International Airport. So safe in fact, that with their tactical khaki cargo pants, tan combat boots, 5.11 polo shirts, they wore *yellow reflective safety PT belts!* After I about pissed myself laughing at this sight, I doubled over once I saw that their weapons, decked out M4 rifles like my own back in our CP, had no magazines inserted or anywhere in sight. Tactical clothing, unloaded weapons, and reflective belts—the truest and finest art of discreet protection was on proud display. Those around me had no idea who I was, or why I was laughing so hard. Finally, one guy grinned wide at me and must've been thinking the same thing. The sight was a highlight for me to see and made the whole journey from BAF worth it.

I arrived in Munich, met up with Sally, and we began to backpack across Germany. We made it from Munich to Bamburg and ended up in Garmisch-Partenkirchen at a military-owned Morale Welfare and Readiness (MWR) resort called the Edelweiss. A few spots in between, and then, we were back to finish up our trip to Munich. It was hard to say goodbye to Sally again as she returned to the states after my first week of leave. We both knew it would still be a long deployment and time apart to endure.

My father traveled to Munich to link up, and he and I then made our way up to Scotland. We traveled to the Isle of Islay via ferry boat. I enjoyed the quiet, pleasant cruise. I was in awe, as I couldn't remember the last time I'd been able to experience such quiet and contentment. Upon arrival, we began to tour the island, distillery by distillery (Laphroaig and Bruichladdich topped the charts for world's finest, if you're wondering). We drove around for days, sampling scotch, visiting with locals, and exploring. Our B&B, Monach House, was fantastic, and our elderly and patriotic hosts found out that my next stop from their B&B would be returning to a small wooden shack in Afghanistan for another seven more months. They surprised both my father and me by proclaiming that my room was free. The old man had a close relative in Her Majesty's Black Watch Regiment, an esteemed unit that also liked to destroy our common enemy. My host's personal scotch bar was opened, and for the next several evenings, he would entertain us by the fire in their living room. For hours, he orated poetic local history tales like those from the ancient days of *The Iliad* and *The Odyssey*.

I sat on the bluff where their house sat overlooking the windswept and beautifully rugged coast of that Scottish island. The old woman quietly brought tea out on a silver tray to my father and me, and their dog wanted me to throw a tennis ball over and over again. I closed my eyes for several minutes, trying to live in the moment and shut away from the thoughts of war. My trip was ending soon, and I tried not to think about my buddies or what operations may be going on right that second while I sat in that beautiful place, feeling the cool wind and listening to the waves gently crash upon the rocky shore below.

I was going to have to go back, the fighting season was coming, and I still had a long way to go before I'd experience any kind of peace again. We made it back to Munich and my father and I parted ways, my dad trying to stay strong as he knew I was going right back into a tough situation. My plane was set to leave many hours later, so I went downstairs in the hotel to a small indoor pool to get one last swim in before returning to the dumbass land of lots of sand and little water.

CHAPTER 7

In the last week of March, I returned to Bagram from my mid-tour leave. After only being in my room for a few hours, I was summoned to our CP, where our troop was having some angry internal meeting. There was also a no-notice knowledge test given, and I was so jet-lagged and tired that I literally fell asleep while taking it. I still somehow scored 100 percent, but had to be woken up more than once to finish it. In my haze of consciousness, I felt as though I should be mad about the whole thing, but I was just too tired to give a crap and made my way back to my room and passed out again.

I began the mental countdown: *In seven months, I'll be home, so that's not too bad. That's only one more month than an Air Force deployment, for heaven's sake,* I thought. For the prior few months, I had mid-tour leave to look forward to and the planning and researching had given me a constructive and positive outlet. Now, all that I had was a countdown clock to returning home. I was again detached from life and events occurring back in the states. My dad kept me apprised of any big news. I was curious as to whether or not our President would make good on any promises to pull us out of Afghanistan. We heard that either he or Congress had even cited a date or two. I was not politically passionate or motivated and had no plans to start. As a young soldier, I believed that no matter what we soldiers thought or said, it would fall on deaf, uncaring ears as far as the political system went.

The conflict had really taken its toll on our armed forces, and it was pretty evident. The easiest way to spot the downtrodden feel among the ranks was that the many soldiers that had originally planned to stay in until retirement were instead planning their exits. I kept hearing media and political statements like, "Send more troops!" and I'd laugh to myself. It was as if there was some magical "troop tree" that I didn't know about. With the way our policies and overall strategy (or lack thereof) were continuing to train-wreck, my future in the military began to generate question marks and doubts.

I began a struggle to stay positive. My personality had never been pessimistic prior to the deployment. In under six months, I noted some real ups and downs. Being a pessimistic bastard makes you sad and miserable to be around. I saw other guys that were struggling; they were easy to spot, and I did not wish to be like them. The last thing I wanted was to be the guy who never smiles, is rude to everyone, and looks like he wants to off himself. I told my family back home to keep me accountable. If they noticed me getting down, I asked them to please remind me that I vowed to not be that guy. I asked for jokes, or to be told to shut my whining trap and go get some ice cream or something. I wanted in my moments of weakness to be reminded that we still had a war to fight, and to "man up, Buttercup."

*

Pilots, on the whole, are a superstitious bunch, and on March 28th, we received the news that President Obama would make a secret visit. My team scowled at me at our briefing table; I had just recently mentioned him, so this one was on me. The President showed up at about 1930 on Air Force One and quickly boarded a helicopter to go see Afghan President Karzai. His total time in the country was perhaps six hours, and I flew for over seven hours in support of his presence. No one got out of flying; it didn't matter if a guy was day crew, night crew, or day off the crew. I was tired because I had still not fully adjusted to the nocturnal rhythm yet. Additionally, having not flown in nearly an entire month, the presidential visit was one hell of a mission to get back into the saddle with. After meeting with President Karzai, President Obama returned to Bagram briefly and spoke to a relatively small group of DoD personnel, contractors, and military members in a tent. Cameras snapped and a speech was given, then, he was quickly routed back to Air Force One and departed our airspace. We learned that news outlets thought it was a great idea to report his arrival to Bagram before he even landed. The story opened up a whole litany of attack planning and coordination from the enemy, which thankfully, was thwarted since they didn't have enough time to execute a hasty operation. Thanks anyway though, media.

After admiring an Apache pilot's gun tape footage, I sat down and met with my crew. Like a song stuck on repeat, we began chugging coffee and listening to more intel briefs, mission objectives and requirements, and getting ready for another long night. There was a village housing some unsavory characters. Recently, activities had increased in the area, and coalition forces had gotten hurt. That would not be allowed to continue.

We had hit an ultra-psychotic period in the deployment, where not only ridiculous policies were being implemented, but we had also begun to routinely receive contradictory orders. We would be told to act, and not to act, at the same time in our daily missions. In the course of receiving contradictory orders and intentions, we had no real choice other than to do whatever it was that our team felt was necessary and correct at the time. Our task force and the rules of sensibility were unraveling right before our very eyes.

It filled many with anger, and at the very least, a rebellious spirit was growing and festering within the ranks. Plans to curtail some of the crazy and cheer ourselves up a bit were discussed and hatched. We thought we might all pitch in and build a deck or porch, complete with a grill. Chico insisted that he could somehow procure decent meat to throw on the flames. This was a good way for many of us to make the most out of an increasingly frustrating command climate and operational situation. Like every other troop or platoon that had been in a similar circumstance, we would adapt and overcome. We just had to rely on our troop from within and give the finger to everyone else outside. Unified through hate, we called it.

*

My team landed at FOB Kutschbach down in the troubled Tagab Valley. As we were conducting our business there on the ground with engines still running, a man waved at me from the left side of the helicopter so I gave him a thumbs up to approach. This special forces soldier instantly became my favorite "bearded one," whom I also sometimes referred to collectively as "the Jesuses." The bearded one produced a small digital camera from his pocket.

"Dude, there's a road up the way that we really need to get some pictures of. Stuff has been going down up there, and an aerial view would be super helpful. Could you, like, take this camera up with you real quick and snap a few photos and bring it back?"

I smiled big, as this was my bread and butter.

"I'll do you one better. Give me the SD card, and I'll take the shots that you need with our camera. Give me some grids of the area and I'll set up a quick recon for you. Our practice is to snap a photo of the grid, followed by a photo of the area so you can garner whatever intel you need, since this is urgent," I replied.

I flashed back to flight school, the night before aircraft selection. This was very much like the instance where a Kiowa had given Marc aid, and I was proud that I would do such a thing myself. My bearded one also seemed like a character right out of a surfer film. The man's eyes went wide and he said, "Oh man, that would be super cool. Thanks, brother! We'll just chill over here until you're done. Can you guys, like, do it pretty soon?" I nodded and said, "We're here for you, man. I'll talk to the other bird and we'll get over there and back in just a few. This area you've indicated is not far and we know it well."

He seemed thrilled with our willingness to help and we shook hands. I called up the other bird and told them we had an urgent request and needed to get back out into the valley. The reason we had been conferring with a Jesus all made sense now, and they agreed that there was no time to waste. We did a fast run-up and take-off directly towards the first grid in the series. As we flew by each grid, we quickly did a high pass and a low pass. I snapped photos like mad, hoping to snag anything in the frame I thought might be of importance for what the SF guys were looking for. Grid by grid, we repeated the process with my aircraft taking Lead and our Trail aircraft covering us. I saw movement here and there by suspicious-looking locals, eyeballing us with hard and careful stares. Most appeared unarmed and posed no apparent threat to us at the moment, but my experience in the Tagab Valley was that situations like these could change in an instant. I had no time to develop any situation from suspicious "farmers" or their actions, so we continued to quickly move on. Before we knew it, we had all of the pictures and notes I thought were needed for our hasty photo recon mission. Even better, no shots had been exchanged with anyone.

Our SWT returned to FOB Kutschbach and the bearded one ran back over to my side of the aircraft, surprised to see us back so soon.

"Dude, that was quick. Did you seriously get pictures of all of those grids?" He asked.

"Yeah man, we got it. I also took some notes by hand on my kneeboard here. I wasn't sure what you were looking for, so I just jotted down anything that looked like you'd be interested in knowing," I said.

I ripped the paper from my kneeboard and handed it to him along with his SD card. He looked at my notes, furrowing his brow a few times, so I said, "Sorry, I knew it was time critical, so we were hauling ass and flying a bit aggressively. Gets kinda hard writing things down in a helo like that sometimes."

He laughed and shook his head. "No worries, man! I appreciate you guys doing the recon and we'll sort it all out. It's a big help and we appreciate it. Stay safe, brother."

We shook hands once more and the man then linked back up with the others of his kind, quickly vanishing into a tent. I never found out what they were looking for. Whatever it was, I hoped that our efforts made a difference.

The following evening, I looked forward to an eventful flight. I'd been getting restless again. In our downtime, we busted out the Nintendo, and after a lot of old-school video game surgery, we got the golden copy of *Zelda* to work. Oh, the fun we looked forward to between missions with that pile of old Nintendo games. Before I knew it, I was on my fourth night in a row logging some serious time. In the few previous nights, we had provided a ton of air support to many different units. It never ceased to make me feel good when we could hear the relief in the voices on the radio when we would show up overhead. As we had suspected would happen all along, the in-between peaceful times we'd been experiencing in Afghanistan dwindled as the weather got warmer. Actions against our forces in the form of IEDs and ambushes had increased. The French operations in the Tagab had become more extensive and elaborate, and although most of the time it was on our own volition and not their explicit request, we mixed it up in the Tagab Valley more frequently alongside the French. Many times, it would be quick attacks followed by retreats from small groups of insurgents, but now and then, a few enemies were emboldened enough to stick around and fight for a while.

I imagined that by the time I returned home, my butt might be flat from sitting in the helicopter doing infinite steep turns. I hoped to find some good workouts to curtail the inevitable and shape my rear back to normal.

*

Our deployment schedule continued forward like a turbulent ocean. At the moment, I was in a period with a tirade of water, having little to no personal time. There was nothing that I wanted more than to stay in contact with my friends and family. I was trying hard not to get too out of touch with the outside world. I couldn't really talk about our current operations at the moment with anyone; however, just the contact and support of those back home did wonders. Our current tempo had gotten me super, super tired. After five high-intensity nights in a row, I looked at the flight schedule and noted that we had no plans to slow down.

While returning from a standard patrol one night, or "BAF Hunter" as we called it, we were ready for a break. It had been a long night and we couldn't wait to land. The Lead aircraft began its approach into Bagram's FARP, with us following a far distance behind as we were now in the Bagram area and didn't need to fly so close to one another. Suddenly, Nick and I saw the flash and explosion from an RPG in the distance. A team of Kiowas would fly toward violence as reliably as a moth flies toward a flame, so, without a second thought, we started to haul ass toward the blast.

As we approached, I observed several MATVs, which were upgraded armored vehicles built to thrive in the Afghan terrain. I called the Lead aircraft, letting them know that a TIC was developing right before our eyes. I watched the tracers from the turret gunners atop MATVs swing and arc out wildly, lighting up the area. The enemy didn't have tracers on them for this ambush, but I was seeing enemy muzzle flashes training rounds on the convoy. Our wingman was moving as quickly as they could to catch up with us, warning us that they were very low on gas. A few seconds after their transmission, our own helicopter began to tell us the same thing.

When a Kiowa got critically low on fuel, she told you so by a loud "Bong!" There was a switch labeled ACK for "Acknowledge" that was used to communicate from pilot to helicopter that whatever message the Kiowa was trying to tell us had been seen and acknowledged. When our fuel level dropped below the 100lb mark, the Kiowa would bong repeatedly. Each flip of the ACK switch would calm our bird down for a few seconds, then she would panic and tell us again.

Because of the ambush below, we were now flying aggressively, diving into the area where the enemy was firing from to get them to shoot at *us* instead of the convoy fleeing the area. We tried hard to get the ground commander to clear us to fire and allow an engagement, but he was too afraid to authorize it. He didn't want to violate any Rules of Engagement (ROE), which were ever changing and increasingly restrictive, so he took the path of weakness and left his guys in danger instead. We were angry and continued to dive into the area as our fuel-critical aircraft continued to panic and bong.

Our aggressive maneuvers caused our rotor blades to loudly slap and pop the air. We got a break once the noise and diving maneuvers distracted the enemy enough to stop the attack. They didn't engage us, and I wondered if it was due to them not being able to see us, as we were completely blacked out on a relatively moonless night. We made it back to Bagram in just the nick of time, with only about 20lbs of gas in each Kiowa. The convoy thanked us and reported no casualties. The nerve-wracking event had been a close call for all involved.

*

Our mission and flight coverage demands seemed to worsen each time a remark was made to the effect of "Surely, this can't get any worse," and then it somehow would. The prior evening, my PC nearly dozed off a few times, and I was getting pretty shaky myself towards the end of a flight. I looked over to see the small green circles from the NVGs illuminating his closed eyes in the darkness. I nudged him and he came awake with a start, cursing and popping open an energy drink. When I finally got back to my room, I hit the bed and fell asleep instantly. The coming evening would be just as, if not more, brutal as the past few.

One evening, in between flights, I was in the gym working out. It was late, and the area was very quiet. Between sets of working out, I was changing the music and the gym was dead silent. Suddenly, I heard a muffled "Bbrraaaaatt!" right outside.

"What the hell was that?" I asked out loud, and the only other soldier in the gym at 0200 with me shrugged.

I opened the door to find several junior enlisted soldiers standing awkwardly outside by the front of our Panda Express short bus. None said a word, and I saw one of them holding a Squad Automatic Weapon (SAW).

"Anyone want to tell me what that noise was?" I asked the junior soldiers. After several seconds and a few uncomfortable glances between the group, the kid with the SAW spoke up.

"It was an accident, sir. I was holding my SAW with my finger too close to the trigger and I didn't realize my safety was off. I tripped and accidentally pulled the trigger... which is the sound you heard, sir." Processing this information, I realized there was a hissing sound coming from our bus.

"Okay, and what's that sound?" I asked. There was silence for a moment, and then one piped up.

"Uh... that's the radiator, sir."

I didn't know whether to laugh or lose my mind. "Holy shit. You shot our bus. You actually not only almost killed your buddies, but you killed our bus," I said in wonder and amazement to the soldier. His eyes were looking at the ground. "Did you at least unload your weapon and put the safety on?"

He nodded slowly, and then a commissioned officer walked outside, asking what had happened. I smiled and patted the senior officer on the shoulder and said, "You've got this one, sir," and walked back into the gym.

On the first weekend of April, after five long nights of missions, I finally had time to relax. With some delicious care-package banana bread in hand, I sat back in my room and couldn't have been more content (unless I had a dram of fine single malt scotch, but booze was strictly forbidden). We had flown three separate flights for almost seven hours total the previous night. The last flight had gone well into the morning. I was overtired and not used to flying when the sun was up, so it was difficult for me to go to bed. I didn't fall asleep until noon, but I awoke the next evening at around 2100 feeling a lot better. It sounded weird to refer to days as going to sleep at noon and considering that evening as an entirely different day.

The flying continued to pick up a lot in the next week, and I hardly had time to communicate with anyone back home. It was a case-in-point for how rising temperatures equaled a rise in our utilization and workload. Our current ground unit utilized us a LOT more than the previous one did, which was a good thing. We'd had quite some time since the last 107mm rocket attack against BAF, thanks to the new guys really getting out there and inconveniencing the enemy.

I walked into the CP to find a group of pilots huddled around a laptop, reviewing footage from earlier.

"Damn, these guys are rolling those dudes up hard," one of the pilots remarked, so I walked over. A thermal video played silently, showing one of our infantrymen sitting on a man's torso, throttling his face with both fists in downward, devastating punches.

"He's Donkey-Kong punching that dude to death, bro!" One of the Apache pilots remarked, and we all laughed. The Kiowa team that had just returned filled us in on the ambush that led to the scene and if I'd been that infantry guy, I would've done the same thing.

We were notified that we may be getting "too aggressive," in fact, and our tactics were not totally in line with the "play nicely" philosophy that was our current expectation. I laughed and surmised that the concern probably had something to do with the Apaches. They had been destroying people lately, with one of their gun tapes clearly showing a large line of insurgents wiped out in under ten seconds. One of the Apache pilots exclaimed to his friend, "Dude, you killed more people than an African virus today!" The next thing we knew, some footage of an insurgent trying to kill Americans having his head suddenly roll off his shoulders and into the dirt under a tree was being rewound and played over and over again.

*

Once again, on a day shift mission to support the French, I sat in the left seat of the Lead aircraft. We were working with callsign Jiffy on one of their Tagab missions, and I was in contact with their forward patrol. Jiffy informed us he was walking down a riverbed, known as a "wadi," and that they were about to enter a troublesome area. He asked me, "Wildwood, please look up in front of us on the wadi? The last time I walked down here, we got shot at. Actually, the last three times."

I was impressed with his English, and I told him we would look ahead and give them cover as best we could. There were a lot of advantageous positions for the enemy, so I could see why Jiffy was nervous. Their small foot patrol continued deeper into the offshoot and highly vegetated valley. As I scanned the area, I suddenly saw a bunch of the French scatter to take cover. They fired their rifles into the dense foliage, and dust kicked up around both friendly and enemy positions.

"Shit, they're taking contact," our Trail ship called.

"I see it, any eyes on the enemy?" I replied quickly.

"Negative, not yet," replied the Trail left seater.

Both aircraft left seaters were quickly alternating between the MMS and binoculars trying to get a quick overall sense of what was happening close below.

"Wildwood, we are taking fire! We're moving back down the wadi away from–"

More dust and dirt kicked up around the French as they hauled ass back down the same way they'd come. French FAMAS rifles and Russian AK-47s barked ferociously at each other, a visceral explosion of brutality tearing apart what had seconds before been a calm walk in the woods. The French did not have the manpower, munitions, or information to counter the insurgents— their only true chance of survival was to fall back. Our team dove in low and fast by the French as we attempted to get eyes on the enemy and a better sense of where they may be hiding. High ground was everywhere. Some dilapidated ruins of structures were intermixed with obviously still-inhabited compounds along the banks of the wadi.

"Jiffy, Jiffy, this is Wildwood, are you or any of your guys hit, over," I called in concern.

A few tense seconds went by and then Jiffy finally replied, half out of breath and laughing. "No, Wildwood. We are not hit and everyone is okay. We are going to continue back down the wadi the way we came in and bad guys are not shooting at us any longer. Your low fly over stopped the shooting. Merci beaucoup!"

I sighed in relief. The skirmish appeared to have ended as abruptly as it had started. Turns out, both the enemy and the French had stumbled into each other and both sides broke contact hastily to get away from the fight.

"Damn, Jiffy, bring more friends to the game next time," I called back.

CHAPTER 8

It was April 20th, quickly approaching the end of yet another month. During the past few days, I'd done the majority of my flying in the early mornings. We'd been increasingly assigned to escorting convoys through a very humbling mountainous area called the Salang Pass. The elevation of the road rose so high that it was above our maximum altitude ceiling that we could use to support the convoy. Our maximum altitude always seemed debatable, but we would stop at about 12,000 feet. Out of curiosity, my aircraft made it to about 13,250 feet before we saw that we better descend or risk some serious aircraft limitation problems. The Kiowa was sluggish, and we knew by the performance numbers calculated that we were on thin ice.

We encountered every obstacle we could while flying the mountain pass that mission. We began in the pitch black darkness. When going through a narrow pass where terrain increases exponentially upward in altitude, it helps to see. When the moon is at a low illumination point, or especially not out at all, even operations with NVGs could become an issue. Navigating through the pass while trying to follow a wingman added another dynamic to the equation.

For the past few days that we had flown our early morning flights, we had continued from the night into sunrise. Flying in the pass was initially doable, but then the sun would crest over the peaks. When turning east, I lost visual on everything in front of me. I could no longer see mountain walls, my wingman, wires, you name it. Until I could get my bearings, I had to use altitude as my friend and trust the instrumentation in the cockpit.

After that, I had to battle increasing winds. Being on the ground and feeling a blast or gust of wind is one thing, but wind does tricky things when mountains get in the way. It was difficult to accurately predict which way it would blow and/or how fast. You could look at the mountains around you and try to guess how wind may be channeled, but trusting a guess was sometimes unnerving. It was usually the only option though. When wind whips downward on one side of a mountain pass, it hits the ground and base of the neighboring mountains, promptly and aggressively shooting gusts back upwards. It was better to be caught in an updraft than a downdraft, as you don't lose points for going too high, but you could lose by rapidly descending.

As if we hadn't endured enough fun, then came the rain. Rain became my most recent mornings' new curse. Bad weather throws in another mixture of problems. Not having doors installed sucked at the time because I was getting soaking wet, but the more important tradeoff was that it afforded me a better opportunity to see. Since we had no such thing as windshield wipers, a pouring rainstorm looked much like it does in a car while driving down the road with broken wipers. We didn't exactly have the ability to pull over and wait it out, either.

Being in the Trail ship, following our wingman in the pass was especially difficult, thanks to the wind and rain. The visibility started dropping quickly and everything was bathed in a grey haze. I was flying my aircraft half sideways at many points in an effort to see the other helicopter, the steep mountain walls, and a plethora of wires.

It seemed the Gods of the Salang Pass were toying with our bravery and seeing how much we could take. The weather began to deteriorate further. My eyes hurt from searching, and my brain began to feel numb from trying to process it all while being starved of oxygen because of the altitude. Our team had reached a critical point where we took the rare path of admitting that we were defeated.

Unable to safely function any longer, we finally had to throw in the towel. Feeling rotten about it, we headed back towards the airfield. When we were nearing the mouth of the pass, our team called up our weather guy in the TOC on BAF and asked for a weather update. He informed us that it had rained at Bagram maybe an hour earlier for a bit, but everything was fine and the weather had cleared up nicely.

He deserved such a square kick in the nuts for not leaving his chair and checking outside. When we were about three miles away from Bagram, I finally started to see some lights. The rain was coming down hard, and I saw parts of the outlying roads and gates were flooded. The wind was gusting hard and the tower was warning all aircraft of multiple weather-related hazards and concerns. About 10 feet before I touched down on the refuel pad, a huge wind gust hit me from behind, catapulting me forward. I drifted far down the pad and scrambled to get control of my aircraft again. Concrete obstacles, light poles, and equipment all streaked by dangerously close. A few ground personnel stood frozen in shock, wondering if I was about to crash. Heart pounding and cussing hard, I managed through the powers of frustration to regain control and spun the aircraft back around into the wind, setting down quickly and safely.

"Holy shit, are you guys okay?!" Erik called up from his position behind us. "That looked like a hell of a ride."

"Yes," I confirmed after catching my breath.

"That was not very cool," added my PC. Erik and Chico chuckled at us from their cockpit.

"Well I mean, it looked cool," Chico said. "But if you need to change your underwear before we go back out, then I'll understand."

Thankfully, Erik keyed the mic, and informed our TOC we would be done for the day, and he graciously thanked them for keeping us in the loop with their accurate weather reporting. I vowed that the next time I called our weather guy, I would tell that fool to go outside before he made another "observation." I figured that might be a tall order for the Air Force, but a guy can dream.

The storms stuck around for three solid days. Weather days sometimes proved a fun occasion because, although we were on shift, there was no real way that we'd have to launch at a moment's notice. Pilots could relax, play poker, and it almost always became movie night. Our time would be complete with popcorn and the "theater" getting fully powered up via the projector usually used for ultra-serious PowerPoint stuff. Sometimes, a weather day was the only fair equalizer in giving everyone on BAF an even break.

I hoped to switch to days soon, since my favorite crew members had just reversed out and were flying during the sunlight hours. I preferred nights, but was willing to switch over to days and be with my preferred team. My troop had essentially split into two factions, and my side was effectively known as "Team Pigeon." I was happy to be on this side, rather than being on with the other half of the troop, "Team Serious." The antics of Team Pigeon were what kept me sane, so I felt it was imperative that I stay with them as much as possible.

One rainy evening, I was informed by my platoon leader that I was in the chute to knock out the PT test soon. I groaned and asked if he was actually serious. He assured me that he was, and we all had to hate it and be miserable together, as that was only fair.

The Army Physical Fitness Test (APFT) was, and to my knowledge still is, an outdated and ridiculous gauge of a soldier's physical state and overall readiness to do soldier things. That being said, the description of me during the two-mile run on our flight line is simple: A sweaty, gasping, shaky mess of a human about ready to collapse. I was thinking, *how in the hell does this hurt so bad? I've never failed an APFT, but I guess there's a first for everything, right?* I wanted to quit—I needed to puke even worse.

Nick and Chico were at the finish line, yelling and laughing while holding a stopwatch. I was the only man taking the test this night. They were playing the song "The Final Countdown" each time I passed by them on the eight laps that it took around the flight line to equal two miles. Running at 5,000 feet made a difference over the sea level I was once used to, and I crossed the finish line like a train wreck and about fell on my ass.

My buddies laughed hard and congratulated me. Nick exclaimed, "Damn dude, you cut that one close!" It was the closest I'd ever come to failing an APFT. The run was an eye-opener, and I'd be incorporating running into my PT routine from there on just for the sake of Army standards, ridiculous as they may be in their blanket applications.

*

The weather cleared, and a sudden new wave of operations struck, so I began to fly a ton again. During the night it was freezing, and for the last several days we experienced very frosty and stout winds. As I pre-flighted the helicopter, I struggled to contain the shivers. I climbed on top of our helicopter to look at the MMS and ensure that it was not frosted up, hoping that it was enduring the cold better than I was. Exhausted, I exhaled heavily and watched my cloud of breath move heavily out and up toward the lights in an instant fog. I was on a longer stint without a day off than usual. Our troop was amid many crew changeovers and leave swaps. The days of surplus pilots were very much over. Our entire troop looked like ragged-out hell.

I hoped that the 25 hours of flight in five days' time type of schedules would benefit my logbook for the future. At that time in the civilian world, Marc confirmed what I had suspected: To train and get experience in a turbine helicopter would cost someone around $800 per hour. This meant that I would get $20,000 worth of flight time in five days *and* get paid for it. *Sign me up*, I thought.

Perhaps it was the cold or the insanity of my current life, but at that moment, I became still and placed my gloved hand on top of the aircraft and patted her like a favorite pet. No matter what, we would continue to ride into the thick and thin. I loved the Kiowa and loved our mission more than ever, despite all the hardships endured. I walked back inside from the quiet and deserted flight line at an unusual peace. I was ready for a cup of hot cider that I knew had to be available from the coffee pot-heated water and tons of drink packets. As I sipped my cider, I looked at the myriad of mission information boards and flight scheduling notices.

"Awe, fuck me running," I mumbled, apparently not only to myself.

"What's wrong, Robo?" Erik asked.

I sighed and burned my tongue on cider. "Well, I guess I get to go to Team Serious, because it looks like I'm back on days."

"What?!" He walked over to see the update. "Damn it! Sorry, man. We'll try to have some fun tonight, and hopefully, this whole non-stop crazy will slow down soon, brother."

I was disappointed to already be leaving nights once again, but the others kept me laughing and we had a good several hours of flying and trying to find bad guys doing bad things. I'd requested to go down into the Tagab Valley, as I was feeling a little froggy that night and the other three saw zero issue with my slightly aggressive idea.

We made it in and out of several areas that may not have been the wisest to fly so boldly into if it were daytime. This ended up being a great opportunity to see Hadji when he couldn't see us; however, I was pretty convinced that by now some of our enemy did, in fact, possess limited night vision capabilities. This last night flight ended up being an early morning flight. The weather turned sketchy, as we had cloud layers building on the ground, and when we were at about 1,000 feet, it looked like we were at 10 times that height.

We flew in support of the French for a bit, and then on our way back towards BAF, the visibility began to rapidly deteriorate. We were all genuinely surprised and alarmed at how fast it happened. We couldn't see the ground, nor could we see too far ahead of us. In a quick manner, we all agreed to call any further flying a no-go and that we needed to proceed toward Bagram without delay. We called the weather people on the radio, who again did not understand that it was not clear blue skies outside. We reported what was going on so that others wouldn't succumb to worthless weather guesses and could receive a Pilot Report, or PIREP. (It sounds like I'm just making these acronyms up by this point, doesn't it?) We saw the haze in the distance that we knew to be Bagram and flew directly to our murky corner of the airfield. As we landed, a thick blanket seemed to slowly and almost gracefully envelop us. It was good to be back on solid ground.

*

Before I knew it, I was reversing out so that I would be with Team Serious on the day shift. Fortunately, several Team Pigeon guys would join me on the day shift soon. I would miss my time in what we liked to call "green world" due to the NVG picture we would stare at all night. Now, I would get to fly in regular world. The area had gotten considerably more vegetated and the temperatures rose rapidly again. This caused Hadji to further ramp up 24-hour farming and extra-curricular activities.

The good news was that we finally had some nice cameras issued to us. We also received some image stabilizing binoculars that I (and apparently only I) had become quite fond of. The only downside for me was that if I looked through them for too long at a stretch, they began to hurt my eyes and give me a headache. Some guys would also quickly get nauseous when using the binoculars, but I didn't suffer from that personally. We had new toys, and I would use them all.

I was in the middle of my reverse out period, awake with the sun and trying to figure out what to do with myself. Idle time always seemed like something many of us wanted, but then when we actually got it, the idle time wasn't as awesome as we'd imagined. We would wonder about our guys flying, how it was going, and even get antsy and jealous that we weren't involved.

To kill time, I worked out like a prisoner. My whole body was one giant ache. "Embrace the pain," Erik would say reverently. He was the priest of fitness in our troop, having made a shocking transformation himself from soft-bodied, middle-aged man to absolute beast. He also surpassed almost all of us in age, so his example was also one of silently saying, "I can kick ass this much. Why can't you?"

A big morale win for some was that we finally got our cable connection working in the TV room. The connection to the world was giant for some, be they fans of horse racing, football, fighting sports, you name it. We all had to have something to hold onto and take our minds off the battlefield occasionally. Funny TV shows were also a great way to pass the time, and the affinity for crude humor distinguished Team Pigeon from Team Serious. Comedy and ripping on one another kept a deployed soldier from going crazy or shutting down. In our downtime, our team would put something on and join several of the Apache pilots, all laughing our asses off in a much-needed respite.

My perceived taking-forever reverse out (in reality, it was only two days) was finally complete—I was a day walker again. On the morning of April 29th, I woke up early, put on my PTs, and joined a few crew chiefs to get chow. After taking our time with breakfast, believing I had the day off, we went back to the CP to relax and catch up.

"Who am I flying with today?" I heard Erik ask.

Everyone looked at the board, then looked at me. There I was, reclined in a chair with my PTs on, feet propped up, hanging out like I had not a care in the world.

"What?" I asked as I turned to the board.

"29 APR, Crew 2: Erik / Robo" was displayed.

"Oh, hell no!" I exclaimed. I had just looked at the schedule a day or two prior and no one had informed me it had changed and that I was now flying. We had a convoy to escort soon, and I wasn't even in the regular uniform.

"You gotta be shitting me!" I yelled, and I ran to my room to change. I ran back to the CP to ready my flight gear, and had to mentally snap myself out of relax mode. Luckily, I moved quickly and made the flight with plenty of time to spare. Even still, I got plenty of crap for it. After a thankfully uneventful escort and landing, my commander looked to our lieutenant who he'd charged with creating our flight schedule, and then back at me.

"Robo, we haven't changed the flight schedule," said my platoon leader.

"No way," I replied. "Do you honestly think if you hadn't made any changes, that I'd go have a long breakfast with the crew dogs and then show up here in PTs like I had not a care in the world?" They looked to each other, then back to me.

"We didn't change it. That's what it's been for several days." Chico started laughing, as did the rest of my usual team and a few onlooker Apache guys along for the fun.

"Okay, so if it hasn't been changed, what's the date on the bottom of the paper from when it was printed?" Chico piped up suddenly, in a cunning defense. I smiled, as I suddenly had a barracks lawyer. Our lieutenant, unfortunately being unreasonably bright and savvy, met the challenge and pointed to the paper.

"Ah-ha! It doesn't have a date, since it is a photocopy of a document made several days ago!" My Apache pilot onlookers-turned-impromptu-jury suddenly sneered and turned against me, the jackals.

"He's got you. You messed up, just admit it!" We all laughed as I shook my head, employing a warrant officer tradecraft skill: Admit nothing, deny everything, make counter accusations. I pounded the table and called them all liars, but then again, everything had all been quite a blur so I wasn't even sure if I believed me.

Once everything settled down, I noticed a newspaper and accompanying military documentation was laying on the table in our CP. I picked it up and my eyebrows raised—Afghanistan was about to experience an infusion of even *more* American military personnel. Apparently, the fun had only just begun.

Soviet tanks and equipment left over from the Soviet-Afghan War.

Rare moment, our team actually shut down at FOB Morales-Frazier.

CW3 Erik Newhouse (left seat) and CW2 Justin "Chico" Chacon (right seat) prepare to launch on a hasty night mission.

Pile of Soviet aircraft near Bagram Airbase.

A soldier trades goods with several Afghan youth as he pulls security.

Armored side panel art, painted by SSG Joshua Allison.

Lead drops down low to investigate.

French armored personnel carrier near their FOB Morales-Frasier, on the western edge of the Tagab Valley.

Afganiya, northern off-shoot of the Tagab Valley.

PART TWO

SURGE

CHAPTER 9

For the few of us fighting and seeing what Afghanistan looked like outside the comforts of Bagram, we finally found what we considered the battlefield lines. The Taliban, Al Qaeda, the Haqqani Network, and many other lesser-reported factions had all established very real control and ownership of certain areas. That's where we scouts liked to go and stir things up. But no matter how many of these enemy groups our forces would kill and/or disrupt, more reinforcements continued to funnel in from the unlimited foreign martyr pool from other nations.

The reality set in that this would all continue until our country finally lost patience and the stomach for such spending and personnel losses, and demanded to call it quits and pull us out. After which time, we believed Afghanistan would slowly deteriorate and enter tribal civil war much like Iraq, a corrupt election would be held, and more than likely, a dictatorship would eventually be installed.

We'd been pretty busy because of the recent U.S. troop surge into Afghanistan. There were now more convoys moving supplies all over the country and to and from Bagram than ever. Our base had become what seemed like the central hub of the country.

Our flight frequency and time in the air increased, thanks to multiple setbacks with our convoys. I didn't mind flying, but my most recent missions were especially slow and mind numbing, so I'd have to drink my energy drink rations. I was living on trail mix and jerky since there was no time for a lunch break. I didn't even know what day it was—everything all ran together.

Below me, a late convoy sat ready to exit the gates of Bagram. I had dealt with this convoy and unit before, so I was prepared when their radio man told me they'd be ready in five minutes.

"We must all pitch in and buy these guys a watch," one of the other pilots remarked, more than 40 minutes after another five-minute promise. We had to refuel and come back by the time their multiple promises of "five more minutes" actually got them underway.

Now that it was heating up outside, the locals were getting a lot friskier and more active. I had no clue where so many people had hidden all winter. To my surprise, many more people were out and about, with some even farming as early as 0100 in the morning. There were GANGS of kids that stood by the road and would shout at convoys for food, supplies, and especially candy. Some little punks would throw rocks if the convoy didn't toss them anything.

Helicopters would make the kids scatter, and I enjoyed helping the ground guys by swooping in hard just a few feet off the ground and dispersing the overzealous ones. We had just had a good conversation on the radio regarding some kids. The culture we were witnessing differed greatly from ours and had traditions steeped way back in time. We had to concede that many of the kids were also like mini-adults, with real responsibilities in their families. They had to know right from wrong a bit better than a young teenager in the U.S.

To illustrate our point, an attack on coalition forces was recently celebrated by the Taliban. In their own official statement (which I quote here but don't care to give the real shithead who said it proper credit), a Taliban spokesman beamed, "A brave, heroic 11-year-old Afghan child hurled a hand grenade at dismounted troops today at 11 a.m. local time. As a result, one invader was killed and three others wounded. This incident shows the utter hatred of Afghans towards the foreign invaders who have occupied our land."

We surmised that it was not at all surprising when a kid aged anywhere from 10 to 15 years old leveled an AK at us and started hammering away. In his culture, he was most definitely a man. An older teenager could very well even be head of the household. We often spoke between aircraft about how alien Afghanistan was as compared to western and modern civilization. There was a stark difference between those kids and American kids, who would probably never understand the luxury afforded to them by merely being born in America. We loved getting letters from school children whose teachers incorporated assignments into their classes to write to us. We always got a kick out of them as any contact back home, even with random American children, was welcome. Their letters highlighted the differences between the two cultures even more.

Dear soldier,

Hi, my name is Lex. I am ten years old. Thank you for fighting for our country. Thank you for being shot at for us. Please don't die, because I don't want to die. I'm sure you don't want to die either. But if you stay alive I won't have to die at ten years old. So please don't die. Oh and thank you again for fighting for our country.

*

The frequency of activity remained pegged to the temperature's rise and fall. As the afternoon showers came in and it cooled down, so did the enemy and strange activity. It was widely accepted as a proven fact that the frequency in activity by Hadji was directly proportional to the weather patterns. Every afternoon, just like in the southern U.S., we began to get a large rain shower or thunderstorm. It would end late in the day, we'd have a rather calm evening, look iffy in the morning, stand off until mid-afternoon, then bam. Repeat daily. We were warned of this well in advance, as it was known as the "120 Days of Wind."

A few days later, it was May 8th. We enjoyed mid 70°F temperatures, blue skies, and big puffy white clouds over the mountains. The terrain was more visually appealing now since the crops and vegetation had taken on many new shades of green. There was little wind and I was even flying with my favorite crew mix of the coolest folks from Team Pigeon. Our bird started off with a little over 500rds of .50 cal, so we were heavy. I managed to shoot about 200rds of it at the range when our basic daily weapon test turned into a few extra marksmanship training gun runs. We were tasked with escorting one of our now commonplace convoys and they had some difficulty with the local national vehicles breaking down within their ranks. To save money and perhaps keep some of our people out of harm's way, the movement of many U.S. vehicles was being conducted via local Afghan trucks. Our vehicles were loaded and chained down to the flatbeds, and the Afghan vehicles sputtered and struggled to drag themselves down the road with impossibly heavy, armored U.S. vehicles on their backs. Needless to say, broken down local national vehicles had become a common and time-consuming occurrence. Our whole four-hour flight was spent getting the mixed convoy of U.S. escorts and local national vehicles to their destination.

After we landed, I was in good spirits. I gathered my gear and noticed a few extra faces out on our ramp. Our commander was there, and a young, attractive Air Force female stood with a small group of other personnel and a camera. Wait, a video camera. A tripod, too.

"Man, what the what is this all about?" I asked Erik and motioned to our welcoming party. His eyes grew wide when he saw them. "Holy crap, ruh-roh," he said in a high pitched voice and we both laughed. The other aircraft next to us had the same reaction, then both pilots threw their arms up in exasperation. We'd finally gotten cornered, and Team Pigeon would be on TV.

We each took our turn being interviewed by an Air Force reporter for the Armed Forces Network (AFN). She asked about the Kiowa and to explain several aspects about our variable missions. I answered her questions the best I could, thinking to myself, *Okay, this will be globally broadcast to all military branches and DoD services and contractors. Don't look or sound like a jackass.*

We ended up going back out to fly another "bag of gas" with a Blackhawk in tow, who carried the AFN reporters along on our BAF Hunter mission set. After roughly two hours of uneventful flying had transpired and the reporter was satisfied, we landed and shut down for the remainder of our shift. Over the following few days, the weather began to roll in and we endured another deterioration of conditions.

By May 14th, we were a few days into experiencing sustained winds in the 25-35mph range, which created much more challenging flight conditions. On a recent flight, I told one of our crew chiefs to stand back a few more feet than usual when we were starting. As I picked the helicopter up, a giant wind gust hit me and the helicopter lurched forward and spun left. I quickly counteracted, but it made our hearts skip a few beats. Hovering to the hold short line of Runway 3 was more difficult. We had an FAA Flight Check aircraft in the area and they were taking up all the control tower's time and attention. This caused significant neglect to the other aircraft trying to get in and out. It was the first time I'd had to wait almost 20 minutes just to get clearance for takeoff. We kept trying to reiterate to the new tower guy that we helicopters did not need the runway, but he couldn't grasp it. Finally, our Erik was fed up and gave him some sharply worded grief, and we were then magically cleared to go.

Because of this, we were late for our convoy, but they were broken down anyway. The crew I was flying with were all gym frequenters like myself, and we all drank lots of water. Not long after getting to the convoy, most of us had to declare a yellow duck already. Erik was praying for bingo fuel (a predetermined fuel point at which an aircraft must return for gas) and was relieved when we had to go to refuel. Getting back into the airfield was still a mess, so I landed directly on the refuel pad and stayed out of the way.

Our Trail bird suddenly caught a wind gust right up his butt while trying to set down and almost lost control of the aircraft. We were all laughing about it because they were about to call me on the radio and tell us to either immediately take off or jump out of the helicopter so that they didn't career into us.

"Dude, Robo. I'm sorry, but we almost took you with us on the way to Fiddler's Green, bro," Chico called over after they caught their breath. Fiddler's Green is the bar in Cavalry lore where all troopers go to hang out after they die, so I shuddered a bit thinking about suddenly ending up on a bar stool there with no forewarnings.

We hadn't been airborne more than 10 minutes when we were called back to BAF because of extreme winds with even heavier gusts forecast. Shutdown was a pain in the ass since the rotor system spooled down wildly with the gusts, which caused the entire aircraft to violently rock and shake. I had to keep a death grip on the controls to stop the rotors from dipping and swinging dangerously in all directions.

The next day, I stopped in at a little Hadji-mart by the PX and found myself a shemagh, or "man scarf." I would need it with all the sandstorms and high winds on the horizon. A side benefit I discovered is that it also helped to keep the seat belts and other things from chafing my neck and throat while flying. It was lightweight and comfortable, and for less than five bucks, I decided that I'd purchase several. It wasn't long before shemaghs became our fashion trend with some in the pilot group.

The one plus side to the wind was that the scenery had never been so clear. I could see farther than ever, and could only imagine what it would've looked like had I been flying. I'd been in the right seat flying a lot lately, and couldn't remember the last time that I was in the left seat, so I decided to cash in on my turn for the next flight. I usually preferred flying, but I'd had my fill of the wind kicking my ass.

*

After looking through my logbook, it was official. On the 15th, I'd just flown my longest ever flight in either an airplane or helicopter to date. I flew an 8.6 hour combat mission. It was a very rewarding and ultimately exhausting day that started as soon as we had come into the CP that morning. We were notified to quickly get ready, because we had a mission before we were even done pre-flighting. I rushed through breakfast and got about half of my plate eaten before I had to abandon the rest to throw on my flight gear. In my haste, I committed the one cardinal no-no for combat flying: I forgot to pack food. I usually had some stashed in my pockets and vest, but my complacency for restocking what I'd already consumed cost me this time.

We linked up with our ground forces and stayed on station with them for two hours, then hastily refueled and returned. In our absence, strange activity from military-aged males (MAMs) had begun to materialize. It was now about lunchtime, and it looked like we'd be needed all day. The MAMs in question were patient and kept their distance, placing phone calls and keenly watching us and our ground guys. Two hours later when we broke station to refuel, we began to hear more and more uneasy radio transmissions from our ground unit. Additional motorcycles and MAMs had arrived in and around the village. The locals didn't seem to be acting normally, and women and children were disappearing indoors. I tried to rob the refueler tent while they were busy pumping the gas, but they had absolutely nothing to eat in there. I was getting a sick feeling from being so hungry, and we had no time to waste. I snagged a few waters from a pallet, at least. The radios were increasingly active, asking how much longer until we came back.

We hurriedly departed the refuel pad and gave our guys two more hours. A tense stand-off was occurring, with the enemy elements below just smart enough to know how to not illicit violence from us or the unit in their village. We could not prove that they were hostile, so we could do nothing but watch. The tension and unease created even more exhaustion and hunger for all of us in our flight. We hit our bingo fuel, so we had to inform the unit we had hit the end of our mission block and must return to base. As we flew away, we were asked to please come back. Every time we departed, it looked as though an imminent attack was about to be launched. After our fourth refuel, we returned at their request, and helped them get back to safety before finally returning home for the fifth and final refuel and parking. It was dinnertime, and the sun was beginning to set. I had only eaten half of a breakfast all day, and I felt like hell. At least our presence had likely deterred an enemy attack and kept the ground forces safe—that mattered more than eating or anything else in the world.

A few flights later, I had another long day. We were briefed that a massive raid would go down among a large grouping of brick factories to our south. The brick factories were large, with a central smoke stack that billowed out foul-smelling smoke as the interior of the structure heated and hardened thousands of bricks. Several of these primitive factories were believed to house, among their piles of bricks, weapons caches and other contraband. Credible intelligence gave us a clue that these were also no ordinary small weapons caches, and our need to support the raids became serious. Our team discussed the plan and our timeline. Nick was the PC in the Lead ship with one of our lieutenants, and I was to fly the Trail ship covering him and supporting our AMC in the left seat. As we approached the first factory, we could see that multinational forces and Afghan police were already moving into the perimeter. A few dirty local workers were corralled and stood waving their arms in wild animation. Everyone always tried to play off a dramatic, over-the-top victim routine, whether or not they were guilty always remained to be seen. A few ANP emerged from an out building near the central factory structure.

"Holy smokes, is that what I think it is?" Called Nick from Lead. I looked at the display from the MMS, and the AMC and I exchanged surprised glances.

"Brother, that looks like six policemen carrying six very heavy 107mm rockets to me," we called back. We watched in growing amazement as more rockets and weapons were pulled from nearby factories, being casually lined up in the dirt in an increasingly long line. The local workers appeared more meek as they were grouped together and intensely questioned, no doubt still attempting to plead ignorance. Suddenly, the ground force radio operator called up.

"Wildwood, we have a white van that's trying to depart the scene. They got past our people and are proceeding to the east at a high speed. We have to stop that vehicle, over!"

The van sped down a dirt road and ignored all of our otherwise non-lethal escalation attempts to stop them. We swooped low over the path of the van just a few feet off the ground, but the van remained unfazed. Our lieutenant in Lead was frustrated and had had enough. I watched from the Trail position as our Lead aircraft moved alongside and slightly above the van. The lieutenant leaned out the left side with his rifle and let a volley of M4 fire tear over the hood of the van. The vehicle came to a sudden halt; they knew that the next rounds wouldn't be a warning. Ground forces raced towards the van, thrilled that the suspects were stopped, and the occupants were still alive for interrogation.

We returned to the brick factory area and flew over what was the biggest haul I'd ever seen; over forty rockets were inventoried. The raids were a huge success, as the 107mm rocket fire had recently intensified since the Taliban stepped up their activity and attacks across the country.

We celebrated the successful raids at dinner. A surprise gift box full of Cajun spices from the Slap Ya Mama company arrived and transformed our chow hall plates full of unanswered questions into more palpable delights. I wrapped one of the seasoning shakers with green duct tape and paracord and hung the shaker from my shoulder holster whenever it was time for chow. It was given the name "Flavor Grenade," and it would be tossed around from soldier to soldier as necessary. We were eternally grateful.

Brick factory, bellowing a foul smelling smoke for miles.

CHAPTER 10

Bagram Airfield was experiencing a relatively calm evening. Our Kiowas were far away from the airfield supporting another mission. The Apache pilots, to my understanding, were playing cards and hanging out in our CP. I was on a night off, dozing here and there in my room. Little did anyone know, Hadji was about to kick off his boldest operation in quite some time. On the western side of the airfield, many enemy fighters had slowly approached the outer perimeter wall. They remained undetected as they took their positions and lay in wait. Everything was quiet, everything was calm.

Multiple explosions rang out, almost all at once. Suicide bombers rushed different gates and points around the perimeter. More thunderous explosions reverberated across the area. Guard towers opened up firing. The attackers on the west side began to run towards the perimeter wall, fighting their way forwards and hiding behind plenty of cover as they advanced. The guard tower guns slowed them down, and the urgent call for help rang out in our CP. The Apache guys were outside in no time, strapping in and firing up since they already had their stuff ready from earlier. More enemy attackers pressed forward, attempting to get inside the wire. Several were successful in making it past the first line of barricades and ended up on the interior perimeter road. The insurgents hurled grenades and attempted to make it through the final perimeter wall. I was awoken early by the gunfire and explosions and ran to the CP half clothed and still trying to dress.

The Apaches had launched and screamed over the runway to the west side, seeing the surprising number of enemy fighters massing and attempting to breach the perimeter. They began firing their 30mm cannon, annihilating anything in its path outside the walls of Bagram. A few insurgents were trying to get inside the outer perimeter wall, like their comrades had, and were cut down by the Apaches and lay mangled against the barriers.

More grenades from inside the perimeter road were thrown by the enemy and caused injuries to soldiers near a bank of B Huts. A few U.S. Army soldiers propped up on a wall and exchanged fire with the enemy, joining in with the already firing guard towers. An Apache laid fire perfectly down the road through the enemy group, "danger close" to friendlies. This volley of 30mm fire had finished the insurgents all off before they could actually breach the final wall to get in and amongst the folks on the west side.

By the time I was airborne, most of the action was already over. One of the dying insurgents tossed another grenade unsuccessfully just as we were making our way to the main point of attack and was promptly put down. A few on the ground were wounded, and most or all of the enemy were killed. In the confusion, I wasn't sure if a few had been able to escape in retreat. When the attack had begun, our troop's SWT out on a mission was called and told to return to BAF immediately. They had arrived on scene to join the Apaches towards the end of the battle, and my rapidly pieced together team relieved them so that everyone could get much needed gas and catch a break.

The "attack" was best summarized by Erik's words, "The Jawas attacked Bagram like a mosquito attacks your windshield..."

The Red Headed Black Sheep put their asses down with extreme force. I was told that even one of the Blackhawks from our task force had joined in with its door gunners. We figured that such further bold moves by the enemy would be stalled for some time to come. I flew along the west side where many of their remains were; I saw bloodied bodies contorted and shredded by the 30mm Apache cannon. It was just after sunrise, and I took tons of pictures, conducting a post-battle assessment and confirming that none of the enemy were still alive outside the wire while we flew low and slow over the bodies. Most of the enemy wore U.S. uniforms, so now we knew where some of our laundry had been disappearing to. I noted one insurgent had an RPG and several rockets, having made it close to an outer wall before he was annihilated by our Apache brothers. If he had made it amongst the B Huts, we would have had far greater casualties and I commended the Apache crews for their expert marksmanship and lightning-fast reaction.

After that, everything was calm. The enemy bodies lay out there for several days before anyone bothered to order a cleanup which I was very surprised by. To my understanding, their culture dictated that they needed to be buried very soon in order to guarantee that they'd get all of that martyr bullshit promised to them in the afterlife. Instead they laid there, rotting in the warm sunlight.

*

We were being utilized a lot more often by the ground task force, which was nice and exhausting at the same time. I'd also finally and officially passed the half-way point of the deployment. Not that the last half would be "downhill from here," though; We still had some uphill battles until the weather would cool down again, forcing Hadji to hibernate once more.

I had begun to miss home, and daydreamed about luxuries like swimming pools. It was more clear to me than ever that Savannah was the perfect place for me to be stationed. I had a great house with access to a large pool, and it was all just a 30-minute drive to several great beaches along the coast of Georgia and South Carolina. We were all at the point where we talked about home. It was normal now to have long discussions of our individual dreams and what we all looked forward to most when we got back home. Our focus was to make it back, all of us, and hopefully in the same condition as when we'd left. I could tell that the missions, the IEDs, and the overall combat experience were forcing a change in me. I had always been a fun-loving, sometimes-goofy guy. Earlier on, Erik had even referred to me as a "free spirit." My outlook and demeanor were changing, and my personality was evening out and hardening a bit. Others from home communicated this observation to me, and tried to keep my spirits up and morale in check.

By May 27th, it was positively windy as hell outside. Inside the buildings and tent hangars, the wind groaned and growled angrily, daring us to fly. On a day where we were supposed to have multiple missions and a lot of flight time, we only flew three and a half hours before being forced to return home. After we shut down and made it inside, the wind was more intense than I had ever experienced. Our satellite dish was smashed while I was on leave and their replacement mount for the windy season was working quite well. Erik was nervous about it all day, but they had really, really anchored that sucker down.

Grounded by winds gusting to over 50mph, a few of us went outside and attempted to fly a small kite that had come in someone's care package. On the kite it said that the wind limits for flying it were 5mph. We had exceeded that a little, and the kite was disintegrating as it was beaten to death above us. It was even becoming difficult to stand up straight as we were also getting sand– and wind-blasted. My shemagh was coming in handy, at least.

Given the circumstances, most of us worked hard to stay positive in light of what we had been given. We watched a lot of funny movies, television shows, and listened to stand-up comedy. We continued to play jokes and rip on each other. We always took pleasure in twisting each other's words and sentences out of context to create obscene innuendoes and stories from it all. We even kept a troop quote book, as was tradition. It was hoped by all that no one important ever read it, lest we all be reprimanded and thrown into sensitivity training for the rest of time.

I finally completed my self-led mission, "Operation Animal Drop." I had a purple teddy bear with angel wings that I snagged out of a church group care package and had been flying around with for a while. I had been waiting for the best opportunity to air drop it to a kid. A little nomad girl was a few hundred meters away from her tent in the middle of a field by a convoy we were escorting. I told Nick to come around and slow down, and to put her outside my door and descend lower. She froze and stared up at us as we approached. I held the bear straight out and wide so that she could see it, then I let go. It whipped out of my hand and fell close to her. She beat feet back towards her tent, so we flew back on another sweep ahead of the convoy. We returned a few minutes later to see about the drop, and the girl waved at us by her tent.

She was grinning ear to ear and held the bear up high and proudly for me to see. I took a few pictures of her and waved back. It felt good to be involved in something so small, yet positive. I decided to continue to do "Operation Animal Drop II, III, IV" etc. for the rest of the time that I was deployed, so long as I could snag more little stuffed animals from packages.

The last week of May had proven to be a long week for me. I couldn't recall how many flights in a row I had conducted, but it was longer than any other time for me during the deployment to date. In all honesty, it had really made time go by and I couldn't believe that it was already the first of June. Our TOC was still continuing to amaze us with their scary level of incompetence. Their abilities were somehow worsening rather than improving over time, which seemed unfathomable. We had a lot of distrust for our leadership and TOC's capabilities and decision-making, causing us to stay more vigilant. Looking at the calendar and talking over dinner, we realized that in a few days on June 7th, we would officially fight in America's longest war, ever.

104 months.

"Juggle that one around in your skull for a second," one of the pilots remarked. It was crazy for me to wrap my head around. I read the words from a book that my brother had sent me, Sun Tzu's *The Art of War*, and it seemed to ring true in our situation: "There is no instance of a country having benefited from prolonged warfare."

I sat next to an Apache pilot, a female lieutenant who had shown up nearly two months prior and was still awaiting a helmet in her size so she could start flying. I felt bad for her; the shortage of Army equipment keeping her grounded for that long was just about one of the best examples of how south the conflict had continued to go. Despite her troubles, she and her husband in the meantime had set up a Facebook page called "Soccer Balls and School Supplies for the Children of Afghanistan." I found out about this after talking with her and volunteered our troop to do the air drops for them, since the Apache could not conduct that operation. We planned on wrapping crayons in bubble wrap so that they didn't shatter after their 50- to 150-ft drop to the earth below. We rummaged through some supplies she'd received and filled up a separate box for my air drops. She aired up a green soccer ball that was sent to us from a young girl's league soccer team back home. They asked me to take pictures and let her know how it all went.

Climbing into the Kiowa, I discovered that one soccer ball fit decently enough on the dash. Erik was in the other helicopter and I told him over the radio of my plan. We were south of BAF, and we linked up with our convoy for a route sweep ahead. We found that everything appeared normal. Fortunately, I'd also located two schools along the route—a boys' school and a girls' school. We weren't sure if the girls were allowed to play soccer, so we decided to try our airdrop over the boys' school first. There were some kids already out in their blue uniforms playing in the yard when we flew over. A team of Kiowas flying low overhead was a pretty common sight for them, so we didn't get very much attention at first. We talked through our drop plan. I sat in the left seat, camera in one hand and the soccer ball in the other. Erik lined the other aircraft up off our three o'clock as we slowed down, descending toward the school yard. I called out on the radio to Erik who was also recording with his camera, "Operation Soccer Ball! In three, tw–Oh, shit!"

The wind had yanked it right out of my hand. We banked hard left and came around. The ball had still managed to land in their play yard, and kids were sprinting towards it. I sighed in relief, as I originally feared the ball had landed outside the wall and that they hadn't seen it. We made a few passes to take some pictures and videos. We later discovered soccer goals at the girls' school and decided that would be the next target when I got another soccer ball. The way that I saw it, many of the Afghan adults were beyond reasoning with. Our own U.S. government official Information Operations (IO) campaign didn't seem to work well, either. I believed that creating self-directed initiatives, such as the toy drop mission, would not have internationally visible results, but maybe those kids in that one school yard would change their views about us.

The Soviet war in Afghanistan had lasted from December 1979 until their defeat and withdrawal in February 1989. As Senator Charlie Wilson said about the CIA assistance we gave to the Afghan resistance fighters:

"These things happened. They were glorious, and they changed the world... and then, we fucked up the endgame."

The Soviet-Afghan War was a mighty financial drain and military failure, and it seemed to have led to the furthering of Soviet struggles and its ultimate collapse. The United States assisted a great deal in this, as well, with our clandestine operations and the arming and training of rebels; however, we then just disappeared. If we had spent an insignificant percentage compared to our weapons budget on building schools and education for the kids left in the aftermath (reportedly only five percent received even a primary education), chances are, there wouldn't be as many of the freaks hammering rounds up at us with AK-47s 10 to 20 years later.

I didn't feel as if I was going soft—I was only thinking about the non-threatening Afghan population. I'd still smoke any one of the people below without question if they attempted to do harm to me or anyone else. The whole mental balance was complex, and it was getting even harder to support our stated mission goals and reasons to be where we were, doing what we do.

*

My days off quickly became less frequent, and I found myself in the air more often. On and off duty, we all dreamt about the freedoms of home. The plans, the adventures, the hobbies, our friends and families, and all the great things in store were awaiting us across the world, in our place called "home." Our endless year would finally cease, and if any of us did even a quarter of what we each dreamed of or planned, it would be awesome. Pure adrenaline and a fierce operational load would keep most of us occupied and in the moment.

When everything seemed to slow down was when the real homesickness would kick in. Like an ocean, the ebb and flow of when each individual wasn't constantly task-saturated with missions and other duties would create boredom and time to think.

We began to take on new operations and explore new areas, which included the capital city of Kabul. This city had the largest population center of the whole country, which included very busy airspace. We were tasked with some peace-keeping duties above Kabul, and I became a bit of an aerial photojournalist. Our abilities as Kiowa scouts to find things out of the ordinary and locate weapons caches had apparently gotten attention. We were assigned several sectors and areas to recon and display a general presence. It felt as though we had flown everywhere possible in our AO and beyond, but we'd been wrong. It was fun to find one of several new playgrounds, especially one so large as Kabul.

I had spent more time flying with CW3 Pete Higgs-Coulthard lately. He hailed from Arizona and had been in the Army and Kiowa world for quite some time. In just the right light and situation, he looked like a Baldwin brother. We were assholes about his last name, asserting that it was the result of him taking his wife's last name, but in reality, he'd successfully kept an old family name going. He became "Dash" to us, and I learned a great deal from him; he was a patient mentor whom I enjoyed flying with.

While over the city one day, I succumbed to my liberal intake of water and coffee. I called Lead from our Trail ship, and informed them of my situation with the one phrase that couldn't be denied, yellow duck.

"Are you serious?! Are you really declaring a yellow duck while we're over Kabul?" Lead asked. Erik was annoyed with me, as this meant that we'd have to find somewhere to go, and we had no clue where that may need to be.

"Affirmative," I called back. "I suggest Kabul International Airport." Pete, my PC, threw his head back, laughing and saying, "Oh my God, Robo. You are such an asshole!"

Because we were in the Trail bird, it would be up to the Lead ship to get in touch with Kabul International and coordinate our entrance into their traffic flow. None of us had ever landed there or had cause to even think of landing there before. We had no charts for it, and we knew nothing but to steer clear of it. The controller of Kabul International was not a pleasant person, so I slightly altered my plan about how this was all going to go down. The controller was giving Lead too hard of a time, so I keyed the mic and said, "Look, we have a safety issue. We're going to land, so tell us where you want us to go." They now had to let us in, and we flew our approach close behind the Lead bird. As we reached the runway and turned off, the man in the tower issued us complex and broken instructions to taxi somewhere far away. With no charts, there was no way that we could comply. We then told the tower that we needed progressive taxi instructions, which put the onus on them to provide us turn-by-turn directions. This further frustrated them, and they were getting more unpleasant in their transmissions.

"Screw it, let's set it down," I called. Erik agreed and set his bird down on the taxiway, with us setting down right behind. The tower guy grew incredulous and demanded to know why we had stopped on their taxiway. I told Pete that I was going to "check on our problem by the tail boom on the left side of the fuselage." He gave me a thumbs up, and then told Erik that I was getting out.

Erik told the tower we had an issue that needed to be dealt with immediately, and to stand by. It was beautiful—I stood back by the tail boom and checked an antennae. I also took a leak right there on the taxiway, feeling much better. I finished "checking the part," then climbed back in and smiled, and gave a big thumbs up. Pete laughed and Erik called me a jerk, then told tower that we needed to depart the area immediately and head back towards Bagram. The tower had no choice but to grant our demand, and I smiled as we took off and turned away, seeing my pool on the taxiway as my contribution to the beautification of Kabul.

Armored side panel artwork by SGT Arthur Torres.
Poem reworked by the same artist, modified and adapted from an originally author-unknown
WWII version said by U.S. B-17 Flying Fortress bomber crews before battle.

Preparing to throw a stuffed animal to a child below.

An excited Bedouin brother and sister admire their new stuffed animals.

A mother and her daughter laugh and wave with neighbors, holding up their new gifts with large smiles.

Villagers and children wash clothes and rugs, as well as themselves, in the Panjshir River.

Team Pigeon about to head out for another round of trouble.
CW2 Nick Payne (left seat), CW2 Kennamer Yates (right seat).

Afghanistan's expansive capital city, Kabul.

CHAPTER 11

In the first week of June, we were given a rather hush-hush assignment, which was so hush-hush apparently that those that didn't know about it were really butt-hurt by our supposedly insane conduct. As we flew over the city of Kabul, we received no special attention since we had become a common sight. We pretended to conduct general reconnaissance, but we were actually escorting a VIP convoy from a small compound in the city to the Kabul International Airport. The convoy was about as unofficial looking as an official convoy could be, utilizing armored civilian vehicles rather than military ones. The difference in their colors, makes, and models only helped them blend in more. Inside sat some familiar high-level people who served in important United States Government and Defense positions.

For a Kiowa team doing such a hasty and serious escort, we couldn't just hang out high in the sky. We had to get down low, and do what we did best. We raced ahead of the small convoy while not drawing attention to them, but to focus any undue curiosity on ourselves. Since we had been operating in the area for several days by then, we didn't turn as many heads as we had originally. In the conduct of our surveillance and checking the rooftops and routes, we flew as aggressively as usual.

An important general who didn't know about the convoy mission observed us, and his feathers got quite ruffled. Here stood this high-ranking U.S. Army general in his little corner office, watching a pair of Kiowas hot-dog flying over the city. We were just a group of damn cowboys, complete with our dumb hats. This foolishness needed to be dealt with, and these pilots needed to be disciplined. An angry call from this individual resulted in a chain of angry calls splintering down the chain. By the time we landed, people were waiting for us. We were told that we needed to explain ourselves, and to do so quickly. There was an intense heat lamp on our task force, and an even more intense one on the Kiowa team who had just apparently pissed off the whole fucking military command in Kabul. We started to chuckle, asking if our welcoming party was honestly serious. Assurances were made that this was no laughing matter. We were in trouble, and it was big trouble, mister!

Our AMC started his first sentence berating our TOC for how dumb it was that we were even being bothered with such nonsense. Our TOC had been the ones who received word of the need for us and had gotten the hasty mission set up in the first place. We could not believe that word had gone from the top to the bottom and had arrived at us, without anyone with a brain intercepting the madness. After a bit of cooling off, we were left alone, as it was more than clear we were completely in the right and everyone who had freaked out had done so out of ignorance. It was amusing to see the serial incompetence finally result in them being inconvenienced instead of us.

Our visiting senior-most warrant officer from the task force stayed stone faced throughout our story and then sighed after we finished telling him the truth of how everything had transpired. He had to concede that there was nothing to lecture us on, and he'd wasted a trip to the east side. We ended up inviting him to play the board game Risk, since he'd already made the journey over, and he was amazing at it.

The next morning, our flight was intense and fast. At the direction of our supported ground unit, we chased some people down and conducted photo reconnaissance. I really enjoyed doing photo recon, and I had gotten proficient at it. The individuals we were chasing had been digging suspiciously by a main road, doing so brazenly in the daylight. Once we showed up and they saw us, the men jumped into a small car and tried to flee the scene. Scorpion 16 was on the radio, giving us an update on what they'd witnessed themselves. Unfortunately for us, the vehicle sped into a nearby village, whereupon parking, the suspects ducked into a building. Scorpion 16 was too far down the road and busy with another task, so for the time being, it appeared the suspects might get away. I leaned out of the helicopter, cursing their luck, but also snapping photos and archiving information. The target vehicle, vehicles around it, license plates, and structures in the vicinity were all detailed with descriptions and times of the events and suspicious persons. Oftentimes patience and perseverance in intel gathering paid off greater than brashly engaging, since the enemy could sometimes lead us to much bigger fish.

*

On June 18th, a rocket attack against Bagram proved deadly, having killed four U.S. soldiers on the west side. The 107mm rockets were placed on small earthen mounds and set to launch at a predetermined time. This was accomplished many times using, of all things, a mosque prayer timer that resembled a kitchen gadget. The cowards who set the rockets would then casually return to the safety of farming and sipping tea while they waited to hear if they had been successful. Hadji was really pissing us off, and that rocket attack had sprung us into more aggressive action for the time being. As it began to heat up outside, we set about traveling into the enemy safe-haven zones. The Tagab Valley still continued to be a humbling location, both in its beauty and for what danger lurked there. We all used our spider senses a bit more when we flew there. With the harvests going on, there were a lot of people out and about in the fields. Down in the Tagab, we always had to maintain a keen awareness of everything moving around on the ground and up on the ridgelines. A shepherd, or any other local for that matter, could easily hide an AK-47 under his robes. Sometimes, they would even openly carry them, and observing anyone with a weapon was commonplace and allowed. It would get our attention, but it wasn't until they made themselves a threat that the individual warranted concern.

Since my arrival in Afghanistan, I could tell that I had become tremendously more observant in the air. A glance from a local towards us was normal, but it was the instant change in behavior from what they'd been doing that would pique my interest. Extremely odd standouts were those who would place their hands behind their backs and walk with large, near goose-stepping strides. On one of these occasions, I called back to our Trail ship, "They're bad."

The AMC keyed the mic. "You sure?" My binoculars were up and I tried not to laugh at the ridiculous Monty Python display of silly walking.

"Who else walks around with their hands behind their backs like some cartoon, trying not to seem guilty while occasionally eyeball-fucking us?" I had a solid point, and was told to keep a close eye on them.

The harder a bad guy tried to look normal, the quicker we would figure out that something was out of place. In less extreme cases, he could simply quicken his walk, pretend to farm, or attempt to conceal an object such as a weapon or radio. Many times, it was the change of behavior from getting spooked that got the quickest notice. It was an adrenaline rush—I could feel that something bad was evolving before my eyes and a hunt was materializing. It might not be me, personally, who would bring their end in most cases, but I'd have a hand in the beginning of that process. Hemingway was right; I was becoming addicted to hunting humans.

*

Because of the Uniform Code of Military Justice (UCMJ) and our additional orders and mandates, I could not enjoy basic American freedoms, such as freedom of speech and of the press. Repercussions from such "disloyal" acts could yield serious disciplinary measures or even jail time, and I had other plans that did not include prison. So, I elected to remain tight-lipped when encountering situations that I seriously wished could be exposed. I wanted to talk, though. I wanted to tell everyone what was happening. Watching and reading the news, even as infrequently as we did, seemed to always kill us all just a little inside. I had recently read the *Stars and Stripes* newspaper (free for deployed soldiers). It was essentially the official newspaper of the U.S. military, and I was pleasantly surprised at how critical some commentators could be sometimes. A week prior, we were being briefed about the attack against Bagram. Everyone sat around the computer in our CP for a teleconference with our TOC. An intelligence guy began, "*Stars and Stripes* reported that the insurgents..." but he was interrupted immediately by laughter and jeering.

"You're the intelligence guys, and you got your intelligence from fucking *Stars and Stripes*?!" One of the senior Apache pilots piped up. It was a perfect example to describe the caliber of "intelligence" that we too often received.

The teleconferencing occurrences only continued to get worse when we'd hope for the opposite. On another teleconference, we were being tasked with escorting a Blackhawk down into the Tagab Valley. The Blackhawk was to fly high and tag along on one of our missions. We figured it was a sightseeing tour for some "important" passengers. The head Blackhawk pilot in the room on the other side of the airfield got angry and spoke up.

"Wait! You want us to go into the Tagab, single ship, with no other air support or cover? What happens if we get shot down? Who's there to pick us up?" Our side of the airfield exploded with angry laughter, as the man had discounted our Kiowas completely. I passionately exploded, "Are you seriously that fucking scared, despite having two armed escorts, to simply fly through an area where we usually fight much lower, and without one of you skirts overhead to pick *us* up?!" We cultivated and encouraged hatred in each other, so my remark was applauded and ended up on our quote of the day board. We could not believe how afraid the skirts (our name for Blackhawk crews) were sometimes. We flew in the Tagab without any means of being extracted all the time. We flew a lot lower and with quite a bit more aggression towards the inhabitants than a high-flying Blackhawk, too. Hell, there were times we'd been so deep into enemy-controlled territory that we were nowhere even remotely close to friendlies. We'd conduct our recon, flying into and up little off-shoot valleys. These were places where I couldn't even fathom how long it would take to be found, let alone rescued. I was so glad that I had not chosen the Blackhawk airframe. Although some pilots were okay, their community as a whole had a much different outlook on operations and life, and I was content with not being a part of it.

We were in the last few days of June and I had the next two evenings to become nocturnal. I was to re-enter green world and fly again. I couldn't believe it had been over 50 days since my last NVG flight. I embraced the night schedule and looked forward to the change of pace and type of operations that green world may once again bring.

We were all aware of a recent *Rolling Stone* magazine article titled "The Runaway General," written about the U.S. Army general who served as commander of U.S. and NATO forces in Afghanistan. The article appeared to have led to the forced resignation and replacement of many in the Afghan war leadership. There were a lot of things mentioned in the article I had been wanting to say to friends and family back home the whole time. Now that the cat was out of the bag, I felt a sense of relief. The American public who were interested could now better understand the conflict in greater detail. The last third of the article dealing with the soldiers out in the middle of nowhere and their concerns and questions during a Q&A session with a general was no isolated incident. One soldier even showed the author a laminated card he was given, which highlighted new platoon regulations. It explained that soldiers should only patrol areas in which they were reasonably certain they wouldn't have to use deadly force, which was absurd.

The story was a core example and universal pulse for how the guys on the ground felt about the war. It was fascinating that one media article could send a ripple effect and bring about such an important change. There was uncertainty in the ranks about how things would go once the next general took over. We had observed and also experienced a lot of frustration since the relieved general's policies took hold in Afghanistan, and we'd been hampered in our ability to actually do anything or win the war. It wasn't so much of a fault of his as it was his underlings. The military had evolved into an ultra cover-your-own-ass-style system. Even at the risk of failing in the grand scheme of things, more and more commands now emphasized policies and directives that would protect them from blame that stemmed from the unavoidable tragedies of war. It was disheartening when the primary consideration was the protection of a suspect and hostile populace over the safety of American service members. Many of us hoped that things would change, but we weren't holding our breath.

*

We sat idly in the CP when a call came in and by the sudden change in the man's face who answered the phone, we all knew to immediately jump out of our chairs. We were all extremely in tune with one another, working like one cohesive, well-oiled machine in our teams. The TIC call for help was very urgent. The phone was put on speaker as we scrambled to gather our things, and were told that an IED had taken out at least one vehicle. The TOC was trying to get us a "grid, freq, and callsign" since our TOC knew that's all we ever angrily shouted that we wanted; everything else could wait until we were in the air.

We sprinted out to the Kiowas, all of our gear was ready to go. We spooled up, popped on our NVGs and were airborne in mere minutes. As we turned from the airfield and began to fly towards the general area in which we'd been told to start moving, we could already see fire in the distance. The TOC was still struggling to get us information, and our Trail ship on the radio told them, "Fuck it. We see it. Stand by and we'll call back later and update you."

It was very surreal to see the MRAP burning far in the distance. As we approached, the fire eerily illuminated the otherwise dimly lit area. The burning MRAP was a beacon for miles under the NVGs. The group of vehicles it had been with had abandoned it and were moving in our direction. Since it was nighttime, we couldn't tell what other battle damage was suffered in the attack on the other vehicles. We didn't even know if there were any dead Americans still inside the burning MRAP. We knew nothing, except for what we saw.

We went over to the remaining vehicles and saw one or more limping back to base after a substantial ambush by several fighters. We spread our formation out to look around the area where the burning MRAP sat. It was dead quiet and very dark except for that burning vehicle, metaphorically burning a picture and memory into my mind forever. The unit it had belonged to were busy with their movement and injuries, so I didn't bother them with my curiosity about the fate of those in the burning vehicle below. I imagined that any bodies would have been removed, and it would be hard to believe that a full abandonment of the vehicle would occur if remains were inside. I remembered the smell of burning flesh from the burn ward working my clinical rotation at Brooke Army

Medical Center in San Antonio during medic school. The sickening smell from the world's premier burn treatment center felt as though it had returned to my nostrils. Scarred and bandaged flesh, and silently screaming men...I pushed it all away and snapped myself back to the present. No movement or indications of human inhabitants in the area were found. No locals dared to chance even a peek off of a rooftop or from a window. There wasn't much that we could do, even if we saw something suspicious, thanks to our restrictions combined with those imposed on the ground forces. Our reactionary stance had reached a tipping point, and I couldn't help but feel desperate for change.

I wished that some "leaders" in charge of the "big picture" could see what we saw. I was convinced that PowerPoint slides and briefings of senior officials grossly underestimated the frustrations of those frontline combatants. They were the ones affected by risk averse policies that put so many into harm's way. Our ROE restrictions dictated everything about the way in which we could (or could not) fight. The who, what, where, when, why, and how we could engage the enemy seemed to tip more and more to the enemy's favor.

The enemy knew our ROE, which was an easy internet search away. They knew that we couldn't strike back at them if they were on or in a civilian structure that we couldn't 100 percent guarantee was devoid of innocent civilians. The enemy knew to surround themselves with women and children as shields. They would launch attacks from the grounds of mosques, knowing we would retreat rather than cause some international incident over shooting up a mosque, regardless of the real reasons why. The insurgents could duck into a building and wait us out, so long as ground forces weren't in the immediate vicinity and they knew we would eventually have to depart, and then they could escape. They could also just change clothing or disguise themselves by looting whatever building they entered, and that would then give us a layer of doubt whether or not the person emerging casually was our target or not.

If our ground guys were not completely pinned down by fire and had any chance of escape, then we were not to engage. If we were asked finally to engage, we then had to take several steps in a chain of approvals to fire. All the while, Americans or other friendly forces below were being shot up while we watched and pleaded to help. If we just said "screw it" and made up our own minds to attack, it could be our last flight ever as we then went under investigation. An act outside of the approval chain or directives in the ROE could do more than end your career, it could (and in some cases did) land soldiers in prison. Our physical enemy wasn't the only one trying to kill us; our ROE and leadership adopting spineless and dreadful policies to protect their own careers had become a threat to us, as well.

By this point, I finally knew why my brother was jumpy for a while at the sound of a loud boom, bang, or thud even after he returned home from deployment. It's an involuntary behavior born from frightful experiences, and I knew that I certainly jumped now, too. I would get angry a lot faster, and my sense of humor was warping a bit. Cynicism was sneaking into my personality and becoming a permanent trait which I recognized and, despite myself, had no choice but to accept.

I stayed terrible at keeping up with news from home. Not that it wasn't available to me with the internet and the *Stars and Stripes* newspaper right there in the chow hall. I found myself always engrossed in other things so I missed most of what was going on outside our Afghan world. In later years, I would come to realize that both of my deployments were like a void in my mind, as if I had left earth and been away from all of society, seemingly on another planet.

CHAPTER 12

We were all looking forward to November and began having talks about the light at the end of the tunnel. Plans were being discussed with loved ones regarding vacation travels, purchases, rumors of when our homecoming would be, and when our replacements might arrive. It was still a ways away, but the prospect of that day to come when we boarded the plane home was an irresistible notion that was tightly held on to.

"The only ones left are the smart ones; we've already killed all the dumb ones." I was sure that the current saying about the enemy we fought with was true. We began a serious mission, and we had a solid plan to finally use our Beggar's Canyon route successfully. We began at the top of our created route, racing down the turns and crevices in the terrain towards the hostile village below. This had been rehearsed numerous times, as we had always figured that our ingress to the area from along Beggar's Canyon would keep us from being seen by the enemy early warning networks. Many sympathizers or insurgents themselves had cell phones and radios, and I knew that they tracked our positions and movements.

We knew that there was a High Value Target (HVT) down in the village on this day, and he was finally set to be captured or killed. The entire village was under siege by coalition ground forces conducting a Cordon and Search. This was essentially a mission to encircle and isolate an area to look for enemies, weapons caches, or other evidence of insurgent activity. As we raced down Beggar's Canyon, my heart raced as well, because this time it was not a drill.

Our ground forces were maneuvering into the area, and we needed to be able to catch anyone attempting to flee out the "back door" toward the high ground. This particular HVT was one that I believed would be better off dead rather than alive. We believed he was responsible for some IED construction classes, and was a strong and senior enemy leader. As we flew down into the last quarter of Beggar's Canyon, we could already see movement in the village. Coalition forces were swarming in, and positions had been set up to funnel those trying to escape into a craggy section of rocky terrain that had been carved out by a long since expired river. As expected, we received word from the ground forces that they had a positive ID on the target, and he was attempting to flee the area right into our trap. The man rounded the corner of a qalat on his motorcycle, stopping at the beginnings of the impassable terrain. He quickly dismounted the motorcycle, now with nowhere to go but up the difficult terrain on foot.

As we neared the man, we saw that he was concealing something under his shirt. My senses tingled as I knew that in a flash he could present his AK-47 and attempt to engage me. I was very close to him and low, looking from my position in the Lead aircraft from the left seat. Quickly, I reached up onto the dash and unfastened my M4 rifle, putting it into my lap and clipping the buckle that hung from the stock to my vest in case it was accidentally dropped. On the next low pass, the enemy and I locked eyes for the first time.

Time seemed to slow down. The man's face was dark tan, dirty, and wrinkled from a hard life of battle and survival. He had a large beard, murderous eyes, and a wild, almost animalistic look on his face. This was the bad guy, the pictured HVT that we were looking for. The shiver down my spine was not from fear, it was from the primal knowledge that my opponent was ready to fight to the death. He was trapped with nowhere to go. The blazing stare from his eyes into mine seared like the memory of that MRAP I had seen burning not long before. My PC asked if I saw a weapon, and I was certain that I did as he tried to conceal it.

This was my kill. He was responsible for hurting all of those whom we had under our charge. For all the casualties in the IEDs and ambushes we'd responded to, this man was party to those acts. My quarry was trapped, and we would remove his wretched soul from the battlefield. We called up to set the engagement criteria and for clearance to engage. Our hostile confirmed target was displaying through desperate body language that he was nearing his last stand. We were quickly cleared, so we began to set up for the shot. As we rolled into our profile to start our gun run with the .50 cal, we suddenly had to break off our engagement. Out of nowhere, one of our Blackhawks had moved into position close to the man and positioned in a static hover. The door gunner then started firing madly, and the HVT ran in an attempt to hide from the barrage. Clouds of earth kicked up, shrouding the man. The door gunner from the Blackhawk kept firing until his machine gun was empty. The air cleared, and a very dead insurgent was visible lying in a bloody pile amongst the rocks.

I was pissed off, along with our team. This was not because the "kill had been stolen," but because the morons in the Blackhawk had come out of nowhere, and had almost gotten themselves killed by a hail of fire from our .50 cal on an inbound engagement. We cussed them out on the radio, and an unpleasant exchange escalated quickly. The HVT was dead, and the mission was a successful one, but it was a damn close call for the impatient Blackhawk. Despite it all, I still thought of those eyes. Those eyes were filled with so much malice and hostility as they bore into mine. Perhaps I wasn't the only one who hadn't properly learned not to hate your enemy.

In the weeks that followed, we Black Sheep all followed the same routine: wake up, eat (sometimes), preflight, brief, and then fly mission after mission, responding to more contact and unpleasantries. By the time the sun came up, we would finally be almost done. After we handed the mission over, we would quickly eat breakfast, shower, and immediately go to bed because we'd be back on shift in eight hours or less once again. We were still in limbo for who or what was going to change, if anything at all, now that a new general was taking over the war. I hoped that an article that I'd read in *Stars and Stripes* quoting him and his apparent understanding of U.S. Service member concerns was accurate. We hoped like hell that he might make some good changes to how business was done. I didn't advocate for a Soviet-style leveling of the villages and killing all the kids to whom I threw soccer balls. I did, however, believe that we could afford to show more force to be successful in our endeavors.

The Apaches had been doing good things in other operational areas that we Kiowas rarely ventured into. The Apache could fly farther and stay longer than we could, which made me jealous. They had been dealing out serious death to the enemy recently, and it was good to hear about it from them and view their gun tape recordings. It motivated me that, in some areas, we were actually bringing the fight to the enemy and stopping some of their advances and operations, but I absolutely hated seeing Americans wounded and killed. No matter how seasoned a soldier may become, watching those things occur was never easy to get over. At the moment, a soldier couldn't afford to dwell on anything other than the immediate needs of the ensuing combat—to take too long of a pause could jeopardize the safety of everyone on our team. When each flight was over, and the debriefings had been completed, the quiet time back in the room was when the emotion could rise and doubt would trickle into our minds. Anything repressed out of necessity could then slowly surface and begin chipping away at the psyche. Haunted thoughts, doubts, and memories mixed poorly with the trippy dream-inducing anti-malaria drug, Doxycycline. The resulting period of sleep would be anything but restful. Sometimes the best and the only thing we could do was talk it through with a buddy who was usually in the same boat, depending on how bad an event had gotten. We all grew very close, and most of us knew virtually everything about one another. The shared experiences of horrible traumas can link soldiers together with a forever enduring bond even closer than with family. We occasionally got pissed at each other; we would fight and bicker to deal with the intense stress and our differences in personality. But, when the chips were down, we would fight to the death for each other without a second thought.

Sometimes, our missions could get so stupid that all we could do was shrug and laugh. I especially liked it when we'd be sent somewhere with some large grand plan, only to arrive and be in contact with absolutely no one. Once, I arrived in a rush after a plea for help from the ANP. We had ensured a rapid arrival to their location as the TIC sounded very urgent. When we arrived, we found them hanging out and in zero danger. I saw no evidence that any skirmish had taken place. The ANP lounging around smoking just smiled and waved. I shook my head in disgust and shot them my middle finger.

The frustrating circumstances were getting to us more and more, so to counteract it all, we became increasingly absurd. Sometimes, we were so loopy that it was as if we were in a slapstick British comedy show. We began trying to lighten the mood by getting into arguments about the most random facts while flying. When we landed, we'd rush to the nearest computer and consult the Oracle (aka Google). To keep from going mad, I would sometimes put my noise-canceling headphones on, shut my eyes, and listen to different nature sounds or rainfall. This was the ultimate luxury, to relax and escape into my world. A lot of the guys on deployment who appeared to be going a little crazy were those incapable of relaxing or taking a break when the opportunities arose.

Recently, I had been entertaining myself while I was sitting in the left seat. Whenever I sat with a camera during periods of low activity, I began "bird watching." A lot of the locals slept on their roofs at night since it was so damn hot in their oven-like homes after the day. Some of them literally had what appeared to be a bird's nest atop their qalat, so I set about trying to find the pimpest bird's nest that I could find and photograph it. I wondered if maybe I was going a little crazy, and I asked Nick. He and Chico laughed like hyenas in response, and I then realized that I had asked crazy people for their opinion on crazy.

*

On July 22nd, my night flight began on the wrong foot. Everyone was kicked back, settled into a rather quiet evening. Suddenly, the phones rang, and the room became instantly alive. The voice on the speakerphone was urgent, shouting "Troops in contact! Troops in contact! Launch QRF! Grids, freqs, and callsigns to follow!"

Everything was interrupted when this happened—in literally seconds lost to anything extraneous, you could cause the death of someone in a gunfight who was counting on you. We went from sitting back and discussing mountain flying to leaping out of our seats and sprinting to the aircraft. Everyone from the CP emptied onto the flight line. Several additional pilots scoured the aircraft prepping from the outside while Erik and I armored up, strapped in, and loaded up critical mission data. There was growing confusion, but we didn't have time to deal with it, we had to go, go, GO! I leapt the aircraft off of the pad and called the tower with our emergency launching phrases to clear us in front of all other traffic. They quickly cleared us as a formality, since we were already whipping around the tower at our highest speed and low altitude while rapidly typing in coordinates and gathering info.

We immediately began to experience serious issues with our radios. Thank goodness Erik was my PC and was a maintenance pilot, so we quickly performed every workaround possible to get our communications system usable. We raced towards the grid for the TIC, located high on a mountain ridgeline. Low cloud layers created difficulty in staying away from zero-visibility conditions, and it was getting worse. Some distant lightning dazzled my senses as I looked on to the nearby fight. Infrared strobes, muzzle flashes, our wingman's aircraft beacon, and lightning in the diffused haze all coupled together into a nightmare light show. The last thing that I wanted was to experience a very disorienting phenomenon called flicker vertigo. We could not afford it.

I stayed out of the lowered clouds, and as we began to get a handle on the fight, our MMS malfunctioned. Erik cursed and tried, but the MMS became useless, so we spun the optics around to the rear and shut it down. Now, all we had were our NVG-assisted eyes to make out the battle. Our sister ship also reported issues. Despite the problems thrown at us, we somehow helped the ground forces and halted the firefight through our presence and noise. Hadji knew his muzzle flashes would give his position away to aircraft, so all that he needed to do was take a break and wait for us to leave.

The ground force assured us they'd regained control of the situation and thanked us, so it became time to escort some Chinooks. We landed at a remote FARP to get fuel, and we thought the Chinooks were bearing down on us, so we figured we'd have to leave quickly. This was a mistake. No matter what, you learn in the military that you never, ever, give up the chance to eat, sleep, or pee, because you never know when you'll be able to do it again. I thought that the Chinooks were about to land, so I decided that I'd just hold the pee until we got home.

It turned out that they were late, and I experienced much discomfort because of their shenanigans while taking their sweet time leaving Bagram. I plotted landing back in the FARP to take a quick leak, but I decided not to risk it. The visibility was poor, with winds growing greater in strength, and more lightning strikes were closing in. Landing at the FARP was dangerous but necessary that first time, but I didn't feel like trying it again. It was an unwritten rule that yellow duck declarations were only reserved for sensible occasions.

We circled and circled until we finally got word from the Chinooks that they would be at the landing site, seriously this time. *Good,* I thought, *we'll just get this over with, then we'll go home and I can finally pee!*

A few minutes later as the Chinooks were landing, we got another call. "Troops in contact! Troops in contact! Vicinity grid of previous ground force location!" Erik and I shuddered in anger and frustration. "Damnit, not again!" I cursed as I whipped our aircraft around. The same ground guys we had assisted earlier were under attack again. We told the Chinooks to hurry the hell up and they finally departed as we hauled ass back to the ridgeline.

Our radios were still in a bad state of affairs, but Erik had somehow gotten our MMS working. Rain began to pour down and the winds rapidly increased. Even with no doors on the aircraft, heavy rain showers weren't an issue so long as the helicopter was flown in a coordinated manner. Add lots of swirling unpredictable mountain winds, and this became a lot more difficult to do. I kept us relatively dry, all things considered. If I had been soaked I probably would not have even known it.

We made it back to the ridgeline, helping until it was time for us to get home due to very low fuel. Right as we were departing, the battle below flared up once more and the pandemonium intensified.

"Break, break, break..(sounds of automatic fire).. Wildwo- (cursing, more shots)..Do you have eyes on the-(bang, boom)!" My NVGs flickered and horrific green pictures danced across my eyes. Lightning, IR beacons, muzzle flashes, tracers, and screaming soldiers transmitted on the radio. My heart rate felt as intense as the raging battle. Luckily, our Apache brothers were almost on station to relieve us. Their sensors were absolutely better equipped to deal with the current situation than ours were, especially given the currently barely functional MMS on my aircraft. We passed them in the air with a quick battle handover while rapidly flying back towards Bagram to avoid running out of gas.

Upon landing, it surprised us to find that the whole series of events had occurred within only a little more than three hours of time. It wasn't even 2300 yet. We all agreed that we were done flying for the evening unless something really crazy was happening. We watched a movie to decompress after debriefing, but first, we discussed the whole flight and thought of new ways to combat Murphy's Law with more effective contingencies. Despite the havoc, a meaningful experience had come out of it, the battle on the ridgeline had ceased after the Apaches had shown their violent proficiency, and our forces were also mostly okay.

The night ended after reviewing some recent photos that I had snapped in the early morning light near a remote FOB in the Dandar area to Bagram's north-east. A pile of school desks sat behind a building in a smoldering, charred pile. The building itself had been repurposed by insurgents determined to deny any educational opportunities. Sitting next to us was one of my favorite Apache guys. Josh and I had much in common, and he was someone I wanted to hang out with when we got back home. He enjoyed reviewing photos with us and seeing the vantage point that we experienced from the Kiowa. I had more than usual, and some of them uniquely showed the details and terrain of the area. The following exchange just had to be written down:

Erik: "You know, this place is pretty; it's just too bad that it's full of assholes."

Josh: "You mean...like Detroit?"

Erik: "Yes, Josh. Like Detroit."

*

Towards the end of July, we were assigned missions back over Kabul again. There were enemy weapons caches and 107mm rockets reported, so we set about our hunt. I was surprised at how effective the ground forces were at securing the sites that were found, and that so many suspects were taken into custody for interrogation.

While over Kabul, a Chinook had an engine failure right as they were on a descent into one of many small outposts within the city. The helicopter was so low and so committed to the approach that there was not much that the crew could do, and the Chinook landed directly on the wall of the base which impacted right in the middle of the helicopter. The nose of the Chinook hurtled forwards, slamming the cockpit and forward half into the earth while the back ramp of the fuselage hung over the wall towards the unsecured road outside. Curious locals began to mass under the aircraft. The Chinook was laying mostly inside of a U.S. controlled outpost, so there was not much time before the crash site was secured. Everyone on board suffered only minor bruises, strains, and sprains to our knowledge. The Chinook looked like it had irreversible damage, but had taken the hit well enough to save its crew and few passengers aboard. We separated from our ground units, who thankfully no longer needed our support, and started to fly security over the crashed Chinook. We tried to relay what we observed to our TOC and to help make a plan. The crew and passengers had exited the aircraft from the forward portion that was inside controlled territory, so there was not technically a crisis going on. Soon, a plan was hatched to have one Chinook come and carry out the other. The damaged Chinook was secured with straps, lifted up, and carried from Kabul all the way back to BAF. It was impressive to see, since the Chinook was such a beast. The act of carrying equipment from a Blackhawk or Chinook was called a "sling load," but never in my lifetime did I imagine I'd escort one Chinook sling loading another Chinook.

It was almost the end of July, which had been a total blur. I hadn't intentionally tried to grow a mustache, but there it was. In the past 30 days, I had flown close to 90 hours, which was the maximum before various extra paperwork was required to waive safety regulations. I looked unkempt and filthy. My face bespoke fatigue, and my stubble was an affront to all regulation-loving Army enforcers everywhere. I still wore my body armor, which covered up my rank, and carried the rest of my gear in my hands. Wrapped loosely around my neck was my once white, now dirt-stained tan, shemagh. As I neared our CP building, a clean-cut man with several sergeant stripes appeared out of nowhere and intercepted me. This senior enlisted man, being a uniform Nazi with a complex, began to talk about how I looked. He asked if I had shaved and spoke of how out of regulation my appearance was. Whatever he was saying sounded to me like Charlie Brown's teacher. As each word came out, the conversation grew more distorted. I wasn't hearing or processing the conversation right. He began asking me to kick his ass. I began to want to fight him. I grew irritable and hostile. An equally dirty guardian angel came to my aid; a senior pilot appeared and intervened in the situation. I was thrust inside and they slammed the door. I heard a loud exchange outside while I put my things away in my locker. My troop-mate came in scowling, but quickly softened up a bit. He told me that the unwelcome guest would not be returning. I never knew who it was or what he thought he was there to accomplish, but the promise to never see him again held true.

Our resident Standardization Pilot had honed in on me with questions. The goal before we were packing up to go home would be that I would receive my PC ride. To recap, this was the next step in a pilot's progression: the coveted title of Pilot in Command. A PC is responsible for the aircraft and its crew, along with the completion of the mission. The "ride" was a long process and conducted just like that of a final checkride in flight school, plus some. Besides oral knowledge and flight proficiency, a multitude of other subjects and critical decision making would be analyzed. In the next few weeks, I planned on really getting back into the books to sharpen my skill set in preparation.

*

August began, and after several days of nasty weather, our team finally got a small reprieve from the downpouring rain. We proceeded northwest to check an area we'd left alone for a bit too long. After all the rain, the river was raging and flooding out the area. I think it was the first time that I was not really able to tell whether I was flying over a river delta in Afghanistan or (from the pictures and videos I'd seen) in Vietnam. Every field was flooded and there was a lot of low fog, humidity, and more drizzling rain. I thought of the Vietnam war, and how out of hand it had gotten for those deployed there. I couldn't help but feel almost guilty for how easy we seemed to have it on Bagram in comparison. Combat was combat, but outside of that, the time spent back in the rear was different for my generation of pilots versus theirs. I looked at the river delta and the haze, knowing that if this was Vietnam, I'd be in a lot more danger flying like I was at the moment. If I thought we were going crazy, I could only imagine how hard it had been for those pilots. The weather began to rapidly deteriorate again, and we left the river quickly after having seen zero inhabitants outside the walls of their qalats. We made it back in time to refuel and shut down, getting drenched in another downpour as we tried to run from the Kiowas back into our building.

We made the most of our downtime by eating some BBQ. We needed something to boost morale, so some guys made an exodus to the west side to the rarely seen BBQ chow hall. They brought us back plates of corn on the cob, potato and macaroni salad, BBQ chicken, brisket, and ribs. Coupled with poker and a competitive game of Monopoly, it was a much-needed morale break. Despite the good BBQ and my plans to study more and keep up the workouts, I was again at a low point, but this time it was different. A lost, hopeless feeling had arrived, despite my best efforts to fight it. I internalized the frustration with the mis-utilization of the conflict. The instances where we had been directed to respond to a false report over here, while a real attack happened over there, were too many. I had finally started to shut down. I was losing my old self—the eager, ambitious, young me with the naïve outlook and plenty of fire and pride was fading away. The change was happening, and it had only taken less than a year. At least I was semi-aware, and I knew it would become dangerous if I let it progress. I confided in my closest pals in the troop. It surprised me to hear that not only was I normal, but I was also not alone. Our senior guys had multiple deployments under their belts and said that, as a first timer, I was right on track to be miserable around then. To keep myself sane, I must try to look to the future, do right by those we supported, and it would all pass.

Afterward, we had some spare time to daydream and shoot the breeze before our convoy was to require an escort. I talked about looking forward to working on my house, as well as getting back to the states and enjoying much of what I used to take for granted. I was hell bent on my decision to buy a camping hammock. I got some chuckles at that one, but was convinced I needed a hammock-tent! Nick owned a few horses and having a lot of knowledge about racing them, he had big plans. Chico, Erik, and Pete each talked about their respective plans for adventure and family time. Another pilot remarked that he would move to Canada and hang out with the Mounties. We all laughed at each other's quirky dreams and desires over breakfast, then made our trek to the aircraft once again to support our litany of impending missions.

CW2 Nick Payne washes down the Kiowa, then anyone who gets too close.

Miles upon miles of winding rivers and wadis abound across Afghanistan. This particular shot is along the Darya-ye-Pamaher River.

Predecessor troop's Kiowa departing FOB Morales-Frazier.
Photo courtesy of Doug Phelps III

A large family gathers for lunch in their courtyard.

CHAPTER 13

Dear Soldier,
Where are you right now?
Are the wars fun? I wish I was big so I can be in a war.
What do you do? Send me a note and tell me all about it. Ok LOL.
Love, Jade.

It was August 11th. In the previous 72-hour span, I had spent at least 25 percent of that time physically airborne. In only three days, I had seen more new areas than I ever imagined I could or would. I'd covered more ground per square mile than the area of which I had routinely patrolled the entire deployment. We had gone deep into other areas and mountain passes that held a surreal beauty and an even more real danger, with no friendly forces remotely close by. We even flew the full route from the western edge of Lake Surobi through the narrow pass into eastern Kabul. Since we'd been flying so much, we missed almost every meal. We had cookies for lunch in the cockpit that were run out to us by a crew chief as we refueled. I had a packet of honey-roasted peanuts that I got halfway through before the wind ripped them from my grasp, sending peanuts flying all over the cockpit and refuel pad. We'd gotten a hot tip that there was, of all things, a pizza oven at our often-visited French FARP on FOB Morales-Frazier. The day prior, we were smart enough to place an order there. We returned later to pick up a few pizzas to eat in the cockpit. I remember that it cost money, but I could have quoted it at $100 per pizza, and we would have all probably said "sure, sounds fair."

We were told that the Muslim holiday of Ramadan had begun, and it could be seen by those traveling outside the wire. Locals had put tents up, and village functions began while lots of people were visiting relatives and moving about. As I understood it, this religious holiday required a day-long fast and then late in the evening, they'd have a giant feast. Their daily tasks and work were regulated, and the cans and cannots of their conduct were detailed. Our understanding of the traditions could be a bit off, we figured, but no one cared enough about their holiday to look up the detailed mechanics of it. I had recently purchased some really cheap, handmade war rugs featuring misspelled English words, such as "rooket" and "Inplanes," and depicting Soviet and American tanks, aircraft, and weapons. A few of our guys wanted to buy some themselves, but because Ramadan was being observed, the locals were not selling them.

We understod that martyrdom was glorified more so during Ramadan. We joked that it would equate to a ten times bonus for killing during the holiday. It would be like an American enjoying a happy feast with their family on Christmas Eve or Hanukkah, receiving a heartfelt send-off, and then blowing themselves up to kill as many people as possible from a rival faction. Each death would be worth more, because it was done during the holidays, earning them jihad bonus points! The holiday brought on behavior changes in the locals, which understandably made us a little uncomfortable. Large groups always got our utmost interest and attention, and there were many large groups scattered all over. This also gave the locals a chance to sit and have philosophical discussions and make plans on how they wanted their villages and local areas governed. The festive and rowdy spirit of the area generally didn't usually begin until the locals were recharged by finally eating and drinking in the evenings. We'd all be happy when Ramadan was over, yet it continued longer than I thought it would. The enemy was doing a good job at pissing off the civilians with their random bombings. The "holy" warriors didn't care so much about *who* they killed, they just cared about killing. I didn't believe that the Afghans would ever embrace us or the government that we were helping to install, but as long as the other team kept creating random terror and mayhem, we looked to be the better alternative.

I was fatigued from the constant stream of operations for several days running. I had to get up very early for my shift, and the growing sleep deficit was catching up to me quickly. I chugged Z-Quil and chewed on Melatonin like candy, trying desperately not to replay the countless missions, grids, FARP turns, briefings, debriefings, frantic radio chatter, and kinetic events in my mind. My troubled brain wrestled with questions and doubts. Could I have done something better or differently, perhaps saving casualties and operations from what had befallen them?

*

We continued to push our boundaries by undertaking flights into yet more uncharted territory for us. We were flying at 8,500 feet with a temp of 95°F. The terrain was still inclining above us, with countless small villages and sights to see in the unattainable heights out in the hazy distance. I took pictures which in no way did justice to what the areas looked like or how it felt to explore them. Some areas had even potentially never seen Americans that close before. We surmised by many of the curious parties that scampered out onto rooftops to see us that visits from outsiders were very rare.

We had some business to attend to in the Tagab, and I had the rare opportunity to do a quick Operation Animal Drop. I had been waiting to spot a loner so that when I dropped the stuffed dog, I wouldn't start a giant fight between kids over who would keep it. Before leaving, I noticed a little girl standing outside a qalat alone. I dropped the dog, and we wheeled around just in time to see the little girl clutching it, sprinting to her qalat. We made some quick orbits around the qalat while the family smiled and waved at me, and the little girl held up the stuffed animal with a big grin on her face. The Tagab was dangerous, and I didn't want to stick around too long, so I took two quick lackluster photos as we departed. The broader Operation Animal Drop had gotten to be a popular and fun game for some of us on day crew. After we landed, my shemagh truly came in handy. The sand, dust and grit blew into my eyes and mouth as soon as the windy downwash from our rotor blades subsided. I was sure that the best few bucks that I'd spent in that country were on that ubiquitous scarf. The crazy wind and sandstorms continued to relentlessly descend upon us. It looked like I would fly every day for the foreseeable future and fight one of our most vicious enemies: the weather.

I wanted to read more about the various perspectives of the war. I had been removed from American news and events and wanted to catch up during my downtime. Of particular interest to me was an absolutely rare article, entitled "Kiowa Helicopters: America's New Cavalry," in *Men's Journal* magazine. Not only did it feature the Kiowa and our mission, but I also felt like it definitely embodied our pilot mindset, to include our near-zealous drive to protect those under our charge.

I also came across a *Newsweek* magazine from late July 2010. It included two back-to-back articles concerning Afghanistan. Reading it, I learned about the frustrations with the conflict felt from those at home. I had assumed no one cared that we were still overseas, since so many people I knew were surprised that I was deployed. I understood that most folks believed the fight was over, based on the depictions painted by the media. Only those with a vested interest would know even a quarter of what was really going on, and that also took some very dedicated research. I read articles upon articles covering political battles and civic strife that I was completely shut off from. My time in 2010 would be very different. The very concept of "time" itself had a different value for me while deployed. There were no such things as weekends, and to us, Monday is a Wednesday and Sunday is Tuesday, day is night, and night is day, depending on when you're scheduled to be sleeping. The disconnected feeling was almost disconcerting.

*

I was flying just along the eastern perimeter of Bagram. A young Bedouin girl stood barefoot in the dirt outside the eastern side of the airfield between us and the mountains we used as a range. The Bedouins would come and go as they pleased, being absolute nomads and living purely by survival. Recently, we'd been assisted by a few of the Bedouin families, especially by their kids.

A UAV had crashed, and the children scurried around picking up parts and jogging them back over to soldiers dispatched to recover the wreckage. In the spirit of saying thanks in the only way that we really could, I took eight stuffed animals and crammed them into the small cockpit space between the dash and the windscreen. On our way to the range in the morning, I wanted to make sure that the kids knew that their assistance a few days prior did not go unnoticed by the helicopters circling overhead. Our impromptu "Operation Saying Thanks" had the kids running and jumping for joy, catching stuffed animals, purified water, and a few snacks from both aircraft. I snapped several pictures as the kids proudly held the animals up high on display with huge smiles, laughs, and waves.

It was difficult taking pictures from a bouncing, quickly banking and moving platform with subjects several hundreds of feet away. Some were grainy, but I could make out the kids smiling, and that is all I really cared to capture anyhow. As September began, I continued to use photography as a fun hobby. It was cathartic to capture the sights I was seeing. On the evening of September 2nd, I was having fun learning new photography techniques from one of our "crew dogs," Specialist Razvan Toma. He was a Romanian-born guy who immigrated to the U.S. and had since gotten his full U.S. citizenship while deployed to Afghanistan. Specialist Toma was a photography and Mac freak, so we got along well. He taught me several ways to improve my pictures, and I was considering many new aspects and techniques as I flew around and took shots. The aerial photography aspect of my job gave me a creative outlet and brought new meaning to my time. This new purpose helped me have a positive outlook.

I renewed my focus on studying and preparing for testing, since I was within my evaluation and request window for a PC ride. It had become very hard to study, because we were all so exhausted. I wanted to make sure that I'd be ready, so I fought through the exhaustion as best I could.

Also in early September, I was forced into a few days off so I didn't go illegal on my flight hours and so I could get my flight physical done. After a giant misunderstanding with the physician's assistant over the phone a week prior,

I showed up at the agreed-upon time and place. Low and behold, she wasn't there. Still, I was accused of not showing up and called many names. It was an eye-opening experience to see the fragile sociological state that we were in. It reminded me of a high school-level crisis, one in which angry notes flew back and forth over unreasonable and foolish nonsense. It relieved me to know that my commander had my back. Our captain said, "Robo, it's clearly documented that you've been pulling 14-hour plus QRF shifts while flying for 25 of the last 30 days. I doubt that they can have any clue what that's like." When I did manage to see the medical officer, she was spiteful, rude, and accusatory. I tried to answer questions and get out of there. At one point, she even threatened to take me off flight status, citing that she didn't think I was mentally capable of flying anymore. I assured her that I was fine and, for the thousandth time, I was sorry that an appointment was misunderstood, but as far as flying and fighting went, I was good to go. Events like these were typically caused by stress and fatigue and it continued to intensify as our date to go home got closer. The more we thought about going home, the testier people got. I attempted to still cope with all of this by gravitating towards comedy instead of cynicism, trying to make fun of it all instead of getting down and grouchy.

*

Operations in the Tagab Valley continued onward. We were briefed on a deliberate mission, one which made our whole team lean back in our chairs and groan. There was a VIP that wanted to fly in a team of Blackhawks to enter the Tagab and visit a remote FOB. This particular FOB was located in a terribly positioned area; it was surrounded by high ground and situated adjacent to a hostile village. Enemy ingress and egress points were everywhere, as well as many other tactical disadvantages for the small FOB. Regardless, an entourage of important folks wanted to land there, meet the inhabitants, and get a tour.

Before beginning the escort mission for the Blackhawks, we hypothesized about what might happen. We knew this wouldn't end well, and after entering the Tagab on the escort mission, we continued discussing our concerns as we watched the Blackhawks orbit around the area for 20 minutes. We keyed the radio, telling them that, by now, the enemy probably thinks we are *trying* to piss them off. The Blackhawks got lower, continued to fly around, burning the area for an additional 20 minutes. Now, everyone for miles knew something was up. They instructed us to hold on one side of a river bed and stay out of the way, but also to observe and provide security where needed. I cringed as the Blackhawks approached their landing zone, and we tried hard to see if any threats existed. The landing zone had a few U.S. forces overlooking it, but the surrounding area was not protected. The avenue of approach taken by the Blackhawks was riddled with places to hide. It was no surprise—as the two Blackhawks landed, all hell broke loose: RPGs, PKMs, AK-47s—everything Hadji had. The first Blackhawk took on a spray of bullets as it frantically lifted off the landing zone; the passengers hit the ground running in utter panic towards the small outpost. The Blackhawk in the second position didn't make it very far before taking between 15-20 direct hits to the airframe. It lifted back into the air from its approach, somehow being just missed by the heavy stuff and the RPGs. The enemy had set up a corridor of destruction for their ambush, and they even had enough time to make tea while they waited.

My aircraft began to set up an engagement with what I thought was an enemy RPG shooter. I had witnessed a puff of smoke, and in the chaos, believed it to be the origin of one of the incoming RPG shots. As we began to work the clearance of fires, I saw another puff of smoke. We rolled our aircraft directly towards the point of origin, only to discover a French tank beginning to move. What I had thought was an enemy hiding amongst dilapidated Soviet armor was a genius French tank commander. They had hidden in the site and emerged just as silently as they hid to join the fight. The Apaches were assigned to the fight later on, and it resulted in a significant operation to get the VIPs back out of the area. Tourism in the Tagab wasn't exactly the brightest idea, obviously.

We ended up flying near FOB Kutschbach in the Tagab a few days later, this time out looking for work. There, I noticed a group of people walking near the top of a high ridgeline. Our aircraft announced the sighting to our wingman.

"Is it just me, or is that a gaggle of lost hikers over there?" Our Trail ship saw them too, and we edged closer. The group of mismatched civilian and military-clothed men hardly acknowledged that we'd spotted them, and we got a few waves as they continued to walk. They were spreading out, a couple pairs each, and appeared to be looking for something. Toward the top of the ridge, I saw a man with an antenna sticking out of his backpack. We radioed Kutschbach and asked if they had any SF teams out in the area and they confirmed that some guys had climbed the mountain walling the FOB to their west. After a few minutes, we ended up getting a frequency and callsign for the man with the radio.

I called up the frequency, introducing us. "Jaguar 16, this is Wildwood 23, over."

The man cresting the ridgeline stopped walking for a moment, turning to our flight to wave.

"Wildwood, this is Jaguar, I've got you loud and clear. What's going on, guys?"

I looked at the other pilot, who shrugged, so I answered, "Not much, we were just passing through looking for work, honestly. We were curious if you could use any support from us today."

I saw him bow his head in a slow nod, as if chuckling at a mildly funny inside joke. He came back, "Well, we could use some help if you're free."

"Jaguar 16, you now have a Scout Weapons Team at your disposal," I replied. "Between our pair, we are armed with approximately eight rockets and 600 rounds of .50 cal, estimated play time before refuel is about an hour and a half, over."

"Cool, wait one," he responded. I could see he was on their internal frequency, talking to the others briefly and pointing up to us. One of the thickly bearded guys smiled big and raised a thankful thumbs up.

You're welcome, Jesus. I wonder what this is all about, I thought to myself.

Jaguar came back onto the radio. "Alright Wildwood, here's the deal. We've lost a Pelican case. It was supposed to be kicked out to us, but somehow, they missed. We really need to find it before some local does. Unfortunately for us, the Pelican case is tan. Just like this whole fucking mountain. Over."

The other aircraft broke into laughter along with us. "There it is! That's why this is gonna suck," one guy remarked. I tried to contain my laughter a bit as I responded and asked for a vicinity grid to start with. We set about looking using a slow, low pattern. After a lengthy search, the case was thankfully located. The guys were visibly tired, but most still managed to smile and give us an appreciative thumbs up. I had no idea how long they'd been searching, so after a bit of talking, we helped organize a Blackhawk ride for them to get back off the mountain a bit easier. As the Blackhawks departed Bagram, we began a slow and wide orbit over a flat plateau of an area suitable to land two Blackhawks. Luckily, the area was devoid of any local movement or hazards, so we could talk the Blackhawks in and get the SF dudes on board with no issues. Jaguar was appreciative and we felt good that we'd been able to help.

After doing a bit more general recon of the area they'd been moving around, I found a cave entrance. I snapped a lot of photos and got in close, trying to see if there were any signs of human traffic or recent use. We then finished up and flew back to Bagram.

During the debrief I informed a bunch of our guys I had found the main target, the enemy of enemies, after carefully reviewing one of my photos. It was a cartoon drawing of Bin Laden holding a rubber chicken, borrowed from the show *Family Guy*, which I had superimposed inside a small cave mouth. My picture became an instant hit and was printed out and posted up in the CP. The Jaguar guys appreciated me emailing it over to them and promised to pass it up the Special Operations Command chain.

CHAPTER 14

Dear Soldier,

We got a new girl in our class. She is nice.

How are things going where you are?

Have you been in your helicopter lately?

My mom went to Alabama. She got me a shirt. She was in a place called

Tunica. That's where she got my shirt.

Love, Daylan

September 11th came and went without too much issue. Protests had started as word came around to the locals that someone in Florida was having a Quran BBQ. Misinformation and propaganda campaigns on the enemy's part deserved a nod. They knew how to rile up the populace by accusing the U.S. or other western country populations of somehow slighting Islam. I realized they were growing in their sophistication and abilities to use social and streaming media. With high level financial backing and support from rich extremist individuals and governments alike, our enemy was not just making amateur videos in caves anymore. They were even able to create videos that tricked the eyes into thinking we were wantonly gunning down civilians. They described the conflict as a fight against an invading force of evil, one that not only occupied their lands but also stood to destroy their very theological system and Allah himself. They were passionate, successful, and a large global following was materializing from these efforts. Our media did not focus on our struggles, opting instead to report on pretty much anything else rather than the tired subject of our war. On the 11th, a few skirmishes and violent activities arose, but in the grand scheme of things, were minor by our standards. Some insurgents were killed or disbanded by our ground forces, and order was restored. I had figured that the September 11th anniversary attacks would be celebrated through more actions from our enemy, since even holidays and violence weren't always separate events for them. I was glad that, fortunately, Hadji didn't exactly have the full level of organization or cohesion to pull everything off that they all hoped to do.

A few days after September 11th, I had a feeling that my day may become interesting. Our job was to cover Eagle 26 while they ran a few checkpoints near the Alasay offshoot valley within the Tagab. Besides U.S. forces, there were also some multinational troops added into the mix. Eagle elements had set up a roadblock and were conducting vehicle searches. Many individuals were at large and wanted in connection with recent attacks in the area. We circled overhead, providing security for the vehicles and their dismounted troops while making sure no one was maneuvering against our guys. A few local vehicles were lined up, and waved forward after a brief chat through an interpreter and vehicle inspection. For us in the sky, it wasn't very exciting at first. We scanned the partially ruined qalats, the foliage along walls and ditches, and every area or movement we felt deserved a look. Suddenly, the radios came to life out of nowhere. A car had stopped a couple hundred meters short of the road block. The driver bolted on foot down the road in the opposite direction. This caused a big shift in priority, as a "squirter" running away could have a valuable amount of intelligence value if caught and questioned.

"Wildwood 33, Eagle 26, we have a squirter moving down the road away from us, just left the vehicle 200 meters up the road from our position. Request you keep eyes on that individual, over!" Our Lead helicopter saw the guy first and kept an eye on him as he sprinted down the road. The running man suddenly collapsed, creating a dusty cloud, then remained still.

"He just fell down in the road!" The Lead aircraft called to me as I worked our MMS to get it locked into the area. I was confused at first. "Like, he tripped?" I asked.

"Uh, well, reference the grid, and the small structure on the corner. Just a few meters to the west up the road from that structure, there's a large tree. Under that tree, there's the dude...lying in the middle of the road," Lead replied.

We got our aircraft set into a good position to observe, and I found the referenced area and fixed my MMS on the guy.

Eagle 26 called, requesting an update, so Lead answered matter-of-factly.

"Uhh, Eagle 26, we have eyes on the guy. It appears that he may have shot himself." There was a pause on the radio.

"You agree, it looks like this guy off'd himself in the middle of the road?" I called to Lead.

It was unusual. The guy lay face down in the dirt, a dark maroon trail of blood slowly creeping down the road from beneath him.

"Dude, this is fucking crazy," Lead called back. "Is there a weapon by him?"

I replied that I saw nothing at all, just a freshly dead guy in the road.

"Wildwood, Eagle 26, say again...the individual is...dead?"

"Affirmative, it looks like he's dead." There was another pause as everyone tried to wrap their heads around it. Eagle 26 came back on after a minute asking, "Do you have any clue how that may have happened?"

Clue. That's what this was. It was a real life game of Clue unfolding before our very eyes. To add more absurdity to the situation, we finally spotted an old man leaving the area with a group of older kids. He only had one arm.

"Lead, Trail. Up the road to the east, do you see that suspicious dude walking straight through the fields away from the area? You know, the one-armed man," I asked?

Lead told me that there was no way that was correct, until they spotted him. We had our suspect. As the man walked in a straight line across the fields, we talked to Eagle 26. The ground guys were interested in this development, especially after the one-armed man stopped briefly in the field and I could've sworn he dropped something.

"He stopped for a second, I just tagged the grid. It looks like he dropped something and kicked some dirt. He's on the move again and keeps looking up at us," I relayed.

Eagle 26 felt that they needed to check the area to see what may have been dropped, hoping to find a weapon, radio, or anything to tie the suspect and his group of kids with what we'd witnessed. Meanwhile, some dismounted troops cautiously approached the body in the road and confirmed that he was dead. From what fate the man suffered, I never gathered. The ground elements moved into the grid I had passed along, kicking through dirt and looking around. I was puzzled and couldn't imagine that a one armed man took a pistol shot that took a guy out, especially a man on the run. Yet, here our only plausible suspect was walking closer and closer to a village, about to disappear into the market crowd a few hundred meters away. We quickly directed forces into the village to intercept the one-armed man, and they nabbed him just prior to him escaping into the fold along with the few kids. Unfortunately, even though they now had him, there wasn't any proof of anything other than him walking from the scene and being shady. Eagle elements turned up nothing in the field where I just knew something important had been dropped. Our guys in the village stood by with the Afghan Police, temporarily holding the one-armed man and his entourage in custody. Unless they quickly received more information or evidence, we'd have to let the suspects go.

We talked amongst ourselves, trying hard to replay it all and go back and forth on the events to see if anything made sense. Ultimately, nothing made sense at all, so the ANP sent the man on his way. We flew around the area for a little while longer, looking at the body, and then the ridgelines and ruined structures. Eagle 26 and his men looked all around, no one finding anything that would have resulted in what happened. Above, we began to joke. It was the one-armed man with the candlestick. It was the butler with a sniper rifle from impossibly far away. My theory was one of the foreign snipers along for the ride with the Eagle guys may have smoked him, perhaps even accidentally. Either way, no one owned up to it. We departed to refuel so that we could return and escort Eagle 26 and friends back towards FOB Kutschbach. Soon after we returned, Eagle elements were ambushed and a large fight erupted, which is the battle described at the very beginning of this book.

*

Finally, in the middle of September, we heard the news we had been waiting for. I was allowed to report to friends and family that I had about 60 days to go until I would board a plane back to the states. The "guarantee" was to have us back home in time for Thanksgiving. We believed it only because high-ranking individuals were telling their wives. We doubted that these leaders would put themselves in a position to piss off their spouses after such a long deployment and during a holiday. In three to four weeks, I would begin seeing new faces as our replacements arrived to take over operations. I would soon be packing up my things, which was definitely an exciting thought. The plans for what people would do upon their return home grew more elaborate and real.

Somehow, a civilian company had convinced our higher ups that we should have a yearbook from our deployment. It looked like a yearbook, had a CD included like a yearbook, and required a lot of yearbook committee-type dedication from each member unit. Being a junior guy who liked photography, I was naturally chosen. I was disgusted and appalled. The requirements were stringent, we had deadlines, and it was all taken very seriously. It required an obscene amount of time and attention from men who were tired and had much better things to do. The 3rd Infantry Division had apparently spent over a million dollars, and it was obviously a terrible scam. We had to interview a few soldiers, submit some cheeky photos, and a couple of cute stories as if we had been at summer camp.

Oh, the fun we had in Bagram and other locations across Afghanistan! Remember that time that we ordered the pepperoni pizza, and got a Hawaiian instead, and we didn't even realize it until we were on the other side of the base?! OMG, that was so funny! Oh, and when the swivel chair broke, and Joe fell from the top setting in the middle of that briefing, slamming down and we all tried not to laugh? Good times, y'all, good times! Sure will miss this place.

We could be so tragically stupid as an organization. This disconnect had gone from being an inconvenience, to life threatening, to blatant insults to our existence. I couldn't wait to have some of our guys sign my yearbook. I was sure that the comments would really show it to be a year to remember, all right.

On September 18th, the Afghan elections were held. Call after desperate call came in from ANA and ANP units saying that they were taking fire. Most of them were crying wolf and just wanted us overhead to thwart attack plans, or they only did it to screw with us. The few that actually were attacked were calling in and reporting that huge, grandiose forces were descending upon their positions. Fighters in excess of 20 or 30 men, with everything from AKs to RPGs were purported to be wreaking havoc. We would arrive to find a few ANA standing outside their Ford Rangers we'd bought them (that's you, taxpayer,) and they'd be smoking and chatting without a care in the world. They would have probably had 10-15rds sprayed wildly and inaccurately in their general direction, only to hide and return the same kind of fire themselves. The one or two aggressors would run off, and they would not pursue. The few actual RPG or machine gun fire attacks against district center buildings didn't do much, other than turn the building less aesthetically pleasing than it already was. The transmissions were kind of like what would happen if a kindergartner got on a radio after something bad happened on a playground, and tried to explain that there was danger. All we were missing were the imaginary monsters.

After flying for nine hours over the elections (the longest flight that I had ever logged, ever) I was informed that I needed to stay awake as long as possible that evening; my time to return to green world had come. I didn't stay up too late that night, but had the next two nights off to reset to nocturnal mode. On my new night shift, I was freezing. We were low and fast operating in a river bed which didn't help, but still, it was getting COLD outside. I began to start pulling some of my cold weather gear out, which is what I did every year when my birthday was around the corner. I kept forgetting how soon my birthday was approaching. Sally liked to make sure I knew how old I was getting. Already turning 27? *Man, I'm going to be considered late 20s now*, I thought.

I sometimes wished that people back home could be able to understand what "progress" was being made. I knew that was close to impossible, as the notion of progress was even elusive to many of us pilots directly involved in the fight. I was not anti-war or some dissident. The only thing that myself and my troop-mates were "anti" about were the manners in which we were restricted from doing our jobs. Fighting with one or both hands tied behind our backs was a very heavy burden to bear for a year while guys depended upon our air support. I hoped that, one day, there would be plenty of history books and authors able to explain and quantify what our restricted rules of engagement practices had cost us.

While I was down on my ass with the flu, a fight broke out in the Tagab Valley involving the French and a town near FOB Kutschbach. Our team overhead watched in disbelief at the brazen insurgent group who fired on the French soldiers, right out in the open daylight. They seemed to believe that they were immune from bullets, especially those that may come from the air. A man armed with a large PKM machine gun fired from around the corner of a mosque, using it as "base" if he were a kid playing tag. They knew that we couldn't put fire into or onto a mosque, but they didn't realize that was only part of the story. One of our pilots pulled his M4 rifle off the dash and briefed the plan, which was quickly accepted. As they circled, he began to hone in on the insurgent; the man on the ground obviously thought the rounds kicking up dirt around him were from the French soldiers that he was engaging. Suddenly, the insurgent fell hard against the wall, leaving a blood spatter against the mosque from the round that had just passed through his chest cavity. He limped away in a slow walk, disappearing into a nearby structure. The heavy weapons fire from the PKM had ended, and the French were safer now. The battle below continued, but with less intensity, and finally tipped in favor of the French, ending successfully and getting them out of harm's way. I was extremely happy to hear the story—it made me feel so much better than the Tylenol that I was taking to get rid of my sickness. Good news always makes a sick person feel better.

CHAPTER 15

Lately, with everything going on, I'd barely had time to respond to any emails or update everyone on my status, so I apologized for being such a ghost. I was reassured that everyone understood, and was told to focus on staying safe.

I tried to better understand some of the operational areas outside of our own. It reminded me that the fight that I was encountering was still very different from the fight just a hundred kilometers east, and their fight differed from that another hundred kilometers north and south, etc. Even though we became frustrated in each of our respective areas and grumpily questioned why we were even in Afghanistan, a large victory could occur nearby and we wouldn't even know it. Some limited progress was being reported by ground elements here and there, which was great to hear.

I was elated to learn that in about two weeks, we would all be forced to pack up most of our non-essential gear. Our supply containers were confirmed to be leaving before us, and it became clear how soon we'd all board an airplane headed back home. I sat through a briefing from Customs about what we could and could not bring home. We were told what to expect about the return trip to Savannah and about the process immediately after. It was great to hear—the realization that I could now start saying that we would be home in mere weeks instead of months was fantastic.

I loved the fact that we were forbidden to bring back any "contraband" movies. The illegally pirated DVD stacks that we had lying around were amassed by ourselves and those that came before us. The best part was that these were all purchased on base, being sold by local merchants, right in the open. These "contraband" movies were essentially sponsored by the U.S. government, but by no means should we have the gall to try and bring such purchased goods back to the states.

We sat in the CP on the last day of September, discussing what a hell of a month it had been and hoping for October to be better. "Beer would make life better," one of the Apache pilots said as he edited a gun tape. We all agreed—if only we could enjoy the occasional adult beverage like every other military around us was allowed to do.

September had been exhausting, as I'd continued operating almost the full month on QRF, with each day being over 14-hour shifts. Our faces said it all. We were spent, but there was still a war going on. We had ground forces that desired overwatch protection, support aircraft that needed escort and landing zones cleared, MEDEVAC aircraft flying unarmed and courageously into battles to pick up our wounded that required us to do anything and everything we could to make sure they stayed alive. Our job was undoubtedly one of the most unique in the Army, and I was very glad that I had chosen to fly the Kiowa over the other aircraft options. I had been told back in flight school that I needed to pick the *mission*, not the aircraft. Coupled with my brother's stories of overhead support from Kiowas that validated such wisdom, I could not have received any better advice than that.

There were still rumors floating around about our departure date for home. I had a good idea when it might be, but I couldn't provide a date until we were informed that the information was okay to release. Even if I had disregarded such orders and provided a date like many did anyway, it was still subject to change and would only continue the cycle of confusion.

*

Over the next few days, I began to pack. It was crazy how much stuff one can accumulate in a year's time while living in a small wooden box. I was giving things away, trashing other things, and a few items would be mailed out. It was all becoming real and before I knew it, we were a week into October and I had turned 27. There were no celebrations for me; the birthday had come and gone just like any other day. I was on shift but we didn't fly at all, so I instead did a few evaluation questions and otherwise was able to take it uncharacteristically easy. I decided to treat myself to eating a frosted Pop-Tart with sprinkles and watching a movie. *At least I didn't get shot at on my birthday,* I thought. I ate the crust around the Pop-Tart first so that I could savor the middle, as if it were a fancy dessert. After my shift, I slept hard. We had some serious mission requirements coming down the pipe, and I had to maximize my battery charging for the QRF cycles ahead.

The past few months had been more action packed than any other times during the entire deployment for us. If someone would've asked me even a few months prior if I thought I might fire a rifle from a helicopter while in combat (and not just do it at the range), I would have said, "No." I had finally gotten my wish, plus some. For so long, I had wanted to go into the fight as an active duty Army soldier. I'd gained the experiences that I so desired, and in some cases, I got more than I had bargained for.

Unimaginably, the war and our requirements continued to increase in complexity and intensity. It would be nice to return to a sector of the globe that was a little more...sane. I knew that I would never forget some of the places I had flown into though, especially those so remote and forgotten. Some Taliban stronghold areas seemed almost pristine and beautiful, but it always brought a strange and uneasy feeling when we were so high up in those mountain passes. It felt far removed from the rest of the world, being so many miles away from the nearest of our remote outposts of U.S. or foreign soldiers who could come find us if need be.

There'd been a lot of talk recently concerning cross-border incidents involving our "ally," Pakistan. The Pakistani military was not to be trusted; many would just as soon shoot us down like any of the Taliban or other insurgent groups they harbored. I felt for our guys who had to work in the bordering frontier with Pakistan. "Border" was a very loose term, a political term only identifiable on a map. The inhabitants that lived along the border may have their village and/or property split right down the middle by it, but wouldn't consider themselves to be either Afghan or Pakistani. As I understood it, they were foremost members of a tribe or clan. I'd talked with our Apaches who routinely ended up down there. We would hear something on the news about U.S. forces pursuing some asshole that shot at them and "fled into Pakistan," but in reality, it was probably only a few hundred meters difference and our soldiers just didn't feel like letting that guy get away with it that day.

We were saddened by the posture that the international community, and even our own citizenry, had begun to take on. Our current climate pressured us into not only avoiding engagement with the enemy, but also safeguarding the lives of Afghans even above the safety of our own forces. Saying things like that out loud were taboo, however. That talk was not in lockstep with the military and government narratives. Perhaps I (and our other pilots) needed more sensitivity training.

What I thought was a hush-hush subject would be commonly talked about and debated across uncountable news agencies and forums, easily searchable using one three-letter word: R-O-E. Our strict Rules of Engagement had directly contributed to the injury, death, and destruction of U.S. and other friendly forces right before my very eyes. It was the most frustrating and disheartening part of our job: not being able to help during a troops in contact event, because to do so without following all the steps and meeting the criteria may land us in jail.

*

On the night of October 12th, we investigated and helped secure a crash site. A civilian C-130 cargo aircraft had slammed into a mountain a few miles north east of Kabul International Airport, instantly killing all aboard. Through my NVGs, I sadly watched the green glow of the flames and wreckage trickle like disturbing lava down the mountainside. We eventually returned to Bagram after recognizing that there was nothing we could do, and the airspace was becoming dangerously saturated with too many aircraft. A Turkish Blackhawk with no lights, not even IR, almost had a midair collision with us, making the decision to leave easier to support.

The next morning, our departure preparations were in full swing. A few of our enlisted guys had already departed for home. In a little over a week, new faces would show up from the advance party replacements. I had cleared out all of my tough boxes and bags from our personal items shipping container and was beginning to pack and inventory my gear. In just a little over two weeks, I would be getting forced out of my B Hut cave. Later in the month of November, I would be listed on an Air Force C-17 manifest destined for the United States of America.

I was desperately trying to get my PC ride done before departing, and I heard that I may get a chance. My APART, or annual flight evaluation that every pilot must do, was already about halfway complete. As mentally, physically, and motivationally exhausted as I was, I had to press on for just a few more weeks. I was not alone—everyone was completely worn out. The pilots in our troop all remained in the top 20 out of many times that number of pilots across our task force in flight hours. Despite how close we were getting to our return flight home, the missions and the seriousness of our job continued. We could not afford to be complacent, especially now that the locals seemed to be having their last hoorah before hibernating again for the winter.

I heard that the news back home reported a lot about what was going on in Afghanistan again, albeit some of it inaccurately. While I initially applauded the renewed interest, unfortunately, some reporters started digging deep and critically questioning every event, which was not helpful. I wasn't against reporting on the war altogether, and I did find it interesting how disconnected our war was from main body America. Again, a friend back home mentioned I was currently deployed to a group of people, only to be met with the familiar response: The war is over... we weren't *really* fighting anyone, right?

The newest media attention was increasingly focused on the negatives, too. I heard plenty about what we were doing wrong, and there existed a ton of critique regarding combat decisions by non-combatants. The situation was detrimental to our morale and sanity, with the negative armchair-quarterbacking literally starting to result in policy restrictions and changes that put everyone in even further danger. Many of us felt genuinely sorry for our replacements. If the war had changed so much during our deployment, we could only imagine what types of pain the replacement unit would have to deal with in the coming year.

On the positive end, though, football season had started again. While I enjoy football as much as the next red-blooded American, we had some serious pig-skin fanatics. Flights were becoming reconsidered along the lines of mission, weather, enemy movements, time, and when the game was on. Not that we really could or should structure everything around football, but if it could safely be done, it probably would be. To me, it was perfectly acceptable and harmless. If anything, it was a distant connection to home that was very warmly embraced by all, so I did enjoy it for that. Fantasy football leagues and some friendly sports wagers had occupied a lot of free time and energy for some of our guys. For a few of them, I was glad to see that they had something to live for again. We got a live stream of the games over our super jury-rigged connection in the TV room, and we were fortunate to be watching live instead of re-runs. Overall, the inhabitants of Bagram Airfield had it made. This was especially true as compared to almost everywhere else in the country when it came to creature comforts. The place had Salsa night dance parties and not one, but two beauty salons, for goodness' sakes. I stayed away from all of that, trying hard not to take anything for granted and remember those living sparsely outside the wire whom we supported. I will admit one stray from this virtuous path however, when a Tajikistani woman that couldn't have weighed 100lbs soaking wet gave me a massage with the strongest damn hands possessed by any human. I was sore for days.

Occasionally, I had taken to procuring empty tennis ball packaging tubes and filling them to the brim with magazines, rare snacks, cigars, and anything else that I could get my hands on that a soldier out in the remote lands would appreciate. Nude magazines were strictly forbidden, ironically, while in a setting where AK-47 rounds whizzing by a guy's head were accepted and expected. That didn't mean that illicit magazines didn't perhaps become occasionally available and possibly make it into said tennis ball tubes. I would fly low, holding the tube out and hinting over the radio to the immediate ground force elements that there was a package to be picked up. There was never any official record or acknowledgement of these clandestine drops, but I knew that they were very appreciated.

Down to counting weeks and not months felt odd. We focused on trying to set up our replacements for the long road they had ahead of them. They seemed like they would be a good strong force, however, and I really hoped that they would kick our enemies' asses even better than we could. As we flew missions, we talked about the areas we'd have to make sure to pass along. There were routes such as Beggar's Canyon, Kessel Run, and Training Wheels that were tribal knowledge to us only and not written down anywhere. Certain mountain passes and off-shoots in the Tagab Valley area were absolutely more dangerous than others, discovered the hard way sometimes. There were villages that we had no reason to bother, and others that deserved constant low fly-by blades popping action at 0300 every single morning for the rest of time.

The town of Charikar, to our northwest, was sizable for Afghanistan, and on many days there were tons and tons of kites flying. We wanted to make sure that the replacements knew that some kites were not flown for recreation, but were likely strung with high tensile strength piano wire. The kids and adults alike who flew them were all about trying to down a helicopter with them. We wanted our replacements to all make it out and stay safe, and we felt a very high degree of responsibility in setting them up for success.

On October 21st, I was experiencing just how much packing and moving sucks again. During the packing, I had been finding tons of itty-bitty mouse turds. As I pulled things from corners, the mouse presence was disturbed and the previous night I had spent the better part of an evening trying to kill one of them. The mouse taunted me, and I still wanted revenge for it running across my face while I was in bed the other night reading, his little turd mouse feet traversing my tongue when I opened my mouth in surprise. I'd lay back down in my bed, and then something on top of my fridge would rustle. I'd jump out of bed with my stick, and the mouse would do a *Mission Impossible*-airborne jump to the floor and disappear. I occasionally found mouse poop on my pillow too, the little bastards. Mice had destroyed much of our survival gear in the CP, and the Apache guys with little league aluminum bats were responsible for probably 50+ mouse deaths, no exaggeration. The battle would continue to rage on long after we were gone.

*

I met an incoming CW5 from our replacement task force and was told he was going to conduct my PC checkride. I was trying my damnedest to get my packing done so that way I had nothing else to focus on but preparing and studying. The next bit of news induced a face palm slap from everyone: We would be sharing a tent with the Blackhawk pilots for the next three weeks. Not just Blackhawk pilots, but the worst bunch of them around. I was sure that this would be an obviously poorly thought-out decision. Not only would I be living in a tent for three weeks with those freaks, I also stressed about my impending PC ride while still flying many mission windows as well. Awesome. I told Nick that I needed an outlet, so he gave me an over the top chick answer, shouting, "Let's go shopping!"

Nick and I went to the bazaar, and a merchant offered us each a pomegranate. Nearby merchants were amused at how excited we got because while abundant outside the wire, there were *none* on Bagram. We tried to pay, but he refused and we didn't press the issue. A gift from the Afghan people was just that, a gift, and was not to be quibbled about. Call it a plus side in their culture; gifts and hospitality were a big deal with the regular non-asshole Afghans. We received his gift with the hand over the heart and head-bow as seemed to be customary. Let me tell you, that was the best damn pomegranate I've ever had or ever will have.

Also in the bazaar, I found four shops tucked away in the corner. They were the local women's crafts area, and the male merchants gave them the stink eye. The female merchants were treated poorly and risked a lot when they left the wire from their shops in the protected safety of our market. I decided to only buy from the female-operated shops, since I'd seen how women lived and were treated each day as we would fly over. I'd seen and heard how the women were considered just above the level of livestock, so I had no qualms paying sticker-price on goods they'd been in the qalat hand making all day.

Some more shady-looking merchants shifted on their feet and eyeballed me and Nick hard while we joked and laughed with a few of the women. They spoke reasonable English, and one particular woman from Kabul appeared to be highly educated. She wore very risky clothing for their culture, including having her hair down and uncovered, and wearing makeup and jewelry. Her beauty struck me. Our curiosity amused her, and she said, "Afghanistan is changing. Women just a few years ago could never sit in a bazaar and run their own shop. Here we are, though, and it's because we have guards making sure that these men do not harm us."

I hadn't ever met an Afghan so articulate or smart until then. It took me back, honestly. I thought about it in a quick rush of wonder—is she an anomaly, or are there others like her? Do the civilians in Afghanistan have more among them such as this woman, taking risks and boldly trying to shift their culture and expectations? I shook her hand and told her I was happy that she could run a shop on our base, and that I would be back to purchase more goods soon. Nick and I spoke about it for the rest of the day, in bewildered awe that maybe we had rushed to judgement too harshly, and perhaps some people in Afghanistan, particularly the women, had hope after all.

CHAPTER 16

Dear soldier,

I am in the third grade. I would like to know what you eat and do in the war. If you drive a tank or a jet. I want to know where you sleep and where you hide in the war. Do they kill you if you fall back?

Have you fought the Germans? What kind of weapons do you use in a war and how do you call in backup? Has somebody been shot in the leg or in the arm and do you make friends?

Sincerely, Jimmy

The winds encountered were crazy as hell again. I had one of the most challenging, and at some points alarming, flights in recent memory just two days prior. We unexpectedly careened close to the Lead aircraft, thanks to a few freak wind gusts, and the wind had also forced my aircraft to roll into an 80-degree bank. Twice.

On the morning of October 24th, we all officially moved from our B Huts to the tent. It was located about a half mile down the road in Bagram's transient area, called "Warrior." This was the same place that we initially had showed up and stayed almost a year prior, but to my surprise, the conditions were much improved. A coffee shop and a few other auxiliary PX-type stores were available, and there were also new facilities such as "shower and shitter trailers," as we called them.

I had lucked out and been cursed all at the same time regarding my bunk position. There was a large fan near me, so although it was hot, I was still getting some air. The bad part was that I was also near the door, so I saw and heard everyone coming in and out. There was also a nice high-pitched car alarm going off right outside, along with steel-on-steel hammering and other wonderful sounds of construction. The car alarm was the backup alarm for construction equipment. Instead of the rather standard and controlled "beep-beep-beep" that may be heard when a heavy vehicle was backing up in the western world, we had to endure jury-rigged car alarms. Loud, screaming car alarms.

It was already 1200, and I had to be up and ready five hours later at 1700. Our night flying was going to be brutal. My PC ride was only days away, so I really hoped that I'd get a fair amount of rest before going through the grueling evaluation where you must be at the absolute peak of your performance. Mine-clearing operations were going on a few hundred meters from my bunk, and would afford random heart-stopping explosions on occasion. I would have thought that there were more rockets coming in if it weren't the middle of the day. I had almost gotten numb to rocket attacks, though. Any time we heard the whistling sound, we'd just freeze and wait. Explosions would happen, and if you were still breathing, it was over. We didn't throw on our helmets and body armor and run to the shelters after the fact, although we were supposed to.

*

Another week of missions and time had come and gone. It was October 31st. There was zero mention of it being Halloween. I could not believe that the last time that I had talked to family was a full week prior. We were in a time-warp. I had switched back over to days again and had more evaluations set for the next two days. Perhaps at the end of that second day, I would even be awarded the coveted position as a PC in the OH-58D Kiowa Warrior, time permitting. There was a lot going on, and we were going to be cutting it close trying to get it done. I was so damn tired and beyond maxed out by that point. I had begun to emotionally shut down, and so close to the end, too. My buddies were in the same state, but knew that I was firing on all cylinders to try to attain PC, so they tried to keep me up and I appreciated their support and efforts.

On Halloween morning, I was forced to knock out my yearly required PT test for record. I awoke at 0330 to walk the half mile over to the troop in order to meet up with our guys and get my test done while it was cool and quiet outside. I shocked myself and everyone in the troop by getting close to a perfect score, absolutely *destroying* my previous records by a very wide margin, to include those logged when I was 19. This was surprising, considering my mental and emotional state by that point. I had the true thousand-yard stare, and my buddies remarked that I looked as if I was in kill mode. My hair was turning grey at the temples as a 27-year-old, and I had very dark circles under my eyes. I was dangerously hostile, being pissed about anything and everything, and badly wanted to get into a fight. I guessed they may have been right to be concerned.

On my Halloween flight that followed, I suddenly banked the helicopter hard, scaring our Trail ship into thinking we must've taken fire and were on pins and needles to hear what was up. Nothing was wrong; I just had to return to a qalat in a small canyon that had pumpkins on the roof. I thought it was ironic that the locals below had pumpkins out on Halloween, as I'd never even seen pumpkins in Afghanistan prior to that. Plus, Halloween was probably as foreign to them as Ramadan was to us. We laughed a bit too deliriously.

We had all been very sleep deprived as of late by living in those transient tents. We had stupid locals and migrant workers literally playing cricket in the middle of the day and their ball kept hitting the tent and rolling off. Coupled with construction noise, car alarms, and locals whooping and hollering at each other outside, one can imagine how much sleep I was able to get. My next 48 hours were about as grueling as I'd expected, and before I knew it, the day of my PC ride had arrived.

I showed up to our CP on the 2nd of November and met up with the SP from the incoming task force. Bearing the rank of CW5, he was one of the most senior Kiowa pilots across the whole Kiowa Warrior fleet. He had picked another of his guys to fly with Erik, who was to serve as the PC for their aircraft. I was relieved to know that Erik would be there, at least as my wingman for silent morale support. Even still, the limelight would be focused solely on me and how I handled the mission.

We began with an oral evaluation, which happens with all checkrides. Once that was complete, we went out to preflight the aircraft (thoroughly and with many questions) and to set up our gear. Our mission brief was centered on me, because not only was I acting as the PC being evaluated, but I may as well conduct the entire team brief and act as the AMC, as well. I was in charge of coordinating how we would do the very real-world mission that we'd been assigned. A flight of Blackhawks were going to be inserting some people on a very high ridgeline deep into an offshoot valley in the Tagab. I knew the insertion area to be dangerous from experience, so nothing was to be taken lightly and we had no time for notional evaluation games. I needed to make a solid plan and perform well. The outcome of our success and the safety of the Blackhawks and those passengers ultimately fell right on me and my conduct. We did our standard brief via teleconference with the Blackhawk crews, and confirmed all of our times and mission requirements. Before I knew it, we were walking back out to the aircraft. As we strapped in, my heart beat quickly and I knew that this was for all the marbles. Every single marble in the whole damn jar.

We linked up with the Blackhawks as we departed Bagram and began to head over to the Tagab Valley. It wasn't a short flight, but I had done it so many times it seemed to speed right by. I entered the area at a specific point as to limit our exposure to spotters or eyes on our team and the Blackhawks we escorted. It was daylight, and the early warning networks employed by the enemy didn't need any additional help in tracking us. As we flew offset from the Blackhawks, I began to get some gripes from my evaluator. He wasn't happy with my distance from the Blackhawks or the coverage we were providing them.

It was not an ideal situation, and I tried to explain why I was doing what I was doing. I didn't trust that the Blackhawks wouldn't surprise the holy hell out of us and do something unexpected and at any moment. I had learned in the year flying in support them out of BAF to keep a respectable distance. Still, this had my evaluator ruffled. I assured him I wasn't making new things up on my evaluation day, and this was also not the time to be practicing some pretty formation flight to show off for him. I was doing what we knew was right and in accordance with what I had learned. I also had no intention of having a mid-air collision. He was ultimately on the ride to support and observe, so he let me do my thing. The Blackhawks surprised me a few too many times, and they validated my point by flying and maneuvering differently than we had briefed. This threw all kinds of wrenches in our plan. I had to think fast and on my toes, and I silently and sarcastically thanked them for being douchebags, especially while I was on an evaluation for getting my PC orders no less.

The Blackhawks slowed and successfully touched down on a thin piece of high mountain, and the soldiers jumped out and hurried to establish a foothold on the ground they'd set about to occupy. The Blackhawks pulled their power in hard and dove off of the mountain and we did a quick orbit to ensure the soldiers on the ridge had no immediate foes in sight. Fortunately, the personnel were inserted and the Blackhawks were kept safe from any aggression by the enemy. I opted to keep our team loitering nearby until I was absolutely sure that our ground guys were solid and secure in their desired positions. Despite the violent off-shoot valley we flew in, we were not engaged at any point, which I was thankful for. For the time being, it was a success and everyone was safe, so we returned back to Bagram.

As we debriefed, I grew uneasy. We apparently did not do things the way my evaluator did in his unit. I got to endure that which he had issues with. The good part was that my evaluator was also wise and professional enough to understand that I was only doing what I had been taught and learned from experience. Despite his own personal feelings, nothing I had done was "wrong" from a standards point of view. Our troop tactics and techniques were different from his troop, but the outcome had been favorable and we had a full success of the mission. They informed me that the people we had inserted on the ridgeline proceeded on to their objective and a lot of insurgents got a nasty surprise from above, attacking them from high ground like they usually did to our forces. No spotters had gotten a sense of what was up or had warned anyone of the insertion, nor were they able to organize an attack against our aircraft. This meant there was also a successful outcome for my decision-making and conduct as a PC. The outcome and successful completion, *as a PC.* I had passed!

Exhausted from the stress, planning, studying, and everything else that went into it, I was in near shock. I had made it. Soon, we'd be leaving the country and my goal had been met; I had attained the status of PC while leading an actual mission in an area which I knew to be terrible in embattled Afghanistan.

*

I continued flying additional mission sets, all while more guys showed up and rotated in to replace us. We were busy, but it felt great to no longer have any evaluation stress hanging over me. I was able to focus on the mission and do my job. I was finally happy, and content. The weather took a cue from my mood, and I was offered clear skies and fair winds. Hadji had a few different opinions on that subject, but at least we were close to being done and the French skirmishes with them in the Tagab ended as usual, with both sides eventually breaking contact with light casualties.

Now that I had made PC, I set about furiously packing and completing a pile of paperwork required for my attention before I could depart. As it stood on November 6th, I was set to leave in 24-48 hours. I was so damn relieved that I'd get to depart with an earlier group. The trade-off was that I would be leaving right before the 365-day mark, so I wouldn't get the extra pay bonus for being deployed more than a year. That royalty was cherry picked unfortunately, but it didn't make me mad at the time, at least.

My last flight was great. We ended up taking one of the replacement guys on a grand tour through all of our favorite spots to fly. We even got to do a quick mission in bad-guy land, so I could get an adrenaline fix before I headed out. I ended up taking a fantastic picture of our wingman by a lone Soviet tank, which I snapped as he followed after us while we dove over a cliff. Later, my commander entered it into an Army magazine contest and it won me 50 bucks, but the magazine only put his name on it for credit, which I wasn't super-thrilled about.

It surprised me to realize that I had mixed emotions about leaving and wasn't even sure it had really hit me yet. On one hand, I was super-happy to begin my homeward bound journey in less than 48 hours. My last flight had been bittersweet as I realized that I would miss the place in some ways. The sights when flying during calm times was breathtaking around our area, and I knew that I would miss the mountains. The adrenaline rushes were also a marked addiction which I wondered if could ever be cured.

Despite what I would miss, it paled in comparison to what I would gain by leaving. I would get to see my family and Sally, and I would be back in our great country. I'd been forewarned that I was going to be a little disoriented at first when I got home, but hoped to soon get over it and be used to life outside a combat zone once again.

I was fortunate to have a great support network back home, and I really felt for some of those who would be returning without much to look forward to. We knew as an unwritten rule that we'd need to keep one another up and help out where needed. I wanted to grill out and be social, but also figured that the initial isolation was what everyone would want and need most. We were all exhausted, but also elated. It was a strange feeling, but still a good one.

CHAPTER 17

On November 9th, my small, five-man group of three pilots and two crew chiefs from Fox Troop linked up with a much larger group of over 100 soldiers from a mix of units across our task force. We departed Bagram after nine hours of formations, baggage shuffling, and Customs inspections. I got severely bitched at for having a handful of loose 5.56 rifle rounds in my vest amongst various pockets. It may have escalated, had they not realized that I was oblivious to the "transgression." I didn't care one bit about the Customs inspectors finding my "contraband," all the while voicing my all-too-honest opinion on how absurd they were being. It's actually a wonder I didn't get into real trouble.

Our C-17 took off at about 2100, and once we arrived in Manas, Kyrgyzstan we could not yet rest. Upon our arrival, we endured more briefings and then made way to the gear yard, where our bags were positioned on a huge palate to unload them. We did this step to simply re-pack the unnecessary body armor and Kevlar that we were all made to carry and not even wear. We were fortunately given a few extra minutes to pilfer through our bags in order to grab any last-minute things that we may need during our 72-96 hour stay in Manas.

I felt strange going to sleep and not having to set an alarm clock...actually so strange that it bordered on stressful, because that was so foreign. We awoke later the next day and ate chow, then ended up sitting in the MWR center established for us transient soldiers. The present crowd was made up of people from every military branch, and I found myself mostly surrounded by Marine infantrymen. Many of the places they lived and fought were hardcore, and I admired them for their zeal and willingness to continue to fight in incredibly austere conditions. Although they "only" did a six-month deployment, the guys were beat and their odor alone spoke volumes about what sort of deployment it had been for them.

Being 11 hours ahead of the east coast time zone, we contrived that we must reverse out to "nights," as we had done the entire deployment. This would allow us to minimize our jet-lag when we got back home. At one point, someone in charge informed us that we needed to be present for accountability formations. Our most senior man in our group of five was Erik, who replied, "No. We won't be there. Fox Troop is on nights." The officer seemed puzzled and was not very bright, so he fell for our off-the-cuff and totally bullshit answer. Our group of three pilots and two crew chiefs became completely insulated from any and all dumb things from there on. When we woke up in the evening, all of the moronic action was pretty much over and everyone else was going to sleep. The whole thing was beautiful.

The MWR center was getting overcrowded, so we did some recon and found a secret location devoid of any other personnel, open 24 hours, and with strong Wifi. The tiny Manas Library inauspiciously located up a stairwell above a laundry building became the Fox Troop hidden little sanctuary.

Our final mission of the deployment was to take on the difficult task of allowing ourselves to relax and convincing our brains that we could stand down; this was earned free time. I hadn't had "free time" in months. On Bagram, even on our days off, we had to get chow and do all kinds of other little things to help out each day due to being short on pilots and high on mission demands and operational tempo. Manas and our trip home had none of that, and my brain could hardly conceive that soon, I would have even more free time to do such things known as relaxing and taking it easy.

During my time in Afghanistan, regardless of whether it was wrong or right, I had developed a sense of guilt for such things as relaxing. There was so much more flying to do, so many more bad guys to hunt, and so many more ground guys that needed our help. There seemed to be no real reason to relax, and I, like the others in my troop, developed a "go-go-go!" mindset. I later learned that this was called "hyper-vigilance," and is a dangerous state to always exist in. It was imperative that I settle myself down once I was sitting in my own house and adjusting my mind back to normalcy.

I was actually afraid to read the journal entries that I had written. They were brutally honest and reflected on-the-spot feelings, and I feared that I would look back on them and see something I wouldn't like. I cannot describe what— maybe shame for whining, being negative, moody, or wrong in several cases. Even worse, maybe I would find an instance where, in hindsight, I should have done something differently on a flight when guys were getting shot up. It made me visibly shudder to think about.

For Erik and our other pilot, they had been on this rodeo more than once. I spoke openly about these fears and admitted that I'd written much of our deployment happenings down, along with taking thousands of photos, which they already knew about. Both pilots looked at each other and then back to me. Erik's eyes went wide, and he said, "Seriously dude? You wrote it all down? That's awesome, man!" To my great surprise, they supported it wholeheartedly and said that I should sort through all the photographs I had taken and create a small coffee-table book. I supposed that I could do such a thing, but it would take some time for me to figure out how I would want to go about it.

But enough. No more worries, sad thoughts, or uncertainties, I told myself. Erik, the other pilot, and I had made a pact of positivity during our Manas stay. Luckily, all alumni of Team Pigeon kept each other laughing, as it should be a joyous time. We loudly sang Bob Marley songs when standing in lines and formations, pissing all the Blackhawk fools around us off for being so crazed and cheery. Their annoyance just fanned the flames. One of our Apache brothers smiled and said, "We're glad that you psychotic Kiowa guys are traveling home with us."

A few pilots from our other 3-17 troops were heading home on our flight, and they told us we'd lucked out having such a good relationship with our Attack guys. Many other task forces didn't even have a neutral relationship between their pilot groups and airframes, some had been downright awful and they despised each other. For us Fox Troopers and Bravo Company Apache guys, we would be sad when we returned to Savannah and would no longer be operating alongside each other as often. The Red-Headed Black Sheep had been a serious force to deal with for everyone we had encountered, and I was proud to have forged such a bond in our joint accomplishments. In my case, I had made good friends within their ranks and knew that I would be hanging out with some of them well into the future.

I was cheerful that for the next few days I could set my mind straight. I began to finally understand that it was okay to sit on my ass in a chair, hidden away in the tiny secret Manas Library, watching dumb YouTube and FAIL-blog videos with Erik and the other pilot while laughing our asses off. For us, the war was over—for now at least.

Madison Square, beautiful downtown Savannah, GA.

Training excercise, Fort Benning, GA.

TWO SHORT YEARS
2011–2012

Upon returning home, we were afforded an opportunity to reconnect with family and loved ones after a reception ceremony held at the very hangars from which we had said our goodbyes one full year earlier. It was overwhelming to see everyone cheering with their homemade signs, the crying families embracing tightly, and the overall emotion of the event. It was a lot to handle. I didn't have a wife or children, but was surprised by my father, stepmother, and Sally. My senses were in overload, and I felt very lost and disoriented by the whole thing. I was happy, but outwardly I'm not sure how well I was reacting. I tried to be normal. My mind grappled and struggled as I thought about how different everything felt, yet looked the same.

We spent a few weeks in Reintegration status. After a brief time at home, we were essentially placed on close watch. We were to report on base each day to attend a series of seminars, beloved PowerPoint presentations, guest speakers, and other lectures aimed at getting us reprogrammed from combat mindset to home mindset. The biggest fear in the world seemed to be that we would be inherently unstable, and it looked as if everyone was trying their hardest to ensure that we would not fly off the handle.

Not long after reintegration, Fox Troop was disbanded just as abruptly and unceremoniously as it had been assembled. There was not a change of command to conduct, so 3-17 Cavalry found no real reason for any kind of ceremony, or even recognition for that matter. Our task force had been under the command of the 2-3 General Support Aviation Battalion, and they were more than happy to rid themselves of their attached Scout and Attack assets, so nothing came from them, either. Bravo Company 1-3 Attack returned to their main unit intact, as they had been an already formed group, but Fox Troop scattered to the wind.

Some of our guys were absorbed by the other 3-17 line troops, while others ended up being moved to different bases across the United States or abroad. Some from our troop and from around the whole Combat Aviation Brigade ended up getting out of the Army completely to pursue a life in civilian careers or to enjoy retirements after 20 years or more of service.

Nick and I ended up in Charlie Troop, of which he was a prior member. It took some time for us to be accepted as one of their own since we'd all served in very different spots and had endured different experiences. Luckily, a good number of my friends from flight school were there, and with Nick being a prior member, it wasn't as hard of a transfer as it could have been. Still, I was the outsider, so I had to try extra hard to prove myself there for a bit.

We shifted our focus to training the new crop of pilots that Charlie Troop had received and trying to get back into the air once more. Months went by before anyone flew again, so we all had to get recurrent in the aircraft before we could really do anything. On my first flight back in the Kiowa, it was as if I'd never even flown the thing. Unfortunately for me, what I had thought would be a "get your feet wet again" flight was really more of an evaluation to see if I could properly function as a PC in my new troop and how it did business. A bit of a difference of opinion was present, but the bugs were finally ironed out, and after a few more flights I was accepted as a full and standing member of Charlie Troop.

Given that we had a pretty large exodus of PCs from the troops, our focus on training up the newest members across the squadron became a high priority. We all flew a lot, with the PCs logging many more hours than usual: NVG and day flights, cross-country flights, and several field exercises. I was no longer a new guy, and many of my mentors had departed. CW2 Dede

Murawsky, whom I'd attended the Kiowa course with, had also made PC during deployment with Charlie Troop. Those of us who were PCs had to be the primary trainers to get our new guys up to speed and try to pass along all of our collective lessons learned. I always maintained that one cannot "learn" experience. I, as well as many of the others, would purposely let an aircraft get near the edge of our comfort levels before intervening to save it, just so that a lesson could be learned by the newer pilot who had gotten us into whatever pickle we were in.

Always at odds with the official military teaching technique (which consists of three pillars: fear, sarcasm, and ridicule), I would ask new pilots who got in the aircraft with me what they wanted to do, not just cover what we had been briefed to do. There were always areas that could be improved upon, and each of us had our various strengths and weaknesses. I always wanted a new guy to get the benefit of the doubt and see for myself where their skill level was before I listened to someone fly off the handle and say that they "suck." As far as the PCs went across the squadron, we were spread thin and got very worn out after a while. Most of our new guys progressed quickly, however, and I was proud of them.

Charlie Troop had a few members with ethnically diverse backgrounds, and the pilot faction had dubbed themselves "Team Brown." They were hilarious to be around and I often tried my terrible Spanish out on them. It was not uncommon to be in the relatively quiet troop some mornings, only to hear a member of Team Brown yell something at another. It was all in fun, but was crass and anything but politically correct. I loved it.

Before the previous deployment, Charlie Troop had been known as a pit of hatred. I had originally been dismayed about joining the troop due to that stigma, but in actuality, an overturn had happened when Nick, Dede, and I became some of the seniors. We were accorded reasonable treatment, all things considered. As additional new members showed up here and there, we, like the other line troops, would play our welcoming prank game for as long as we could. Other troops would be apprised so that they wouldn't blow it, and a few could also take part if they had a slow day. New pilots would not understand who was actually who, and several of us had settled into certain character roles. Since our names and ranks were affixed with velcro, we traded all around and crew chiefs became pilots, pilots became crew chiefs, and our commander and lieutenants knew to just not be around much that day. The good commanders would even leave a uniform hanging so that we could steal their rank and name to impersonate them, and we hid a camera to record everything. It was cruel (but hilarious) as we made new guys go through hell.

One slow day, Nick and I were out in the hangar with not much to do. We saw that a lot of troops were flying with several Kiowas out in the air around Hunter. Nick had a superpower within him to mimic an old creepy pedophile character from the show *Family Guy*. We decided that it was time to start some trouble, and went over to the nearest Kiowa and flipped on the battery switch. We each put on a pair of headphones and plugged into the radios, pulling up the various team internal frequencies to see who was out there. It wasn't long before we found our first target.

Across the airfield, a Kiowa remained in a high hover, almost perfectly still. The pilots were presumably doing an airborne calibration, which required a bit of checklist work and good control coordination. To the surprise of those two pilots, they suddenly had a creeper inside their heads. "Mmmm, look at you boys hover that helicopter. I like those strong arms, keeping that drift down to a minimum. You guys over there, sweating, keeping it up like that…"

We watched as the helicopter dipped and twisted a bit, our transmissions obviously breaking their concentration. They came on the radio, laughing, demanding to know who was talking to them. Nick persisted, "It's your neighbor. I've been watching you, meaning to invite you over. I've got some popsicles in the basement…"

The helicopter lurched, and they cursed us more, so we switched frequencies. Much of the same type of banter was exchanged, and we creeped out almost every Kiowa in the air. A few of our crew chiefs had walked over and were about to piss their pants laughing, and soon the squadron had someone on the frequency demanding to know who was dicking around on the radio. We quickly killed the battery, swore our crew chiefs to secrecy, and then snuck back to our troop. We heard mention of the event, but no one really knew who it had been.

During the deployment, the award medals that had been passed out were a sham. They were granted by position and not necessarily by merit. Nick had not received an Air Medal, but rather a lower Army Commendation award, or ARCOM. He was still bitter about it, and so were many others since he had done so much for our unit and 3-17 Cavalry. Whenever something stupid would happen to us, I'd look at him and yell, "Do it, Nick! Show 'em what you really think!" At that, he would pull the ARCOM medal out of his pocket and slam it down into the ground, as if it were a penalty flag at a football game. The pilots all got a kick out of it, while others who didn't know the story were taken aback.

Our troop prepared for our flight to Fort Benning, where we would support a large training event and conduct live fire drills in support of ground units there. Nick was close to getting out of the Army and our commander really wanted him to go with us, as he was a senior PC and AMC in the troop. Nick didn't want to go, and the commander was quite amused as we stood in the troop talking about it. Nick was shaking his head in the back of the trailer that served as our troop, saying that he was done. I leaned in and said, "Come on, Nick. One last go. Do it for your boys. Besides, when is the next time you'll get to shoot some shit from a helicopter, anyhow? You know I'm right…"

The commander's face showed surprise when Nick bowed his head, patted me on the back and quietly said, "Okay, Robo. One more time, and then I'm done."

The fake battles on Fort Benning got so real to those involved on the ground at one point that it took several tries on the radio to get them to acknowledge that an *actual*, serious forest fire was beginning. I ended up having to swoop down over their command tent several times and interrupt the fake war to tell them to get the hell out, or they would catch on fire. It was a good experience and the pace that was set gave the newer guys a taste of what an upcoming deployment would be like.

After we returned from Fort Benning, Nick left 3-17 Cavalry and the

Army. Despite his contributions as a mentor, AMC / PC, Squadron ALSE Officer, Tactical Operations Officer, and loyal soldier, his exit was with no mention outside our troop. I was both shocked and intensely angry about it. Each individual soldier was said to be valued, but it was made apparent to me that in actual practice, we had no value. I saw that we were each an unappreciated part of the machine that would be replaced and not missed, which really pissed me off and further degraded my personality. We had a new 3-17 Squadron Commander who liked to huddle everyone up like a football team before the beginning of each weekend and throw out ideas and information. These huddles were also usually the venues to recognize and award soldiers from the unit. Instead of any mention of Nick or several others quietly exiting for transfer to new units or civilian life, we focused on the mundane and unimportant.

The Cavalry did participate in a military tradition known as the "Hail and Bail" to recognize and introduce those incoming and outgoing members of the unit, but it was a more informal event centered on a lot of drinking at the bar. This setting was really the only spot that our new guys or old guys received any kind of welcome or farewell. One of the new platoon leaders in our troop was a good guy, and he later noted that he saw a change in me when Nick went away. I was angry at how dismissive our service from Fox Troop had been handled, and even more so with how individuals from both Fox and other troops were sent away.

*

How business back in the states was being conducted over the next year was difficult on everyone. The Army was changing, with more politically-correct movements and requirements continuing to move in and take up our time. We had endless Safety Stand-Down Days, Equal Opportunity classes, Sexual Harassment and Rape Prevention (SHARP) classes, Resiliency training to curb everyone from violent behavior (we joked our behavior was because of all the classes), and several others too exhaustive to list or worth mentioning. The Army "Warfighter" mentality was being stripped before our eyes and replaced with a new, more touchy-feely and respectful force that may engage in "quarrels" rather than fights, it seemed.

Our Cavalry Stetson hats, a piece of headwear mired in proud tradition and history dating back to the Civil War (and before) became a new target. We were to remove all pins and/or flair from our hats. Aside from the rank, wings, and Cavalry sabers on the front, we were no longer supposed to have anything else on the hat. This included prior or current unit affiliations, awards, you name it. A Standard Operating Procedure (SOP) was attempted in order to dictate how and where the hat could be worn. The whole thing was ridiculous, and it pretty much killed the morale and drive to even wear the Stetson. Around the same time, unit patches were also targeted. We had all sewn velcro onto our flight suits, wearing our troop patches with pride. This practice became outlawed, and was to end immediately. Morale and happiness sagged further, as any shreds of pride that any of us had remaining for our respective troops, the squadron, or 3-17 Cavalry were being ripped away.

For those combat veterans among the ranks, it was almost too much. I was casually asked by a civilian what I did for a living one weekend. I replied without thinking, "When actually allowed, I hunt the enemy in his homeland, with pleasure." I realized that I wanted war again, as anything in combat could be better dealt with than what we were currently enduring. I missed it. As soon as I heard mention that we were in the running for a future deployment to Kandahar, I was on board. It seemed far less painful than the crazy direction that our ship was headed. At least combat made sense to me, and I began to yearn for my marked adrenaline addiction.

My personal struggle intensified when Sally and I broke up. This was due in part to my changes in personality and attitude. My maturity level had progressed at a faster rate than my age. At age 27, my hair had continued to prematurely grey and I wore an almost stoic expression with serious worry lines on my face that had never before been present. Although I still laughed and joked around, it was deceiving as my sense of humor had critically warped. My whole outlook had changed in only one year. It didn't help that Sally and I had a long-distance relationship between Tallahassee and Savannah, either.

Sally was pursuing a doctorate in finance, and her career and my career were finally at their tipping points. We realized that professional coexistence would mean one of us would have to drastically give something up. Neither of us were willing to do so, and our drifting apart had been more and more apparent, so it was without much malice that we parted ways.

In the following months I was very down and felt lost. Initially, I was fortunate to have one of the Bravo Company Apache guys living with me at my house after he had a renter squatting in his house he'd rented out for the deployment. A real piece of work, the lady was covered under multiple laws and technicality issues that made evicting her a grueling six-month plus process for him. He wanted to pay me rent, but I honestly enjoyed the company in my otherwise empty house so we settled on rent payment via shared bottles of scotch to consume at my bar and ammunition to share at the range. After a while, he married his fiancé and moved out. That's when I truly was, and felt alone.

Our work situation continued to deteriorate as did my lonely existence. I was becoming disillusioned with the Army and what was becoming of it. Decisions from the deployment haunted me. I knew that I had matured much more by the end of the year, but I had wished that I had been more of a hard charger in the early periods. By then, I knew that initially I had lacked life experience and was naïve, but despite it all, I wanted to have done better.

I wanted to have been on more useful missions for our troop. I wanted to have been utilized more properly by our stupid task force. I grew angry at remembering leaving wounded on the battlefield due to technicalities outside my control. I grew even more angry at the loss of ground guys in IED attacks or ambushes that we had not been able to stop. I felt guilty for those who died under our watch. I saw an American vehicle burning in a crystal clear green NVG picture in my mind. I saw dark dirt caked with the blood of Americans along a wall riddled with divots made by AK-47 rounds. I watched a MEDEVAC take a barrage of fire while trying to hoist a medic down to save a wounded soldier, as we desperately tried to lay fire down and an Apache leveled a building to stop the madness.

Like many returned single veterans, my path ahead began to look bleak in a hurry. I was unhappy with our unit at present and how we were once again being utilized and treated back in the states. I squatted down in the motor pool with all the other pilots, hand-picking tiny weeds and scraping them out of the cracks in the concrete with my fingers. We painted rocks and conducted lawn care. The policies and treatment that were being levied against our average soldiers in the ranks was becoming too much. My very future existence was uncertain. I doubted things I had never doubted before, and a very real darkness was beginning to envelope me.

Much of that changed one morning when Lindsey Shankle, my old college girlfriend, sent me a text out of the blue about something funny she figured I'd like. We had dated a lot in college and parted ways afterwards, only corresponding a handful of times between then and the present. She was a steadfast friend and someone with whom I had always had a great relationship and fun time. We ended up talking for several hours all at once, catching up and laughing like old times.

She didn't really know, but it was an immense comfort to talk to her. My immediate family has always been supportive, but they also had their own lives and lived far away. I was very thankful to have a friend back in my life almost instantly, and one who wasn't tied to my military career. After several weeks of catching up, I asked Lindsey if she would like to go to our small family cabin in the Ouachita Mountain range near my home in Arkansas. We had great memories there from college, so she agreed and I soon had my leave authorization to go. We spent days at the cabin lounging, cooking delicious meals, and having deep discussions. I needed it much more than I had realized. A lot of time had passed, yet we knew each other so well that the connection was immediate and one that healed me in a way I had not yet experienced.

After our trip to the cabin, I felt a lot more hopeful. I asked if Lindsey would ever consider leaving her job and life in Louisiana to come out to Savannah. It was a huge step for both of us, but she thankfully agreed to join me on the journey I was on with the Army. She knew that I would deploy again and seemed to both know and accept what she was getting herself into. Lindsey moved to Savannah, and we settled into a year of adventures and fun as a couple, while also trying to combat life within the Army. Lindsey transitioned into the group of wives and girlfriends very well and was welcomed with open arms. They were a great resource of comfort and unity. It was a tough life being an Army spouse, and even more difficult being an unmarried companion of a soldier, since they were not afforded as much recognition or credit for their efforts or sacrifices. Not long after Lindsey moved in, we got a female black lab puppy; I'd both wanted and needed a dog for quite some time. We named her Scout, which seemed only fitting. The Kandahar deployment rumor became a confirmed reality, and it was time to get ready. Our training began to focus on that eventuality, and things began to get real again. Some of the dumb focus we'd been enduring was finally subtracted, and the proper focus was being restored. War. Preparations for war. Training for war. Planning and knowing and gears turning, jet fuel burning, .50 caliber machine guns, and rockets flying in target practice all in preparation once again for war.

Bravo Troop was selected to spend a month out at the dreaded National Training Center, or NTC, and required a few additional PCs to volunteer to help them. I was unmarried and had no kids, plus, they were the first troop I'd been originally, albeit briefly, assigned to when I'd arrived fresh out of flight school. I volunteered to go on a journey with them that I was glad for the experience from, but would never want to ever do again. It was all centered around big, nation-on-nation battlefield warfare. The training provided very little value in respect to preparing a pilot for our current asymmetric warfare demands in Afghanistan. It was also insane in that we were strictly forbidden from possessing or using cell phones, or any other means of communication, to speak with our family or friends while there—unlike the actual war I'd previously endured. The part of Texas we were in was absolutely a dead ringer for what Afghanistan *looked* like, though.

Lindsey seemed to have resorted to the understanding that if I would propose, it would probably be after the long road ahead from another deployment. Still, she had begun to drop engagement hints when we passed jewelry stores, so I tactically snuck in the movie *Blood Diamond* one evening, which resulted in a stand-down that gave me a few additional months to plan. Little did she know that I had already set things in motion. I selected a very nice diamond ring after long and relentless research. Her parents received a call from me and both gave their immediate and excited blessing. Soon thereafter, I set about secretly organizing a wedding. I called up family and a few groups of immediate mutual friends with the plan to have it at the Sandals Royal Bahamian resort. Everyone was in, everyone was excited—except my potential and clueless bride-to-be.

I kidnapped her one day after work and brought her blindfolded downtown through Savannah to our favorite B&B called the Dresser Palmer House. They had also been apprised of the plan and promised to keep quiet. We had a fun day around Savannah, and for lunch, we packed a picnic basket full of goodies and wine to enjoy in Forsyth Park. Nice wine, a picnic blanket, and everything was set up. We ate, talked, and laughed. I got nervous because I knew that my window was closing and this was my chance. I reached into my pocket for the thousandth time as I'd done all day to ensure that the ring was there, and put it in my palm. I looked her in the eyes and said, "I have a question."

She set her wine down, not knowing anything out of the ordinary was going on. "Okay, what is it?" she asked. I got on one knee, and opened my palm, placing the ring between my thumb and forefinger. Her eyes grew wide, and she froze. "Will you marry me?" I asked.

The park was quiet, squirrels played nearby, and a car drove by. She sat motionless and staring in shock, unable to speak, and I stayed transfixed, waiting. Finally, she caught her breath and exclaimed, "Yes! Yes, I'll marry you!"

We embraced in a joyful hug of tears and happiness. I told her it was all set up. We would travel to the Sandals Royal Bahamian resort, our family was apprised and would attend, as would a few close mutual friends. Lindsey stuttered and tried to think, and I told her that there was nothing for her to do but find a dress. That's all—just find a dress and everything else is handled. Our wedding date in September 2012 was fast approaching.

The wedding and honeymoon in the Bahamas was spectacular and entirely stress-free, save the night before our wedding when an Apache pilot and I were late returning from a shark dive. We stayed after everyone left for a few extra days to enjoy, as we knew that once I returned it was going to be full throttle getting ready to return to Afghanistan once more. After we got back, Lindsey was the newest official member of the Charlie Troop wives' club and received all the military benefits and support entitled to, and deserved for, a spouse.

Weeks moved quicker, and the intensity in our unit grew as we edged closer to the reality of imminent deployment. This time around would be different too, as our operations were going to be conducted right in the center of ultimate evil itself: Kandahar. It was the birthplace and sympathetic region to the Taliban, and all the extremist douchebag offshoots stemming from it.

Reports coming back to us were of intense combat and operations dealing with a very dug in and sophisticated insurgency literally fighting in their own backyard. To make matters worse, America and the rest of the world were losing the stomach for further war, and the current administration had been decimating our funding and shrinking our ranks and operational capabilities. The recipe for this deployment differed greatly from my previous one. Around Bagram, I could not only fight, but also drop stuffed animals and soccer balls to kids in an attempt to try and do some good. I had no illusions that this sector of the country would come even close to affording such opportunities.

Soon enough, we were doing our final packing and experiencing the all-too-familiar litany of briefs, classes, and preparations. The last two years had seemed to fly by, and our time was up. It was time to return to war again.

PART THREE

OPERATION ENDURING FREEDOM XIII

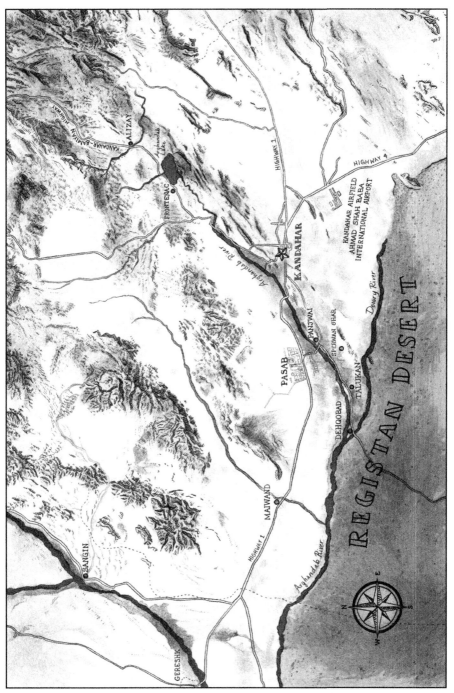

Area of Operations, Kandahar, Afghanistan, 2013
(rotate to view)

Loading up on a C-17 in Manas, Kyrgyzstan.

Mountains around Kandahar, Afghanistan.

CHAPTER 18

Monday, December 17, 2012: "It looks all the same, but it feels a bit different" is the best way to describe our journey to Kandahar. Instead of jumping into the ocean the day of departure, I settled for about 20 minutes in the pool on base and 5 minutes in the hot tub. I also ate a steak fit for a king. We departed Savannah in much the same manner as before, after teary-eyed goodbyes and similar advice from my father: "Fly safe and smart, and make it home just like you did last time." My new bride sobbed and nodded in agreement with his words, and I once again promised to be safe and hugged everyone tight.

We took off late at night and crossed the ocean to refuel in Germany. Fortunately, we were refueled and re-boarded within only two hours, continuing on into Manas, Kyrgyzstan. Our commander told us he knew it would all be a shitshow, but please just go with the flow, adding: "If you fuck us in Manas, I will fuck you, and leave you in Manas." I liked our commander.

It was freezing in Manas, with temperatures in the day hovering in single digits and definitely dropping below zero at night. Where we were staying looked like an Antarctic expedition site. The one nice thing though was that the heaters in our tents worked very well, but we all started sweating when some genius cranked the damn things up.

The Manas facilities had even improved. I snagged a few trusted friends whom I allowed into my secret club, guiding them to the same hidden WiFi library spot that I'd found two years prior. The little Manas library was eerily undisturbed, existing both in my mind's eye and before me in the exact same state as it had been when I was last there. The small space may as well have had the same magazine and pencil laying on the table, as if it had all been locked in stasis. This set my brain a bit to unease, as I remembered sitting there with pilots no longer with me, talking of how glad that we were to be leaving Afghanistan. Now I was in this same, once jovial room, thinking about it all as if it were a continuation of the same situation turned into a nightmare.

I set up my communications link with those back home again and wrote my first report on the journey over and what we expected next. It was important to give a good glimpse of our forgotten war that still raged on in Afghanistan to those who cared.

Dede also kept a journal, and this is her account of our first day in Manas.

Journal, December 12, 2012

CW2 Dede Murawsky

I swear this tent is 90 degrees! Every time the door opens, I see thick snow flying by. It's about -3 outside, and I actually really like it. My contentment here is not compared to America, but if you compare it to where we are going, even though I have not yet been there, I know here is better. I love the quiet, clean air. The landscape is not covered in sad filth, nor is the air full of its scent. Starting later today, the pure white sparkle of this snow-covered silent Army retreat will be replaced with the sounds of American Air Superiority and smell I can only describe as Afghanistan.

Here in a few hours, my job will hit me fast and furious, and I can't wait to get on the ground in country and spend every possible second "soaking up" everything the 25th CAB has learned.

I am scarcely dressed and still tempted to go jump in the snow! Before I go shower, because I cannot stand this heat, I want to take a moment to talk about the amazing female pilots we have in my task force this time around. Not only are two of the four flight companies commanded by tough, level-headed pilots, we have a female lieutenant who is on her way

to filling their shoes in no time. We also have me and another CW2 PC,
both with prior enlisted service and another two CW2s who went into
flight school directly from being civilians. Together, I think we are going
to provide a good balance in each of our troops/companies.

Dede was excited to have more females in our task force, especially since there had been so few in the first deployment. The only other female in Charlie Troop with her had been seriously injured in a crash and airlifted out, and I think that was harder on her than she let on.

As a simple orientation to this deployment, our Task Force Lighthorse was one of several other task forces that had deployed together in the same spot under our 3rd Combat Aviation Brigade. We arrived at Kandahar Airfield (KAF) after our brief stay in Manas, only to find that insanity was in full effect. We sat through briefing after briefing, class after class of the same information taught from different entities so that they may feel special. On December 21st, we got up at 0600 in the morning and returned to the room at midnight. My roommate and I were smoked. We lived downwind of a treatment plant on KAF, affectionately known as the "Poo Pond." That's exactly what it was; an enormous pond of feces and fluids, being heated by the Afghan sun and releasing its olfactory majesty for us all. Why the poo pond was located right in the middle of most of the major living and trafficked areas was beyond me. Biohazard signs warned of the dangers from getting too close, but a few mannequins managed to make it to the shoreline in lounge chairs, one complete with a fishing pole.

Our living situation was much different on Kandahar than it was on Bagram. We were all living in a two-story, shipping container apartment-style complex called the RLBs (short for Relocatable Buildings). Each container, called Container Housing Units or CHUs, had room for two soldiers with their gear and two bunks. My roommate and I both had placed a desk and little personal area below and slept above on the respective top bunks. My roomie was CW3 Matt Vaccaro. He had joined Charlie Troop from another squadron after we had returned from the 2010 deployment. Matt was blonde where he wasn't bald, and was a strong and proper soldier. He had a gruff voice and was always trying to make sure he did the right thing, even despite it being at his own peril sometimes. In addition to being one of the most senior warrants in our troop, Matt was also our Safety Officer and an experienced AMC. He was coasting down towards retirement and had been an NCO in a Bradley tank unit that participated in the initial invasion of Iraq. I always gave him crap for being old and having his own substantially large army of children and pets back home. Matt and I had found prior to our deployment to KAF that we got along great and flew very well together. We decided that we should call being roommates with one another early on before anything such as that was assigned. By doing so, we both avoided living with a potential weirdo or personality conflict.

Although this wasn't our first rodeo, (in fact, it was his fourth deployment), we were both still unprepared for how especially dumb the whole situation was going to be right from the moment we stepped onto KAF. The silly games were just a foreshadowing of what was in store to come. The next day, with all due importance, my morning consisted of going to a shooting range with 300 other people. There, I proceeded to walk up in a large line of 20, load FIVE rounds into my pistol, shoot said rounds for no score, and then walk a mile back to where I came from. Magical, I know.

A fun fact about our budget: We left the U.S. without enough weapons. We had enough M4 rifles to issue one for each pilot, but the shortage of M9 Beretta handguns would force us to share. A soldier always had to be armed with something when deployed, and typically, pilots would carry their M9 in a holster wherever they went, while their rifles would be left in the arms room to take out only on missions. A rifle should be sighted in to the specific soldier it's issued to, but the M9s were not user specific. The lack of enough M9s was only an inconvenience in the grand scheme, as the shorted pilot could at least carry their rifle, but it still was pretty telling of our military state when we ran short on guns.

*

From the start, our communications inter-troop were rocky. Soon, I would be getting a Hadji phone so that information gathering might be easier to contend with. The 25th CAB Hawaii guys that we were replacing were still conducting missions and training our guys to take their place. I had not begun flying yet, but was slated to in just a few more days—perhaps even sooner than I thought, as had happened to some of our pilots.

The operations tempo was fast-paced. KAF, furthermore, was the busiest airfield in Afghanistan. When I was out on the flight line, it looked like some over-the-top action movie. Helicopters were constantly taking off, hovering, and landing. The battle space we were in was a challenging place, and one senior pilot simply put it, "It's fucking game time out here, boys." We returned to the room for some much-needed five hours of sleep before the next big day began.

My initial orientation flight was fast approaching. The prior few days, I had stressed over the ALSE shop and the fact that our entire brigade hadn't figured out what to do or who was going to run it. The officer in charge might become me because I'd bitched so much about the disorganization. The ALSE shop itself was very well set up and supplied. I set about orienting myself with what and where everything was in case I was placed in charge, especially since I indeed had at least become our Squadron ALSE Officer. Matt and I had gotten our room squared away, and we were fortunately located in a convenient spot. The Afghan Coffee Shop was only 50 yards away, a small PX annex was almost right out front, and bathrooms/showers were a few doors down. This was most definitely an improvement over my last situation.

Christmas Day came and went unceremoniously, and on the morning of December 26th, I woke up much too early for my show time, so I walked to the coffee shop and then managed to get a ride to our troop far away out on the flight line. I began to do the performance and weight and balance calculations to see how much fuel, .50 caliber ammunition, and rockets that we could carry given the aircraft weight and then adding both pilots and their gear. Our maximum total gross weight that we could fly the Kiowa Warrior was only 5,200lbs, and believe me, every pound counts. Even 100 rounds of .50

cal ammo weighs 33lbs, which could send us over the limits. Our fuel load was calculated in pounds, rather than gallons, thankfully, and our absolute maximum fuel that we could ever take was only a little over 700lbs.

After the paperwork was complete and calculated, I met the others over at the Intelligence brief. Here, all pertinent information was passed out to us and we could ask questions to get a feel for what may be going on in our operations area. When that was done, the SP and another pilot went out to take off and I went to lunch, with instructions to be ready to get picked up by 1530 for my turn. After a rather bland lunch (I already regretted not bringing along any Slap Ya Mama spices), I donned all of my equipment on and stood in a rocky area way out on the flight line, fidgeting with my gear. I figured out right away that some adjustments were in order. I had trouble with my small go-bag and bandoleer that carried four spare rifle magazines of 30rds each (120 extra rounds besides the 90 on my person and 30 in the weapon). The magazines did not sit right in the bandoleer and were prone to falling out, so I would need a new one, and soon.

As soon as the bird landed and the other pilot swapped with me, I was more than ready to roll. I was a little anxious because I hadn't flown but twice in the preceding three months, but I was surprised to find myself very comfortable the second after I had strapped in. I brought us to a hover and maneuvered to our refuel and rearm pad to get gas and pick up our rockets and ammo, as the munitions were not co-located with each aircraft like we'd (preferably) had set up with on Bagram. Once fueled and armed, I was back up in the sky over Afghanistan once again. This time around, our callsign would be "Wrath," with each Kiowa having its own distinct Wrath callsign number such as "Wrath 53."

Another surprising thing to me was how instantly everything came back to me; my head was on swivel and I was calling out nearly everything that I saw, any movement from anyone at all. It is uncanny that even though I was in an entirely different area, and despite the rules and fight having changed drastically, it was all still familiar. The SP pointed out a bunch of different references and waypoints, programming our onboard navigation system to direct me with a little waypoint carrot from place to place. Once satisfied with the basic orientation, we ended up at the test fire area.

At first, I sucked at shooting and it pissed me off. Accurately using hard-mounted weapons fixed directly to the airframe with no ability to articulate them was a perishable skill. I grudgingly knew that I would get better again, especially since we would do it every single day we flew to test fire the weapons. This was in stark contrast to the two or three times (if we were lucky) in an entire year we got to shoot back home. That still didn't give me much comfort, but by the time I was running low on ammo I was more satisfied with my progress on the gun runs and was less discouraged.

I successfully conducted a landing into a dusty intersection without incident and was happy that the SP was satisfied. My approach and landing on a few mountain pinnacles and ridgelines also went a lot smoother than I had expected, and I was pleased not to have wasted a lot of time trying to get it right. Satisfied, we decided to return to base for more gas and ammo and await the sunset so we could come back and do it all over again under NVGs. In a nutshell, the second half of the flight went just the same as the first.

After landing, I was marked complete with the evaluations with no additional requirements or discrepancies noted. I'd needed a good flight and was happy that it went so well, especially with our senior-most pilot in the troop evaluating me. In a few more days, I was set to have my official Local Area Orientation (LAO) with one of the experienced Hawaii guys that we were replacing.

There really was not much to an LAO but to sit in the left seat, hold a map, and learn and absorb as much information as possible. After that flight, I would be fully mission qualified and put into a mixed team. The Hawaii guys were still helping us take over, so the teams currently consisted of both our pilots and those of the outgoing unit until they all departed for home.

Two steps forward, three steps back. That's how it all was feeling to me. I was supposed to fly my LAO on December 28th, but got weathered out because of a sandstorm that kicked debris up to 13,000 feet which had slowly been settling ever since. I hoped to get another crack at the LAO soon.

*

My commander and I walked down the dusty shoulder of the road by our flight line, talking about some of his prior experiences in Kandahar and what the year may hold for us. As we walked, we both caught an odd sight at the same time and stopped in our tracks. A contractor pickup truck was about to pull out of an area near our flight line, but it wasn't the truck that was out of the ordinary—it was the passengers. The windows were all rolled down, and our troop's Team Brown sat staring at us looking half guilty. The commander's face was that of an expert poker player; I couldn't tell if it amused him, or if he was about to lose his mind on them. We waited in silence, as obviously he wanted to let Team Brown speak first. The driver put his hands up slightly, and said, "Sir, I know that this may look bad, but it's not what it looks like…"

I laughed and said, "That's good. It looks to me like Team Brown stole a truck from the contractors." One of the guys in the back chuckled a bit, declaring "Robo, I cannot believe you just blue falconed us." I smiled back. "Blue falcon" in the military stands for "buddy fucker," and we'd throw each other under the bus occasionally just for kicks.

"Stealing a vehicle is exactly what it looks like, but you're saying that whatever you're up to is legit, so I'm going to walk away now," said our commander. They began to try and all speak at once, but our boss just raised his hand and started to walk again. He didn't want to know, and I laughed and told him that we should probably erase the whole thing from both of our memories—plausible deniability and all. The commander agreed. No one ever wanted to know what Team Brown was really up to, so long as they remained experts at getting us the unobtainable and working their behind-the-scenes deals at our most difficult times in need as a unit. Their methods were better left mysterious, but their success was always welcome.

I admired that Team Brown ended up with a set of turntables and a projector in one room back at the RLBs. Their room was a mini-rave and the flag of Spain hung proudly on the wall. They even had a damn light ball much like a disco, and to top it all, they'd installed an actual fog machine. They had obtained all of this on KAF. It was wonderfully impressive.

Everyone was getting along decently enough in Charlie Troop. There would be a few cliques that would no doubt form, but mostly we were a much tighter knit troop than any of the Blackhawk or Apache companies. A Blackhawk ALSE officer assigned to our task force made a note of how cool it was that we all ate together. I thought that what we had was normal, but then realized that we honestly were the only people who seemed to have "family mealtime." I was happy about that and hoped we'd continue to be a solid troop together.

I already missed Lindsey and our puppy, Scout. I was thankful to have Skype and email available and hoped that those in the outlying areas had access to such things. I felt guilty once again for the facilities and niceties available to us, as I could only imagine how hard it was for people before such technology. My maternal grandfather was a prisoner of war and then listed as missing in action for more than three years during WWII. He'd emerged from the jungle alone months after escaping and fighting alongside French commandos, not even knowing about the Japanese surrender. I can't comprehend how hard that was on our family, and I always appreciated the few seconds that someone took to send a message over to support myself and our unit. It truly was always one of my favorite little parts of the day to read those messages.

I visited the Bravo 1-3 Attack guys who were only a few doors down. I was happy to still fight alongside some of my old Red-Headed Black Sheep comrades, and we all had a few spare moments to catch up. Over the course of a few more days, I tried to fly two more LAO attempts, but failed due to weather. We sat down and it was finally agreed that we could make my LAO happen on a real mission, given that combat flying was not exactly brand new to me. My next flight would fortunately be a productive one to support our war efforts instead of checking boxes on a piece of paper for legality. The games were over.

CW2 Dede Murawsky on her way out into the frontier.
Photo courtesy of SPC Jessica Janes

Bringing the flag along for a ride.

CW3 Matt Vaccaro flies as my wingman in Trail.

Charlie Troop CP, sitting in our only real "lounge corner."

CHAPTER 19

Dear Soldier,

How are you in Afghanistan? What do you do when you are not fighting?

Have peace on earth.

Love, Kenzie

Suddenly, I went from sipping tea and messing around on the internet, like everyone else on KAF, to being directly involved in the fight. I'd been flying like mad the previous 48 hours. The outgoing unit was finishing up the last orientation flights with our troop, and I was paired up with one of their pilots for the day. I sneezed and cursed "the crud," a tell-tale illness signaling that you've been away from Afghanistan for a while and your body is mad at you for returning. It's a miserable booger infestation and feeling like crap while you adjust to the poor air quality and majesty that is the Middle East. I was on the downswing luckily, so I was still able to listen intently and appreciate my tour guide's shocking amount of knowledge regarding the area he'd called home for so long.

Like an encyclopedia of Kandahar, my guide pointed to almost every single hut and trail as we flew, citing what made it significant, when that happened, and the details surrounding every event he'd witnessed. It was an amazingly useful transfer of knowledge that I had not at all expected. As we did our tour, the radios came suddenly to life. A ground unit nearby was receiving sporadic AK-47 fire. They were being forced to hold their position along some rooftops in a destroyed and deserted labyrinth of qalat ruins that was once a village. We flew low and fast, trying to get a quick take on the situation.

"Wrath 52, this is Saber 33. I don't know if that last burst of fire was for us, or if you pissed them off and that was for you," said the calm and matter-of-fact ground guy on the radio. I cocked an eyebrow. This was getting pretty interesting. My pulse quickened and I couldn't hide a slight smirk. The adrenaline rush hadn't been felt in quite some time. Antagonizing Hadji with a Kiowa was my most favorite game in the whole wide world.

We moved in closer again and the ground forces attempted to talk us into the area that they believed the fire was coming from. One of the infantry guys propped up quickly onto a wall and fired off a few rounds from his M-14 Designated Marksman's rifle. A burst of AK-47 fire answered him from the ruins of a structure which I estimated to be about 200 meters directly across from him.

The proximity of the incoming U.S. rounds had signaled to this insurgent that the bead the Americans had on him was a bit too close for comfort. He ran out of the back of his destroyed hideout, and magically emerged on a motorcycle. We knew that the fleeing motorcyclist was the same man who'd just been lighting up our ground guys, but now, we had to prove it. Our aircraft got right above and just slightly behind him, and I attempted to hit him with a smoke grenade. Had this been earlier in the war, he would have definitely been hit by a barrage of 5.56 rounds from my rifle. He stopped suddenly, and to my disbelief, another man sprinted out from his hiding place in one of the heavily entrenched grape row fields. The man jumped onto the back of the waiting motorcycle and then the two sped as fast as they could out of the dirt and onto the highway.

"Did you see that?!" I called to Trail. It was quick, and had all the hallmarks of a well-executed, pre-planned extraction if the enemy needed to bug out of the area in a hurry. Trail confirmed that they'd seen the whole thing and believed also that these were the two responsible for the attack on the ground guys. They were displaying all the signs they weren't just confused civilians, scared up in an abandoned village and attempting to escape Americans at breakneck speed out of fear alone. We'd had enough of this.

Like something out of the TV show *COPS* intermixed with a Hollywood action flick, we were now in a high-speed helicopter vs. motorcycle chase. Our helicopter edged in very close, and I then saw the genius procedure that our predecessor troop had discovered for using the newly-installed flare buckets on the Kiowa. Designed to thwart surface to air missile threats, the bucket was mounted to the belly of the aircraft, and had been done so in a forward facing orientation. Over 30 flares were loaded on board, and although the system was designed to save the aircraft with these flares automatically in the event a missile was detected, we also had a manual override button. The flare dispense switch was right by the weapon fire switch on the pilot's cyclic flight control. I smiled, then began laughing in disbelief as our aircraft angled its nose slightly upwards and we began launching very accurately aimed flares. Our Kiowa was hauling ass less than 50 feet above the highway in a tight chase, launching fireballs like *Mario Brothers*.

I pulled my rifle off the dash and ensured I had rounds chambered. The motorcycle continued speeding as fast as it could towards a fork ahead. "If he goes right, we're not gonna be able to catch him," said my counterpart. I quickly looked at my map, and saw what he meant. Up ahead once the road forked right, there were no checkpoints, outposts, FOBs, or other assets we could warn in time to interdict the motorcycle.

We sped up to arrive right beside them, with me staring at them out my left side. I pulled up my rifle with my right hand, and made a cut-throat gesture with my left. The man driving paid no attention to me, and the man on the back of the motorcycle looked at me with a killer's icy stare. *Looks like blue eyes on Hadji, how interesting,* I thought. We locked in time which slowed for several seconds, staring at one another, each face-to-face with our own mortal enemy. I thought of the man back in Bagram that had stared at me in such a way near Beggar's Canyon, and a visceral feeling of disgust and hatred washed over me. We had witnessed this duo of insurgents firing upon Americans, and although I wanted these men dead, I could not prove my innocence in court if I shot them. It infuriated me.

Our plan to influence their escape route worked. Since we were harassing them from their right side, the motorcycle driver hooked a left at the fork in the road. I began hurriedly calling on the radio, trying to move from frequency to frequency to get a hold of a small checkpoint up the road. Someone finally understood what was happening and got the ball rolling, placing the call ahead on our behalf while there was still time. Now, only a few hundred meters away and with the motorcycle in danger of speeding right past their compound, I suddenly saw soldiers empty into the courtyard towards the gate. We dropped over them low and close, and I waved and pointed frantically out the left side towards the motorcycle.

The checkpoint flung their compound doors open and soldiers poured into the street drawing up their weapons just in the nick of time. The motorcycle came to a screeching halt, and I witnessed the soldiers yelling at them to put their hands up and kill their engine. The two insurgents did as instructed, then pulled the same typical innocent and confused victim routine they were all trained to do. An interpreter was on the scene, and the motorcyclists flailed their arms and pointed every which way, acting as if some insane injustice was being brought upon them. The soldiers kept their weapons up, looking between us, at one another, and then back to the motorcycle guys. Apparently, they'd been told to quickly find the Kiowa chasing a motorcycle and then stop said motorcycle, but from there, they didn't really know what else to do.

We passed very low and slow now, and I attempted sign language by pointing to the two insurgents, motioning as if I was shooting, and then pointed to my American flag on my sleeve. I did not have their radio frequency and was having trouble establishing direct communication with those below. The NCO in charge out in the road suddenly put it all together. He perfectly mimicked my sign language motions, and pointed to the two from the motorcycle. I nodded emphatically as we slowly circled. The NCO grabbed the motorcycle driver by the neck, pulling him close to his own body and pointing an inch from the insurgent's face. He then pointed to me and moved his trigger finger, while I saw his mouth move deliberately and I lip read, "This asshole shot at you?" *Close enough,* I thought, and nodded in affirmation.

The next thing I knew, the insurgent was taken to the ground. The other man accompanying him was thrown down next to him and both were flex cuffed and roughly led into the compound. We were elated and laughing, not believing that we'd been able to pull off the chase and have the dickheads apprehended in such a spectacular manner. I complimented the *Mario* flare-launching tactic and swore to pass it on if our troop had not already begun to employ it.

Not more than 10 minutes later, I spotted something that looked odd and mentioned it to the right seater, asking him what he thought. We came around and observed individuals and actions that just didn't feel right; something was out of place. How the military-aged males we witnessed were moving around, communicating, and eyeballing us wasn't normal. I was quickly learning that "patterns of life" traits in these local Afghans weren't all too different from my previous experiences.

Our team dedicated special attention to the area, and kept eyes on a few more suspicious-looking characters. It wasn't long before we began to notice the tell-tale signs that there was an IED close by in the road, and that some of these guys either emplaced it, or knew who emplaced it. At any rate, they were there to cause harm to our forces or, at the very least, the ANA or ANP moving frequently through the area. We pulled up grids and descriptions, all the while trying not to draw too much attention to the fact that we were looking very specifically at a particular group of people and spot on the ground. Our ruse to feign disinterest appeared to work.

After landing and several hours later, I learned that our report and my little tingle feeling that something was not right had caused a stir. Once we had departed, other eyes were trained on the bad guys doing bad things, who must've thought since we left they were then free to resume being scumbags. Hostile intent was declared and the proper authorizations were worked up, so a Hellfire missile had come out of nowhere and sent one or more enemy to the afterlife. I was especially proud of this and claimed that drone missile to be mine, stating that it was great news and the perfect way to celebrate the coming of the new year. I happily got a celebratory piece of dessert, figuring that it was well in order.

*

It was becoming readily apparent that KAF was a place that could definitely keep us on our toes. Initially, work found us much more frequently than my previous scouting ventures had deep in the mountain passes and regions surrounding Kabul and Bagram.

I hadn't been able to go out to the ALSE shop for a few days. I was still not getting what I wanted from higher, but I vowed that they'd get to hear me gripe about it non-stop until I hopefully did. We especially lacked the maxillofacial shields that were installed onto our flight helmets as an added safety precaution for those that desired them. The shield I used to refer to as a "Vader mask" was most beneficial during a crash sequence in keeping a pilot's face from slamming into aircraft controls, or for the safety of the crew chiefs riding in the back of Blackhawks and Chinooks. It was beyond me why we couldn't receive more.

I was happy that we were staying busy. Not having the mid-tour leave break would be rough, as we were all acutely aware. Two weeks of mid-tour leave was only offered to those with a year or more on deployment, but ours would only hit the nine-month mark, so we'd be going through it all straight on. Those warriors who had come long before us had it much worse though, and I tried to remember that.

My reliance on care packages had been critical this time around, and I was extremely thankful for package drops. There had been many occasions where I'd been unable to go eat, so it helped having snacks and little emergency meals on reserve. I'd missed lunch the last two days because we were so deeply engaged in protecting guys on the ground, so having some snack bars and jerky in the cockpit made a world of difference. A rumbling belly was annoying, but the hypoglycemia that could come from a loss of nutrients and salt shed through excessive heat and poorly-met nutritional needs could become much more than just annoying.

On January 5th, I succumbed to another bug that had been ravaging our ranks. All the miserable symptoms included lots of snot and aches, fatigue, sneezing, and a chapped nose from one-ply toilet paper used as tissues. My roommate, Matt, looked at me, helpfully remarking, "You look like dog shit. Stay away from me." I was officially down on bed rest for the day.

The previous two flights had been decent. We spent most of the time escorting ground convoys and canvassing the area in the difficult attempt to learn the complex operations zone. There were so many different little towns, routes, FOBs and COPs, checkpoints, and visual waypoints. It all could get mixed up and very hard to remember, especially with the vast majority of the above having mainly local names. We'd all get it down after a few more weeks of constantly flying around the areas I knew.

Matt had a great way of looking at the remaining time for our deployment, and I set about adopting his mindset. Since we traditionally did 12-month deployments, we were already a quarter of the way through. That meant that in about three months, we'd be halfway through the deployment already. It sounded much better that way. He hung a calendar to do a daily countdown, which I wasn't so sure about, but whatever floats his boat was fine with me.

CHAPTER 20

We Carried the Stars

"Let my daughter be remembered.
Bring her memory with you into battle."

Back in the states, Matt had met a grief-stricken mother by coincidence. Her daughter had been killed in Iraq, and the woman had flown the flag which was draped over her daughter's casket for years over their house. The flag eventually became tattered and torn, and had to be retired. The woman then cut out all 50 stars from the flag and she placed each in a small clear bag. She placed a sticker on each one, with the name of the soldier who had died and a few sentences imploring whoever held the star to bring it into battle against America's enemies. Each star would carry her daughter's memory. The woman had turned many of the special packets over to Matt, and he handed them out to me and several other pilots. I ordered a stout bullion coin holder, and neatly encapsulated the star in it. Every mission I went out on, and every subsequent day that I served in the Army, I carried the star in my breast pocket over my heart. I often thought about the star; what it meant, where it had been, and I would pat the holder carefully protecting it. Her memory joined us in the skies to avenge those who stole her life away.

By January 8th, the Hawaii unit was gone and we'd officially "taken the battle." There were a lot of missions going on daily; not a moment passed by that there weren't helicopters in the air, except in the most inclement of weather. I flew another eventful five hours in a steep learning curve. We'd begun to understand the area piece by piece, settling in while the motions became routine and the sense of groundhog day started to take hold.

I was dropped off on the opposite side of the airfield to knock out a few chores, and subsequently, was left on my own by accident. Stranded, I walked the area known as the Boardwalk on a rainy, yet also dusty afternoon. The Boardwalk was a large covered wooden walkway lined all the way around with all the junk that your deployment money could buy. There were shops and eateries, creating what was essentially an outdoor mall. There was even a damn TGI Friday's. Locals who had been fortunate enough to be merchants elevated from bazaar to full-time shopkeeper status sat near the entrances of their shops, beckoning potential customers to come forward and claim their most special deals.

As I walked the entire thing, I was struck by how built up and permanent the place seemed in comparison to those shops and food trailers I'd encountered just a few years prior. I laughed aloud at the tourist T-shirt proclaiming 'TGI Friday's - Kandahar' for sale. That's exactly what I wanted, to wear that around in public and have people ask me about how dangerous and badass my time was in Afghanistan while eating my burger at TGI Friday's.

The thought even angered me more, as I tried to push it down and away.

Friday. "Thank God It's Friday." We don't even know or care when a Friday is! It's all the fucking same! It seemed asinine and ironic all at the same time, and I fought hard to drop it and move on. Needless to say, the Boardwalk wasn't my cup of tea, so after getting a sandwich, I took a main bus line back to the living area just to get out of there. As I rode back, I overheard two guys talking about how delicious the melon smoothie drink over there was. *Wow,* I thought, *what a great war.*

I did not feel completely settled in yet, as I hadn't been on a set schedule for flying. For whatever reason, I felt almost displaced. The two years between deployments had taken a lot out of me. Both our command climate and the attitude of the American public of indifference and frustration towards our current government had mixed to make the lives of the soldiers rough. Unlike the previous trip to Afghanistan, where I was full of Cavalry pride and an unquenchable thirst for fights and flights, this time around, I felt more discontent. It was readily apparent that our military was going through the motions, and what I had thought were restrictive policies and rules of engagement before had morphed into an even more damaging and terrible monster.

Lindsey could tell that something seemed different in me. She sent a calendar with family photos and a large blanket with her, Scout, and I pictured on it. I hung it in the classiest manner with fancy duct tape on the metal wall behind my chair. Outside, the dusty, nasty weather was back in full force. High winds were accentuated by even stronger gusts, and a torrential downpour occurred. While I traditionally loved rain and thunderstorms as much as the next guy, the muddy trouble it caused on KAF was dreadful. There existed practically no drainage, and the water would remain for over a month in some places.

I flew another four and a half hours on the 12th while dealing with ever increasing dust and wind. It's never really that great flying in high winds, but this was definitely made worse by the "Rej," which was the gigantic red Registan Desert just to the south and west of us. What was most fascinating to me about the Rej was how prominently and suddenly its northern stretch of desert ended. A steep slope dropped right into the Arghandab River banks—a river which ran the length of our AO, ceasing at the base of a dam along the large Arghandab Lake. Anyhow, the wind was blowing right across the stupid Rej and directly into our faces. Luckily, a fluke downpour settled a lot of the crap in the air in the late afternoon and early evening. The air quality marginally improved, at least.

We had a very long day still scheduled after flying though, as we had several follow-on classes and briefings. That put me into one of the longest duty days that I had yet experienced. After a certain period, we'd turn into pumpkins and have to be whisked away back to our rooms so as not to break our regulations for duty day.

I was informed that I'd be on duty to drive a van for the next week from 0800-1600 each day. Our living area was far away from the flight line, and the regular transit system on base left something to be desired. Our missions involved very real time hacks to contend with, and I knew that the creation of a transportation schedule made inter-troop was only a matter of time with our rickety little van. I cringed at the thought of the next morning, where I would wake up and begin shuttling people around at 0800. Unlike a cab or bus driver, I didn't know my way around and would most certainly get lost as hell. We had no maps, and there were no such things as road signs to help me. My days would entail hours of frustrated circles and twists and turns around a dusty, crappy airfield in Kandahar.

*

On January 17th, I arrived in our troop to fly and looked at the faces around me. I could see that many were soberly realizing and understanding that we still had a long time to go in Kandahar before packing it up. The focus on building schools, repairing roads, and training up a populace for agricultural success was not as evident or widespread as it once had been. The new focus was on being incredibly passive and risk averse, and orchestrating an unnecessarily slow withdrawal. The ANA were patrolling under our supervision, yet we still had Americans going outside the wire and being targeted. The mission of our ground guys in my estimation appeared to be something like what I figured they were briefed each day:

"Don't get killed walking around out there... and, uh, support the Afghans while they get shot at and targeted with roadside bombs and other booby traps. Don't step on or drive over those yourselves, either. The aircraft will be overhead to scare the bad guys, but don't expect them to always be able to protect you and shoot anyone because we don't want to upset the media and have an incident."

The TV in our area played a sad song of mourning while listing many names of those most recently killed. It was sad to read things across the screen like: PVT/SGT "Joe," age 19-35, blank-blank province, Afghanistan, __ January 2013.

I sure didn't hear about anything like that anywhere other than a closed circuit military television network on a commercial break in the middle of its regularly scheduled programming. The war shit was starting to get to me a little bit. It wasn't just me, but we all kind of kept it in for the most part. We couldn't or wouldn't really talk about the difficulty of any of it right then and there. We had a job to do, and we needed to file everything away to deal with another time down the road. Sourly, I watched the TV, betting that the ground guy blown sky high very recently in front of us would never get mentioned once on any news network back home. In all irony, the small tribute on our television ended with "Never Forgotten," and faded out.

Many among us were having increased difficulty coping with our unpopular war. This was especially true for those on multiple deployments. In the outgoing unit, and within our own ranks, the consensus seemed to be, "Let's hurry up and get the hell out of here." This sentiment only climbed up the rank structure chain so far though, until it reached those that gained career advantage and profit for staying and maintaining operations. It showed their unique and special leadership skills and potential to be considered for further promotions in order to "do good things."

I was finally resolved in my intentions, and admitted my plan to discontinue my time in the Army upon completion of my current contract. By leaving in this manner, I would be eight years short of the 20-year mark that would guarantee a retirement. Despite 12 years and two deployments, upon my exit, I wouldn't even be able to buy groceries on a base in the future, let alone receive any other benefits. Still, I didn't care any longer. There were an increasing number of pilots admitting that they were going to, like me, get out at the earliest opportunity. Not many would just come out and say it, though. In my case, I was lucky that my contract would be up within a year after I returned home. I knew that after the dust settled and the gigantic reduction in our budget, the Army would be a tough place to continue to work.

Making such a thing known was akin to coming out of the closet as an exuberant homosexual in front of a bunch of nasty, intolerant relatives. I knew this, but still flung open those closet doors to admit my intentions to vacate the Army as an aviator. It felt good to not hide the dirty secret anymore. With nearly two years remaining, I'd still be a competent crew member supporting our ground forces by diligently scouting, fighting, and remaining proficient within my current profession. But I would no longer have to hide my desire to plan and prepare for other jobs to come as well. I'd committed a sin that the Army hated most though; I announced that although I was a member of the team, I would no longer blindly follow and instead put my own family and personal future to the forefront of my life-goals priority list.

*

On January 22nd, I had a nice day off after the previous 16-hour day with a five-and-a-half-hour flight in the middle. After that finale from several long days at a stretch, I figured it was time to enjoy the one day out of 14 that I may truly have to myself. I again visited the MWR and walked half of the Boardwalk, only to be reminded how much I loathed it. I slurped down one of those melon smoothies I kept hearing so much about. There were dudes out getting blown up on the roads, running qalat to qalat, and fighting to stay alive among the fields and grape rows. The Boardwalk was a nicety that irked me, despite it being the only place to go sometimes to not eat chow hall food and pick up a few items. I couldn't figure out what upset me so much about it, and I finally settled on it being a feeling of guilt. I felt that it was so far and away a perverted representation of what our military required in a combat zone, and I was just as guilty for using it as the next guy. I later learned from Matt that while gallivanting around on my day off, others were taking their turn in the fight as I had expected. They were whom I thought about while standing on the Boardwalk, aggressively slurping on a smoothie.

In the next few weeks, I was slated to fly a lot more than I had anticipated. The pairings showed that I was set to be on a cool team composition and I was really looking forward to it. I was also definitely going to bring my camera. Aerial photography with a personal camera was not nearly as easy or acceptable a feat as it was in the past. We'd entered a cycle of being examined and scrutinized at every turn. Anything that appeared extraneous or couldn't be defended for a "professional" reason had become taboo. The lower enlisted soldiers admitted to having worse morale as of late than I had previously thought. They had been subjected to recent and more common "sensing sessions" to address the blatant unhappiness and alarming disciplinary issues that were multiplying.

Nothing bespoke our situation better than the simple, telltale example that a downward spiral was in effect. While the unit from Hawaii was in KAF for an entire 365 days, there was one soldier who accidentally discharged his weapon. This type of accident has always and unsurprisingly been seen by the Army as a massive no-no, and the poor soul is usually dealt with harshly.

The kicker was that our brigade had so far experienced *nine* accidental discharges, being at only 39 days in country! Hell, two of them happened on the same day. We didn't know whether to laugh hysterically at the absurdity or be completely horrified at how screwed up we were.

The situation had caused some sort of short circuit in the brains of the leadership and there was a massive briefing to address it all. Reactionary measures like that always cracked me up, as the problem was honestly not that hundreds of trained soldiers did not know how to properly handle a weapon. In response to the numerous accidents in prior weeks, every single person would randomly encounter someone walking around with a clipboard. We would have to show this suddenly appointed "weapons expert" that we each knew how to properly unload and check our weapons. The list of "check-the-blocks" would then get forwarded up to the powers that be so that they could say that they had completed retraining to fix the problem. It was tragically comical.

The increasing complacency, apathy, and lack of discipline continued to weave into a near epidemic. This wasn't as apparent or severe in the pilot and officer ranks, but a troubling number of soldiers looked worn down and didn't seem to give much of a damn about anything. A week prior, one soldier had actually shot another soldier in one of these accidents, but luckily, the bystander had his M-16 rifle slung across his chest. The bullet struck the weapon, bouncing off the metal buffer tube component inside which spun the weapon and sent the bullet on a ricochet off course instead of ripping through the guy's heart. We joked that as an Army unit, we must have made history for The Most People Accidentally Trying to Shoot Each Other in the History of War. If we couldn't get that, then at least we should get the honor for setting the record of two in one day.

I couldn't wait to fly. Drama on the ground in Kandahar was amazingly pervasive. My fortune of gaining a solid spot on the flight schedule would help keep me somewhat insulated. Unlike my last deployment, we had a pilot surplus rather than a pilot shortage. The flight schedule was the only saving grace to escape the madness on KAF.

*

By late January, my goal to avoid the circus by focusing on flying had been successful. I'd logged 11 hours in the previous two days, almost the whole time being to support ground forces. It continued to make our job rewarding to hear the relief in their voices when we arrived overhead to cover them. There was no shortage of enemy activity around our area, which was referred to en-masse as The Security Zone.

"Holy shit, where is that coming from?" I called to Lead as I covered their aircraft. I could hear the tell-tale snaps of AK-47 rounds. If they got really close, the internal communications system of the helicopter would transmit them through our radio. Our ground guys ran through the nightmare of clustered ruins below. They were having a rough day, and Hadji was starting to include us in the game. "Wrath, we're taking contact from our north and west. Be advised, we believe insurgents are also attempting to engage your aircraft each time you make a low pass, over!" Tomahawk 43 was in an elevated position atop a partially collapsed rooftop. Other elements from his formation were situated among tightly grouped ruins exchanging fire with their dug in foes nearby.

Scraggly plants and debris from decades of abandonment and neglect rose up from the earth to reclaim the area. The remains of human construction through mud and rock were sun bleached and worn from the harsh climate, some being so brittle that they easily crumbled under the violent impacts of bullet strikes. We switched radio frequencies momentarily to monitor Tomahawk's internal communications, and they were keeping it together well.

"No! Not that one, the second building! Put fire from your gunner on that second structure. The bastard is just behind that wall facing 2nd squad, maybe 50 meters out." The turret on one of their vehicles slewed about 30° to the right, and the gunner went to town. The ancient mud constructed wall began to disintegrate, and a few of the men below noticeably cheered and high-fived as the remains of a tiny, dilapidated ruin was torn apart. For a few minutes, everything became extremely quiet.

"Wrath, we're moving in to check that area where the MRAP engaged, do you have eyes on? Can you see anything?"

"Roger, I'm reasonably certain that I see someone with our sight. He isn't moving. I don't see his weapon, over." Lead moved in for a closer look and I positioned to cover them. A relieved voice came over the radio several minutes later, "Wrath 52, Tomahawk 43. One enemy KIA in the vicinity of the last engagement. No more contact is being received from our north. Request you keep eyes on the northern structures and fields while we regroup and prepare to move back towards Sperwan Ghar, over." We edged in closer, and I glanced over at the picture in our MMS as the ground guys searched the body of the enemy fighter they'd alleviated of his life. The dead man wore a grey traditional flat wool hat, and had the standard Taliban beard. One of his arms looked to be attached only by his ragged clothing, and he was a mangled bloody mess. *One more down, an infinite amount to go,* I thought.

*

Since there was so much talk of the war effort being shut down, we were ever increasingly starting to see the effects of drawing down. Budgets were already being thinned, orders and purchases for supplies were being scrutinized. None of it had affected us too badly yet, but if we were seeing this thing already, then we could only imagine what our situation may be like as we progressed in our deployment.

With that knowledge, I was doing everything that I could to ensure that our ALSE shop received the supplies to support the hundreds of pilots and crew chiefs requiring their gear be serviced, repaired, or replaced. Sourcing replacement parts for more expensive equipment was becoming increasingly difficult, and in a few rare cases, impossible to find. When we returned home, who knew what sort of shoe-string budget we'd be operating on. I was rightfully upset that I still couldn't get any more maxillofacial safety shields for our helmets. There were several pilots who had requested them, and I could not for the life of me get an order for them to be approved and sent to us.

Potentially life saving equipment was negotiable, but the subject of unit baseball caps became a sore subject with our Combat Aviation Brigade. Most of the units in our task force believed such a morale building implement had been approved, so they wore their hats around proudly. Our brigade commander walked into Bravo Troop one afternoon, saw a pilot wearing a Bravo Troop ball cap, and subsequently freaked out. The poor pilot had absolutely NO idea why he was getting yelled at by a high-ranking officer, being his boss' boss' boss.

The Bravo Troop lieutenants immediately travelled from unit to unit after the event, warning of what lay ahead if they were caught with such contraband as a morale building unit baseball hat. The quote that was written down (that I could never make up):

"This kind of thing has to stop right now! Baseball hats like this lead to poor unit discipline, and drug use!"

The leaping connection between a baseball hat and drugs had many of us laughing our asses off for days. The fact remained as it always had been: When the high level foolishness increased, so did the backlash from the soldiers who were literally stuck on an island with nowhere to go. At least we were trying to find humor where the only other alternative would be to go utterly mad.

Matt and I watched a comedy show to cheer ourselves up. We were nearing the end of the show's season, but knew we could get follow on seasons easily.

The U.S. government pretty much sponsored pirated media on KAF just like I'd seen back on Bagram. Local merchants were openly allowed to sell thousands of obviously pirated movies, television shows, and computer programs. I heard of cases where the computer programs sold had been found to be laced with fairly advanced hacking software to gather intelligence for the enemy. It was pretty slick stuff, especially since it was all still openly allowed to be sold despite that knowledge. I also figured that some merchants probably even turned over some of their selling proceeds to enemy fighters.

Naturally when getting checked while returning home, the Customs enforcers would remain high and mighty, confiscating DVDs from soldiers, saying that none of the items were allowed to be brought back to the states. "It's pirated stuff, which is illegal!" They'd cry. Due to this, we'd donate whatever we purchased to the ever growing pile in each unit library for the next guys. It was definitely an imperfect system.

Matt and I were set to fly together the next morning. It had been a long day, and I envied him for his loud but comfortable sounding snores. As I began to drift off to sleep, I thought about how I felt after talking with many back home. It was hard to even consider going back over everything in my mind, so I pushed the thought away. I needed to sleep; we had people who would be depending on our performance soon. I took some NyQuil, which finally did the trick to knock me out, but my dreams were unfortunately unsettling and violent.

CHAPTER 21

Dear Soldier,
Are you winning the war? I hope you win. I hope you do great.
I wish you a happy Valentine.
Thank you for saving us.
Love, Nathanael

It was almost the end of January, and right away, my team found our services in need. Ground forces had been taking a decent amount of harassment and one of their vehicles had trouble on top of it all. I looked through our binoculars at an MATV which, despite usually being hearty, could not overcome its current position. It sat at an extreme angle, two right side tires buried into a deep and muddy trench on the side of the narrow dirt road. The belly of the heavy armored vehicle was partially dug into the earth.

We conducted a battle handover to relieve the SWT who had been covering them into the sunrise. After the standard informational exchange, I asked, "How long has that MATV been stuck like that?" The Bravo Troop left seater replied, "Man, it's been a bitch for these guys. They got stuck at least three hours ago. They're trying to figure out who or what can be brought out here to drag the vehicle out, especially since the few attempts they made on their own only dug the thing deeper and made it worse." I watched the tired men below pulling security and walking around a bit slower than usual. "You said they were taking contact earlier, but that it ended as your team arrived overhead, and has stayed quiet since?" Bravo Troop's pilot responded, "Affirmative. Now if you'll excuse us, we've got some breakfast burritos to eat at Pasab. They even have strawberries today. We're gonna eat them all, too." I snorted; strawberries were an incredibly rare commodity. I watched their team turn away towards Pasab, one of the guys grinning ear to ear, flipping me off and blowing me a kiss.

Two more hours passed before heavy equipment arrived to free the MATV. Suspicious local men huddled around to watch, but knew to keep a safe distance and to leave their weapons hidden while we were overhead. As the MATV was finally freed, the soldiers below weakly cheered, then got the hell out of there. Our team arrived to refuel at FOB Pasab, and I rushed into the shack where the meals were served. A lone strawberry sat on a paper plate in the middle of the table, with a bite taken out of it and a smiley face doodle was drawn on the plate.

*

A few days went by and operations responding to troops in contact remained high. Two days passed and I then found myself flying in the same area as before. We'd consistently experienced successful mornings keeping insurgents off of U.S. forces, and this time around we could see that there was still trouble in the area.

Our ground guys, callsign Hulk 26, were lined up in "grape rows," which were giant, plowed fields with at least four-foot-high dirt embankments. These farm fields were everywhere. The friendlies in their position among the grape rows had decent cover due to the natural bullet blocking properties of giant thick mounds of dirt, but then again, so did insurgents who employed the exact same tactic. This wasn't entirely uncommon and would literally become a somewhat familiar version of the accounts of trench warfare.

Located sporadically among the grape rows were always a few grape huts. These were large, two-storied structures in the middle of the rows that the locals would use to house anything from equipment to crops, almost like a barn. The tops of the buildings were technically open, but were covered with interwoven wood and thatch grass roofing replete with holes. The grape huts themselves were made of mud like the qalats, and had multiple slatted holes in the sides looking much like an old castle to me. The problem with grape huts was that we could not see inside of them, and we were punished for shooting at them pretty much no matter the reasons. Here, our guys were taking fire from one of the grape huts.

"Wrath 52, this is Hulk 26! We're taking small arms fire and believe it's coming from the grape hut just west of our position!" They were currently hunkered down behind the safety of earthen grape rows, and we had begun to run exceedingly low on fuel. Unfortunately, we did not yet meet the criteria for an engagement, as no one would approve our close air support due to the possibility of potential collateral damage to civilians or their property.

Hulk 26 kept their attention on the grape hut cluster that had just lit them up, and our team of Kiowas begrudgingly had to depart for a quick refuel. In our absence, the seasoned enemy knew that this was their cue, and many insurgents started gathering in a village 90° off the stranded ground elements' side.

We rapidly received reports that the enemy were active on radios and cell phones, planning on attacking our guys who were stuck out in the open in the grape rows. The Americans would surely bend to Allah's will this day, and the enemy transmissions and their emboldened stance grew more dangerous by the minute as we yelled and cursed that we needed to get the fuel onboard and weapons reloaded as soon as possible. Our FARP turn at Pasab needed to seriously speed the hell up.

The overall situation was also tragic in itself, as the reason the U.S. forces were actually there in that area was to improve the road and some of the walls and structures. They were engineers, and had been dispatched to try and help rebuild an area destroyed by local conflicts and not even by any malicious acts on our part.

The situation was front and center indicative of the level of local appreciation our forces received for these types of efforts. It was a dirty secret that the media didn't discuss and higher ups didn't want our public or even serving military members to know. Our tax dollars and our lives were risked to "help the Afghan people," but they would kill us and destroy whatever infrastructure that we wasted our money on, regardless.

We returned from the FARP and I quickly checked in with Hulk 26.

"Wrath 52 back on station, 600rds of .50 cal and eight rockets, approximately two hours of playtime. What's your status, over?"

"Wrath 52, Hulk 26. It's getting pretty bad. One ANA is wounded and we're working up a 9-line MEDEVAC. No U.S. casualties yet, but some close calls. We are continually receiving effective small arms fire from a few different positions besides the grape hut. We haven't located the other insurgents yet. We also have military-aged males massing in the village to our north, over."

They were in a tough spot; covered at present, but unable to safely move. He told me of his concern with the group on the other side of the village and asked if I could give him more information. It didn't take long to get eyes on the ever larger-growing group. After a few passes, I was pissed off.

I knew that those gathering in the village were bad. As we conducted some fast and extremely low passes that would usually make a civilian think twice and go inside, these badasses stared hard right back at me and held their ground. Many wore bulky clothing, more than likely concealing weapons. In my experience, every mannerism and behavior that they were exhibiting didn't fit the norm.

"They're bad," I announced and explained how many, what I saw, and all the pertinent details of where they were and other tactical jargon. I was then asked my favorite thing by the engineer team: "Wrath 52, can you disperse the crowd in a non-lethal manner?" I heard the crackling fire of M4 rifles in the background as Hulk transmitted, no doubt drawing in on the insurgent position in some dense foliage nearby.

Hell yes. We can make that dream come true, I thought before replying more professionally. I told the right seater to get me going fast and low, quickly relaying my plan. This was going to be difficult. I pulled a red smoke grenade off the dash of the aircraft and pulled the pin. I held tightly to the grenade spoon so that I could time the grenade, and I outstretched my left arm along with a third of my body hanging out the left side of the helicopter. My rifle was ready in my lap, corded to my vest in case it fell, but also quickly available in case our plan went south.

Up ahead, I saw two tall trees about 30 meters before the group that was gathered in one of the village's tight alleys. I hurriedly informed the right seater of my revised plan, and he flew me fast as hell right towards the field-goal gap in the trees. The distance that the grenade would still have to travel forwards when I threw it had to be perfectly judged.

Right at that special moment, I screamed out the door "Goal post motherfuckers!" and chucked the grenade with all my might. It sailed forwards while I roughly fell back inside the helicopter as we banked away hard right and steeply ascended up into the air. All that I heard the Trail ship say was "Holy shit, Robo!"

When we circled back around, I was elated. I had put the grenade between the trees and right into the midst of the group, and like roaches, they were all scurrying in whatever direction that they could to get away. The Trail ship was laughing and then told me what happened once they caught their breath.

My grenade had gone screaming towards the group and one of them had to duck. The grenade hit the opposite wall of the alley, bounced momentarily up in the air, and landed right in the middle of them. They informed me I had basically almost killed a guy with a smoke grenade, as would surely have been the outcome had I hit him. That was my biggest failure of the day, I was told—it had missed his face since he ducked just in time!

The main goal was met. The insurgent forces were flustered and tamed, no longer talking so much trash on their radios and cell phones. This gave Hulk 26 an opportunity to move as the slightly rattled enemy tried to regroup. We flew low and aggressively over the grape huts and fields while Hulk elements beat feet back to the safety of their vehicles. The wounded ANA soldier was stable and was picked up by a MEDEVAC bird dispatched from nearby FOB Pasab. None of our U.S. forces were injured, and they finally arrived back at their base safely. The next day was a mirror image of the first; the engineers were out trying to help the people of that village, and were met with the exact same response.

*

Although we were tired, Dede and I organized family time to watch a movie. We got some pilots together and watched *Tropic Thunder*, a comedy of the making of a Vietnam war movie with a hilarious cast. We ate junk food, laughed, and I killed a fly and smashed it on a junior guy's shirt. It was good to take a little time off and have some normalcy. We agreed that we needed to do such things more often, just so we didn't all go crazy.

In the morning I went to the ALSE shop to get a few things done. For whatever reason, we were still receiving new lieutenants and warrants sent straight from flight school to Kandahar. No one told me, so they would show up needing a full issue of survival gear and we were already at the point of trying to scrap something together. It wasn't pretty, but we were making it happen. Apart from shaking my head at the whole thing, I also felt bad for the poor pilots being thrown into our mess like that.

February kicked off with increasing operational activity. I logged 13 hours in a two-day span, with the second being my longest flight thus far in the deployment at 6.7 hours. We had begun flying joint missions with the United Arab Emirates (UAE), who also had Apaches stationed at KAF. We were increasing joint missions with them, which added an entirely new dynamic to things. I was on the schedule for February 2nd, tasked with being on the second bird in a standard Kiowa team, unless the UAE Apache pilots showed up for the brief. In that event, the mission would then shift focus and we would get bumped from our slot so that the pairing would become a Scout/Attack Team. The reference for this pairing of one Kiowa and one Apache was officially known as a "Pink Team." I showed up and pre-flight checked my aircraft, did the paperwork, and went to the brief. About 10 minutes before the brief started, in walked two UAE Apache pilots, kicking us off the team for the day.

Under normal circumstances, that would have been the end of the day for me. We usually stayed around, however, as a stand-by crew in case the UAE Apache broke. This was not actually a phenomenon specific to the UAE Apaches alone, however. As I hung out with the maintenance pilot I would have flown with earlier, he was informed that he needed to conduct a maintenance test flight. The flight was going to take three and a half hours—the particular Kiowa in question needed some special attention, and I volunteered to help. I liked maintenance test flights, since it was always a great opportunity to learn and observe a few things that you didn't usually experience or see. I sat in the left seat like a sandbagged sponge, occasionally reading something from a special checklist and a sheet of paper. The maintenance test pilot was doing all of the real work; I would observe and take a free helicopter ride.

The MTP went out to the flight line to ready our flight, and I proceeded to the maintenance area to wait. While there, I talked to my commander who was reviewing his logbook for a separate flight shift. His team typically took off a few hours after my usual team I'd been assigned to in the past few months. As we stood and chatted, one of the senior U.S. Apache pilots entered our troop with a big grin on his face, telling my commander, "I have great news for you."

In the Army, this situation was a complete flip-flop from what this sort of happenstance would look like amidst some cubicles in an office building. In effect, "I have great news for you" could almost always be counted on to actually mean the complete opposite, like "prepare to be destroyed, have your plans crushed, and be completely pissed off. All in one delicious taco."

The U.S. Apache pilot did not fail to disappoint. He put his hand on my commander's shoulder and informed him that every single U.S. Apache in our task force fleet was officially broken. My commander had just lost the wingman for his own Pink Team, and there was no hope of getting another (at least for that day). The commander's eyes got wide and he asked a few questions while trying to soak it all in.

Our own Kiowa helicopters had been continually flying from KAF for over three years. Usually, they must be sent to a reset facility in the USA to be recertified after a maximum of two years of service, regardless of where they were stationed. Our Kiowas and many other aircraft out in deployment areas had received a "waiver of responsibility," if you will. Risk/Reward formulas came out in the dollars' favor, and there was only a limited amount of maintenance that we could conduct in KAF with some civilian contractor support. The neglect had really begun to show, but as tired as our birds were, they continued functioning as hard as they could for far longer than the Bell Helicopter company guaranteed that they would. The Apache helicopter was not as hearty, however, and in Afghanistan their systems seemed to get all sorts of messed up.

When the Apache pilot told our commander that although they had five Apaches available the previous evening but zero were available that morning, it really wasn't the largest shock any of us had ever thought we'd see. As I chuckled at our collective misfortune, the commander looked at me and said, "What are you doing today?"

I replied, "I guess I'm volunteering to fly on your team and will skip a maintenance flight."

The commander selected a pilot who was on a day off and had me place an urgent call to get their ass up to the troop ASAP. Luckily, I already had all of the paperwork and preflight stuff accomplished for the bird I'd originally been assigned before being replaced by the UAE Apache. After a few pencil changes and a signature or two, I was on the commander's team as his left seater. My commander was aggressive and I loved that about him, so I was totally happy to oblige. The original left seater he'd been assigned and the pilot that was called in occupied my original bird. Shifting around like that allowed his previous left seater to give a down and dirty of what was going on to the pilot coming in that had no clue about the day's operations.

The largest limiting factor for the day then became myself. I'd been required to show up to work many hours prior, which meant I would have to monitor my "duty day" constraints. If we reached a certain flight-hour-level of work in the day, it was Army law that we must be turned loose for rest. We could request an extension from our chain of command if we deemed it was necessary, but the approval for this got more and more complex as the overage grew. We knew right away that this was going to be an ass kicker for me, but I happily accepted the mission.

It was not long after take-off that I became busier than all hell. I was monitoring three of the five radios that we had on board at practically the same time while the commander managed the other two. Even though we would split up the particular communications responsibilities between both aircraft on the team, it was still necessary to tune in to all five, in some degree or another, in order to maintain situational awareness. My lap was full of gear and packets, and I was furiously flipping through maps and scribbling notes on my kneeboard. Hadji apparently liked the windy, crappy day outside enough to be inspired to start acting like an asshole.

Our team dove, turned, and buzzed mere feet over the ground. Rounds flew and frantic ground forces called for help and reinforcements. The four pilots in our team of two aircraft each worked in overdrive at our respective duties. An explosion and dust cloud appeared close below. More yelling, more rounds. We now had wounded. We dealt with more unnecessary casualties from Hadji's actions, and that subconscious knowledge was all getting to me a bit.

We cleared a few landing zones for Blackhawks. Soon, we needed to find and clear some pickup zones for MEDEVAC Blackhawks. I wanted to fucking kill everyone. Guys were in a bad spot, and we needed to get them out of there. I saw more red crosses zipping around the area than I'd ever like to see. The flight was much like my two back-to-back, six-plus hour flights that I'd had earlier in the week in the MEDEVAC aspect. The real war stuff was happening: I witnessed wounded and dying Americans and ANA being desperately worked on by their buddies before being transferred to medics trying to save their lives.

It was like Hadji had suddenly gotten new AKs with barrels that had rifling in them, or some new players who actually knew how to shoot had come into the area. Rumors were that even a new and reasonably skilled bomb maker was in town. The bad part was that we still hadn't even begun the official "fighting season," yet. A few rounds snapped a bit too close to my head, missing our aircraft, but the burst returned me from my angry mental sidetrack. A

MEDEVAC had also just taken a hail of fire, and we needed to get nasty about it.

Once there was finally a lull in the action, I started cracking up. The commander wasn't monitoring the FM frequency that I was on, so he looked at me quizzically. We had some ground guys who were in a pretty tough situation, and it made me laugh and respect the hell out of them when they relayed that their biggest concern or wish in the world was if we could please air-drop them some TGI Friday's burgers that evening from KAF while they fought. There are just some things in life that only a small percentage of people will ever understand, and for these guys, I got a glimpse of that profound mentality and wished like hell that I could drop them some burgers. I doubt that they got their wish that evening, but I hoped that they made it through the night unscathed.

We landed at sunset, with me utterly tired as hell and yawning uncontrollably. I ended up sitting in the troop for another hour and a half until a van came to take people back to the rooms. During the ride, I realized that all that I had eaten was an energy bar in nearly seven hours of flight. The hunger hit me hard, and I was low on rations in the room, so I unwillingly carried my ass to the chow hall for a late dinner as they were closing up. The personnel were visibly irritated that a dirty, stinky warrant officer had arrived looking for lukewarm scraps of whatever was left over while they were trying to call it a night. I was too tired to get sore about it. The recent flights coupled with the intense flight that day made my week seem like it had warped forward considerably. There was really no more remarkable feeling than to look back on an entire week and really, truly, ask yourself, "What the hell just happened?"

Up close and personal.

The northern border of the Registan Desert.
Put another way, its what a desert looks like when it suddenly ends.

Grape rows, along with tightly vegetated corridors (not pictured) give the enemy a lot of freedom to maneuver.

Ground guys respond to harassing fire in the dilapidated ruins of a village.

CHAPTER 22

My day off had come, and I vowed to not shave or put on a uniform. My plan was to hide and not even leave the room. I had just gotten plenty of food rations thanks to a plethora of care packages arriving from home, and it couldn't have been timed any better. I was so well set that I ended up giving a few things away to some very appreciative buddies who had received no packages from home, sadly ever. Despite wanting to do nothing all day, I'd have to study. A little birdy told me that we had a test coming up soon. Oh, how I could not wait until the day that I didn't have to sweat random tests filled with utter nonsense that I must remember. Some stuff I emphatically agreed and understood why we must keep fresh, such as critical emergency procedures. Those events required such swift action that everyone was doomed to death if only seconds passed without corrections being rapidly made. I knew that no matter what aviation job I pursued in the future, I would succumb to the same types of requirements for memorization and proficiency. In the Army's quest to remain the dumbest organization that it could be, we were additionally tested on an exorbitant amount of very irrelevant, very stupid shit such as anatomy of the eyeball, the ear, and certain other engineer-level aspects of how our gear and bodies operated.

At least I had my peace and quiet, though. It was a rainy, cool day outside. My mind still replayed the MEDEVAC kicking up dust to fetch the wounded. I thought about the medics in the back, how they would analyze the casualties and triage and treat the wounded. Smeared with blood, they worked desperately at giving someone their best chance of survival while being rushed to emergency surgery in a hospital. I shut the thought out of my mind and peeked out our little window in the room between the metal slats I'd mostly closed up. I doubted that anyone was flying, but almost everyone was up at the troop handling their additional duties or getting quizzed. I bet that whatever test being brewed up would be served nice and fresh that afternoon since there were so many idle targets up there and boredom equalled trouble. Just in case, I lounged in my room in solitude and prepared myself for such things, and otherwise tended to relax.

Although I was off of the flight schedule the following day, I had plenty of things to keep me busy out in the ALSE shop. The issues and failures that continued to arise from some of our crew members and their gear never ceased to amaze or impress.

Since all we had was jet noise, explosions, and the smell of poop from the poo pond, I quietly imagined the days when I would return home to Lindsey and Scout. The thought of sitting down and enjoying the idle time and nice weather outside at a cafe on Broughton Street in my favorite town in America (Savannah, at the time) was enough to banish the bad thoughts of the recent weeks. I promised Lindsey and my friends and family back home that, once back in the states, I was going to enjoy those first few months home like no one could imagine. I was going to swim in the ocean, even if it required a wetsuit. I'd enjoy the outdoors like never before, and would relish those usually overlooked sensory stimulations such as wind in the trees and birds chirping.

I felt so fortunate to have a loving and supportive wife. A wife. That thought alone was so new and wonderful, and it just so happened that she was a great friend. She continued to talk and be available whenever I needed her. She and the other wives of our troop had banded together to do whatever we needed done while away. I couldn't ever describe how vital of a component it is to have support back home while you're in a war zone.

*

Matt and I decided it was time to get back to a workout program. Despite the well-intentioned zeal that we started out with, our productive weight room day came at a high cost. I was damn sore! There were moments of pure hilarity in our room when one of us would reach for something, or worse, try to climb up into a top bunk. We sounded like some pitiful bastards as we cried out in anguish trying to lift something or attempt to bend a certain way.

After working in the ALSE shop all morning one day, I arrived and asked around our troop to see who hadn't gone to lunch yet. It was then, of course, that one of my buddies over in the schedule board area did a double-take at seeing my face, and curiously looked back at the schedule. He then asked me if I knew what day it was, and I replied, "Who knows, but by the looks of it I'll bet you're about to tell me something that I'm not going to like."

He didn't know whether to laugh at me or feel bad for me. I was then informed that I was on the "Gym Guard" schedule, with a shift that was set to begin at 2000 and end at 0800 the following morning. So, a 12-hour shift lasting all night, while I had erroneously been up working that whole morning and into the afternoon. I said a few choice words and then promptly found transport back to the other side of the airfield to get whatever sleep that I could. *Bus driver, gym guard, who knows what they'll dream up next,* I thought as I lay down.

The shenanigans in order to stay in good spirits began to increase. A few Kiowa pilots snuck into a Blackhawk company area, and casually walked over to a side table with a microwave. A lookout scanned around, and confirmed they were alone. One man reached into his pocket, and produced an impossible number of little yellow marshmallow Peeps. He quickly opened the microwave and stuffed them inside. They tried hard not to laugh out loud as the pilot jammed about 20 minutes onto the cook timer, then hit start. The men quickly escaped and we later heard that some asshole(s) had made a terrorist Peeps attack, setting a microwave on fire and destroying it.

*

I went in to work before lunch where it appeared that the world was ending and we needed all hands on deck. Our aircraft fleet was in a bad state of repair, so everyone had to contribute to maintenance, aircraft washes, test flights, and troubleshooting. I was also busy with ALSE shop memorandums to obtain things we really, really needed but couldn't afford. That's what I was told at least, but I knew that there had to be a secret pot of money set aside somewhere being jealously guarded. I could easily justify the purchases that I was trying to make and hoped that our crash survival gear would be a priority.

In the meantime, we needed flyable helicopters. Our "special case paperwork" that we had received said that our aircraft could conveniently stay deployed for an entire year, then could add in our units' duration of another year. This was far past their due date for major maintenance and inspections. The case was nonetheless blessed off so that the Army could save money, and the whole situation had unsurprisingly now bitten us in the ass. This wasn't exactly the type of scenario where I liked to be correct and say the words, "told you so."

The last flight that I was on had been difficult. It had been one of our longest missions yet, and time-wise, we logged my record flight time on the deployment. Once again, I was really growing tired of watching MORE of our guys get blown up and dealing with multiple MEDEVAC helicopters and ground vehicles hauling ass down to the nearest U.S.-controlled outpost to try and get help.

Normally, I would understand that this was war, and that's what happens. This would be most especially true if we took the fight back to the enemy and made them pay for what they had done. Meanwhile, we still struggled with clearance to engage those who tried or succeeded in doing our forces harm. The noose on our own aircrews regarding what we could and could not do continued to tighten. I really feared to what extent we were willing to go to allow the enemy such freedom to maneuver. Emboldened fighters could expertly take our people out while we sat and watched, unable to react due to orders stemming from cowardice and a desire to not upset any media or have the tiniest chance of injuring a civilian. Our safety was being compromised by leaders so that they could be protected from any career harm as best as possible.

The shifting of schedules would fortunately end for me once my next evening flight was over. I would then be moving back to a day shift again. I'd be happy once the flip-flop stuff was over. It was incredibly rough on the body and mind over time. I discovered that I'd also get the honor of driving the bus again in about a week. I couldn't believe that we had the whole bus schedule stuff in the first place where we took line pilots out of the regular schedules for flights and had them drive a bus. This was even more damning for those that really needed every hour of flight time that they could get.

We sat around in the troop, hearing the most recent sunny news. When we returned to the states, substantial intelligence confirmed our fears that we would barely ever fly. We would be so budget constrained that it would be impossible to remain proficient in the aircraft. The current estimate was that joe-pilot would receive around seven to 10 hours of flight time, not exaggerating, *every six months*. A pilot would live an existence rife with endless additional duties, random taskings, classes, and ultimately, PowerPoint presentations.

As I surveyed some of the newer guys, it seemed that every single one of them was secretly hatching some sort of scheme to move somewhere else, and even fly a different aircraft that may potentially be less affected. A few had talked to other services such as the Coast Guard, and others were putting in request packets to be selected to fly Army airplanes. The Army did not have many airplanes, and once that training was completed down at Fort Rucker, the pilot would incur an additional five-year contract.

When I was training to fly the Kiowa at Fort Rucker, I never dreamed that I would bear witness to the slow deterioration of the Cavalry and watch such a drastic clearing out of its people. The obsession with UAVs (a.k.a., "drones" in the media) would likely phase us out completely. This would seem like a great idea to everyone except for the immediately affected war fighters on the ground, who would no longer get the personalized support and one-on-one coverage that they so desperately wanted and needed. Unfortunately, the job of what was once called an Aeroscout seemed to be slowly and painfully dying.

Luckily for me, at least, I'd seen the writing on the wall and had set about devising a plan to escape whatever madness would later be in store after we returned home.

After midnight, I still sat at my desk, diligently writing and keeping myself awake. Matt walked in right as I pulled up an email from my niece, Emma. She had written me a very cute and funny message. Emma was five, and I enjoyed the email very much, as did Matt as I read it aloud. It was the little things like that which threatened to keep us human. It brightened up my evening from the thoughts and troubles we'd recently had, and I was able to hang on to that sweet message and sleep uncharacteristically well.

*

On the 15th, while I was out working in the ALSE shop, I noticed that I was having a hell of a time focusing or concentrating on anything at one time. My brain was moving off course in many directions, like a ship adrift in an ocean. As I struggled to figure out what was wrong with me, I was asked by one of the guys when the last time I had a day off was. It had been a while, so I had to look it up in our troop on our digital pilot tracker that's specifically designed for such things. Even when not flying, if one worked non-stop and stayed too engaged, they risked running into real life self made emergencies in the helicopter. They could also endanger the guys on the ground by not being on their A-Game. That's what the digital tracker had been developed to prevent as best as possible. Aside from keeping tabs on flying, it also would show when someone was in the caution zone and needed to take a break. I was officially in the caution zone, and couldn't believe that my situation had proved that the damn thing was actually accurate.

The schedule flip-flopping continued to suck, but I could manage. We departed under NVGs to escort a few Blackhawks that were dropping passengers off, and to provide cover for a convoy. Given the exceptionally cold and hazy weather, I was surprised that we were even able to pull it off. The conditions held out just enough for us to complete our escorts and get our own team back safely. The ground convoy guys that I talked to had no desire to be any part of it that evening. They were tired, run ragged, and ready to get back inside the wire and call it a night. Fortunately, Hadji took the night off as well.

I managed to dodge bad weather an additional time about two days later when I flew a little more than six hours, but this time with the task force commander (a.k.a., everyone's boss). I wasn't too happy to go on that flight initially because I'd been at odds with some of the policies, but tried hard to not show it and keep as professional as I could. The flight did not actually end up being as bad as I was thinking that it would be. It was straightforward and moved along quickly because we stayed busy. The wind was terrible, however, and the clouds kept threatening to come down and swallow us up. I ended up taking the controls to give him a break for a while and it was a serious battle to refuel and hover around on the ground. We were literally operating right on the razor-edge margins of the aircraft capabilities at many points. I was happy that under the boss' watchful eye of scrutiny, I could control the aircraft like a seasoned vet and not encounter any issues or incidents. He expected me to over-torque the aircraft on takeoff since the conditions were so bad, but I held my own and told the Kiowa to just work with me so we both didn't look like idiots. The bird did her job, and I did mine, so we got out of the landing area without a sound of warning.

The weather patterns continued to affect the locals like that of zoo animals. They would go into a state of hibernation on cold and windy days, which was not so surprising since no one wanted to do much on either side. We still found some work to do, and luckily, none of our forces were blown up that day under our watch. The same couldn't be said for a local Afghan who was probably just in the wrong place at the wrong time. Getting in the report, it sounded to me like an old Russian landmine. Those things were still peppered across the earth everywhere. I really wondered what the Afghans would end up doing once all the outside influences were gone and they'd finally be left to fend for themselves. I'd rather us spend the money in our own country and our own problems, so I was glad that seemed to finally be the running consensus with the rest of our populace. At least I hoped that was really the case.

Team Brown set out on a self-led mission to get rid of some of our troop's discards and essentially trash. They snooped around Mustang Ramp, searching for a dump site when one of them suddenly got excited.

"Bro! There's a container hidden back here!" One of them called out. Among a bunch of empty, dusty shipping containers one sat with the shipping seals and lock still on. It was obvious it had been forgotten for a very long time. "I say we get it opened and we get first dibs on the treasure!" The others agreed, and almost giddy, they raced off to find a property book officer. Team Brown had gone global; the one they located was on their side, so permission for cracking into the container was quickly granted. They stood in anticipation as the bolt cutters struggled and the lock finally gave way, and the creaking old doors were thrust open.

"Dude! Holy shit!" They all cheered and high-fived. Inside amongst various pieces of equipment was a large case full of brand new M9 Beretta handguns, and tons of laptops. The original owners were unable to be found, so Team Brown's treasure hunt resulted in solving our unit handgun shortages while the rest of the equipment was divided amongst units in need. Their exploits never ceased to amaze me.

CHAPTER 23

By February 19th, I had gotten very busy, very quickly. We completed a six-hour flight, debriefed, and then learned that my schedule once again changed and I needed to go to bed immediately. My bus was at 0330 and I would need to fall asleep as soon as possible. Back and forth, back and forth.

While the flying had picked back up, we were accepting American flags to take out on missions for people. A soldier could drop a flag off to us, and we would in turn take it out on a mission so that it could get seasoned by a bit of war. Afterward, we'd read the note in the box about who it was from, to, or what message they had for us. We'd print a certificate with the day that it flew and with which pilots, and then put it back in the stack for pickup. We knew that a lot of people appreciated this unofficial volunteer service that we provided, and it was nice to make our comrades smile.

On the 20th, I was not prepared for the blitz that would come. I didn't have time to do anything but sleep or be at the troop engaged in flying or preparing to fly. The first day that I flew was normal, and was in fact an uncharacteristically nice flight. There was little going on, weather was rolling in and the wind was nippy which caused Hadji to predictably not feel like playing too much. The scenery wasn't too bad, and what we thought was going to be a crazy day ended up being fun. In rare form that reminded me of my first year up near Bagram, we were actually given decent free-rein to go on our own and properly execute our job of general reconnaissance and finding work to do.

Toward the end of the flight, we supported a small group of guys out in some grape rows a few kilometers from their base. We were observing things and calling out and distracting any individuals they wanted us to. I got to disperse a crowd that was just a little too curious by throwing out some smoke, and they got the hint that they should go about their business. Luckily, they looked to be random village neighbors and farmers who went casually and peacefully back to ignoring all of us.

We were asked before we left if we'd do a morale boosting fly-by, and we happily obliged. The ground guys waved and cheered as we buzzed by a few of their positions. I'd created another small morale kit in a small plastic tube, hoping that the magazines and odds and ends crammed inside may be useful to someone. As we were departing, I did one final low pass and chucked the package out towards the patrol heading back to their base. Unfortunately as I threw it, I saw that the guys were moving slowly and cautiously. My package landed around 50 meters short of them, and not along their intended path. It was then that I saw the lead guy carefully operating a mine sweeper. A few looked at the package, then back at me. One man's face could have been mistaken for sadness.

The poor guys were stuck moving at a snail's pace through grape rows on foot back to their base while following a man with a minesweeper. Their biggest mission of the day was to not get their legs blown off or killed by a mine or IED. I felt bad for assuming that one of them could stray from their path to get my dumb package. After landing, I couldn't shake my concern for them, but luckily, I could finally confirm that they'd safely returned to the confines of their small outpost. Usually we never knew the fate of those we supported, but it was nice to occasionally find out that they were safe and had no casualties. There were other times that I regretted asking, as my heart was ripped out and felt sick to my stomach to learn of casualties once we'd left our position of watching over them. No matter what was happening in our own units and lives, we never let it affect us to where we'd allow the ground units to suffer for it. We all continued to feel a very intense responsibility and drive to protect them.

When I arrived back to KAF after about six hours in the air, the blades were still spinning slowly down when my phone rang. I was asked if I was all set and knew everything that I needed to know for the next day. The caller was cryptic, but we were on unsecured local cell phones, after all.

"I'm running the shutdown checklist, and the blades are still turning. No, I have not been briefed and don't know what the hell you're talking about," I replied simply. The caller sighed, a bit irritated, but we both understood that it wasn't directed at me.

"You used to be in Fox Troop, and you guys worked with many ODA teams outside of your normal AO, right?" Asked the caller who had yet to identify himself.

"Yes, and I miss that shit a lot," I replied.

I had absolutely no idea that any special mission was set to begin soon, or that I was even on the flight schedule the next day. As it turns out, I was involved. They required me to immediately go inside and put my things away and report for a briefing at the squadron. I was also required to leave immediately following that briefing, go back to the room, and sleep since I would only get maybe six hours in the room, if I was lucky.

*

It was game time. I woke up, quickly got ready, and then met with my buddy CW2 Brian Fullen. Brian was a lean man of about five and a half feet tall, with a face that appeared much younger than his true age. He had previously served in analysis and counter intelligence, so his background was a great asset for our troop. As equally brilliant as he was hilarious, Brian and I had attended WOCS together and subsequently hung out a lot, both during and after flight school. We functioned great together as a crew, and I was very glad to find that we would be flying together on the upcoming high stakes mission. Brian put a dip of tobacco in his lip, smiled at me, and asked, "You ready to go do some secret squirrel support shit?" I nodded and grinned back, passing him a pair of NVGs.

"Totally ready, dude. I think this is gonna be awesome," I replied.

We linked up with the other crew from our team and made our way into the squadron briefing room. Right as we sat down and pulled out our respective notepads, the briefer and intelligence guys began to recap the mission and what to expect.

"Good morning, gentlemen. As you know from yesterday's pre-brief, today, the Afghans will be conducting one of their first ever independent Air Assaults. ANA forces will be inserted via three Mi-17 Afghan military helicopters in key locations just outside the village of Girdahzi. Despite our best efforts, we strongly believe and suspect that the enemy will know of the operation and will have forces in the area to disrupt and attack the ANA in the course of this mission. Although this is an Afghan planned and led operation, U.S. and other select coalition forces will be nearby in order to support and assist as necessary. Your team will be instrumental in providing overwatch and surveillance to ensure that no enemy forces are successful in their efforts to move against the ANA or our supporting personnel. An ODA team will be situated atop a small plateau in over watch of the village and intended LZs."

A series of grids, descriptions, callsigns, and locations were read aloud for us to each copy down and reference against a mission packet that was prepared and handed over to both of our crews. The mission briefer allowed us a few moments to get our bearings and talk the information over amongst ourselves before turning the floor over to an intelligence briefer.

"Gentlemen, as you know, this area is on the fringes of our AO and it is a hotbed of insurgent activity. This Air Assault is being conducted against quite literally where many enemy fighters live. It is our understanding that neighboring villages and structures near Girdahzi are filled with, at the very least, Taliban sympathizers, and even probably members of other terrorist cells like Al Qaeda. The enemy in this area are equipped with AK-47s, PKMs, and RPGs. We do not anticipate a heavy weapons or high surface to air missile threat, but it cannot be ruled out, either. The most difficult factor in this mission has been keeping the ANA in the dark about the details until the last moment. We hope that enemy operatives within the ANA ranks cannot give enough specifics or notice to insurgent groups in time to impact the outcome."

Our AMC nodded and without looking up asked as he wrote, "Expected enemy presence?" The intel man shuffled a bit at his podium, and then answered truthfully, "We believe that this whole area is essentially infested with an unknown number of fighters. Expect any military-aged male, weapon in hand or not, could be a potential hostile. They have a solid network of communications in the area, and the second any early warning spotter sees those ANA helicopters, you can bet that a lot of 'farmers' will stop farming and take up arms. It's also possible that the Air Assault could even be already compromised, and insurgents may be waiting."

"Well then, isn't that pleasant?" I remarked as I wrote. The others smirked. Lucky us. The remainder of our questions were answered and our tactical maneuvering plans were ironed out. We would act as a distraction and attempt to lead fighters away from the village and the LZs. After the briefing, we walked out to our aircraft and prepared to head out.

Brian and I discussed our plan, and I had agreed earlier to fly in the left seat. We would be the Lead helicopter, and I would be busy as hell on the radios and conducting recon. As we strapped into our Kiowa, I checked my gear a little more carefully than usual. I moved my magazines around and placed one in my rifle that was a mix of half regular rounds, and half tracers. If I needed to use my rifle in a hurry, I wanted to quickly walk my rounds onto my intended target with that initial magazine.

"You ready, brother?" asked Brian after we finished our preliminary checklists.

"Hell yeah, dude, let's do this," I responded, followed by sticking my head out the door and shouting, "Clear!"

The engine came to life and the low rumble of the turbine light off from the explosion of jet fuel gave me a rush. It never got old. Our blades turned hard and fast, and before I knew it, we were finishing loading ammo aboard and then proceeding to the north of KAF. It wasn't a short distance to our objective, so we talked everything over one more time on our team internal frequency.

The further we ventured, the more we could recognize that there was less and less of a security presence—U.S., or otherwise. We passed the remains of what used to be U.S.-controlled areas, which were now either occupied by

Afghan forces, or in other cases, lay in plain ruins. A small U.S. outpost I had once supported sat deserted, a pile of smoldering trash let up light plumes of smoke in the center courtyard and the doors to any remaining plywood structures were ripped open with debris and broken furniture scattered about. We continued forward. The area became more and more unsettling, and a familiar feeling came back to me.

This was becoming deep recon, and we were actually doing our real jobs again for once. On my previous deployment, we encountered many areas like that which I was now traversing, and had gone into even far more desolate areas. The difference between then and my present situation was that some of the areas last time had reports of suspected enemy believed to be around. The area I was in on our mission had absolutely *confirmed* enemy around. They were also very experienced and seasoned fighters, not just random jihadis from foreign lands. We were preparing to kick in the doors to their actual fucking houses.

"Okay guys, we're approaching the first grid. The ODA team should be there already. I'm gonna get the MMS on it and see who's around." I told Trail. I scanned and sure enough, there was my expected gaggle of bearded ones. A few lay on the rocks with large, scoped rifles from light cover overlooking Girdahzi. To my initial surprise, the remaining personnel in the position sat or stood in the open. They had the high ground, and they didn't seem very concerned who may see them. I figured perhaps they were overt like we were, ensuring focus remained more on them than what was about to happen. An older man in civilian clothes, complete with a windbreaker, baseball cap, and dark sunglasses paced among the men while talking on a satellite phone. I nudged Brian and pointed to my screen showing the man. "Must be his show," I remarked and Brian agreed. "Yeah, whatever agency he's from probably really wants this to go well."

Like an unusually well-oiled machine, we watched three Russian-built, Afghan military Mi-17s approach, suddenly dipping down low and fast in unison over the terrain towards their LZ. We raced from our position to the predetermined coverage point and triple checked that the LZ appeared clear.

The helicopters moved very quickly and settled into position on the ground. The doors flung open and a less impressive mass of ANA poured from the helicopters and raced towards the village, a few of them literally tripping over themselves.

As the first two Mi-17s lifted off the earth, the third was still unloading its people and had to pause the takeoff due to the giant dust cloud kicked up from the rotor wash of the other two.

"I think they just took a few rounds! That last bird is yelling on the net that they're taking fire," Trail called out. I watched as the bird shimmied and lurched up and forwards just as the last ANA soldier tumbled out and into the dirt. Luckily, if they were hit, the rounds seemed to have only hit non critical parts, and the helicopters raced away from the area. "Where did the fire come from?" I asked quickly, scanning with my MMS and then in frustration ditched it in favor of my quicker to use binoculars.

"Not sure," replied Trail. "No one is talking about any more shooting, so it seems it was just a quick, yet well-placed burst of opportunity." It was also just as likely that a single round hadn't even been fired.

The ANA continued to race on foot into the small surprised village, stopping people in the road and moving house to house. Soon, squirters began leaking out of the perimeter, with the ANA unable to effectively stop them all. I watched as a few men placed calls and made it to outlying structures and even a few vehicles. I casually looked low and left below our aircraft, and then quickly did a double take.

"Dude, shit. There's a bunch of guys materializing in that field out my left door," I called out. Trail responded, "Whoa, that's a lot of armed guys pretending to farm." We widened our orbits to get more comfortably outside their weapons range. I peered through my binoculars and watched the men for a few minutes. Soon, I could figure out who was generally in charge, and who their communications guy looked to be. The well-armed farmers below were a calm and disciplined force growing in size and organization. I called the ODA team atop their plateau. "Raven 11, Wrath 56, do you have eyes on this group in the field approximately one kilometer to your east? We're just flying back over them now." I waited, watching one man struggle to unsuccessfully conceal a large machine gun. *Why do you dumb bastards even try to be sneaky?* I thought.

"Wrath, we have eyes on that group. A few more appear to be descending down the hill to join them. Request you keep an eye on the group and deter them from moving against the village or the ANA, over." I looked at the gently sloping terrain, a lush green tract of terraced farm fields that increased in a graceful ascent towards the top of a saddle between rocky topped ridgelines. More men with weapons casually walked down the field towards the edge where it met a small valley bowl below. A light wind blew the waist-high grass, cannabis, and other crops gently as the men moved into their positions, seemingly undeterred by our presence. They spoke amongst themselves while a few stared intently at us, likely being the ones charged with engaging us if they were ordered to. A slender, notably unarmed man with a flat wool hat, tan weathered skin, and long beard spoke on a cellphone, looking between our helicopters and the besieged Girdahzi village. Less than 100 meters in front of him lay a small footpath leading right to the village. "Raven 11, Wrath 56. It looks like they're about done reinforcing their numbers, and this guy on the cell phone seems to be weighing out the pros and cons of moving into the village with so many of us watching, over." Raven responded, "Copy. Wait one."

The unarmed man hung up his cell phone, but kept it in his hand. A fighter near him passed either a cigarette or most probably a joint to his buddy. They were waiting, and we were waiting, so a tactical game of chess began. A similar-looking fighter to the man with the phone nonchalantly approached and started talking with him while the others around them decided to at least pretend to farm. The second man was slightly taller, and he was armed with an AK, which he had slung. Something about the man had the little voice in my head telling me that he was important. Once again, I ditched the MMS for the binoculars.

"Brian, I need to get low and close to the edge of that field. I wanna get one good look and also a few bursts of pictures with the camera." Brian's eyebrows went up.

"You mean the field with a ton of openly armed bad guys that are looking for a reason to fight?" I smiled.

"Precisely, my friend." Brian's face soured a bit, conflicted as to whether this was a smart thing to do or not in the risk/reward arena. "Just one pass, man, that's all I need." I persisted. Brian and I trusted each other, so he muttered quietly, "God damnit…" and called up Trail to let them know what we were about to do, and why.

In our next orbit, we began a steep descent and picked up speed. Brian wasn't going to make it easy for them to suddenly engage us, so I understood and accepted the erratic altitude, speed, and directional shifts. We were set up to pass by close with the field out my left door, so I could still get what I wanted. The other men in the field had all squared off and were facing us, at least 15 fighters having temporarily abandoned their farming ruse were now giving us their full attention. In a mild surprise, the two men that I was most concerned with froze in time outside my left door. I took several shots with the camera in my lap with my left hand and held tight to my M4 rifle. The two men glared at me. The stoppage of time afforded me a close glimpse at their faces, and to momentarily peer into each of their eyes. They were dark, intense, and foreboding. I could feel their hatred pierce into me. My veins tingled with the rush of hot blood while my body momentarily shuddered from my own primal and visceral flood of adrenaline and hate. The man with the AK held it low and tight, wise enough not to raise it.

Our aircraft rapidly turned and ascended. I placed my rifle back on the dash and immediately began flipping through the digital photos I'd just taken. I was surprised that several had turned out and were usable, and I began counting the fighters and attempting to identify their weapons. The taller of the two men I'd locked eyes with held an AK that was decorated and adorned with artistic style. My instincts were correct: He looked important.

"Well," I finally said, breaking our tense silence, "that went surprisingly well. The two I'm most interested in are pretty disciplined. I think that taller guy is in charge of the group." I zoomed in on the camera screen and tilted it close to Brian's face so that he could see it. Brian nodded in agreement, then dryly remarked, "He looks like a fuckin' pirate." I laughed and called Trail, "You guys aren't gonna believe it, but the guys below are being led by Blackbeard's first mate." Trail responded, "Argh! Copy that."

As I watched the group of fighters pretending to farm below in our MMS, I saw all of their heads suddenly turn towards Girdahzi. I wasn't sure if I heard a thud, or if I imagined it. Our radio suddenly came to life.

"Wrath 56, Raven 11, ANA are calling troops in contact, northeast corner of the village!" Both of our aircraft immediately turned toward the village. Right as I began slewing my MMS towards the vicinity grid for the TIC, I watched the fighters below grouping towards the man with the cell phone as they looked towards their village. We told Raven we'd be overhead of the ANA in less than a minute, and Raven informed us that they'd closely monitor the group of concern in the field. For the time being, our low fly-by had given the enemy group enough doubt to force a tactical pause and give their plans more thought before attacking.

We began aggressive flight maneuvers over Girdahzi. The ANA below darted around in the street and civilians ran for cover. An ANA soldier with a PKM machine gun fired wildly at a low wall near a dilapidated qalat, kicking mud and dirt clouds up everywhere. We circled the scene, and I saw nothing on the other side of the wall being decimated by the PKM. "Trail, do you see-" I began, and then cut myself short as a burst of fire peppered the road and walls around a large group of ANA who dove every which way. Most jumped back up and sprayed AK rounds in a loose general direction from where they must've heard the firing originate. The ANA had become disorganized and chaotic, firing wildly at an unseen foe. One ANA soldier fell to a knee, and I couldn't tell if he was hit. I resumed, this time calling to Raven, "I cannot tell where that shit is coming from! Are they talking to your terp? Do we have any info?!"

It was a frustrating game of telephone, with information going from an Afghan commander, through his radio man, to the interpreter, who relayed the info to Raven, who then passed it along to us, where our team then tried to dissect the reports. If we didn't get a handle on it soon, our next step would be a MEDEVAC mission. A wall spit out mud and dirt as an ANA soldier ducked, just being missed by inches from eating the string of rounds aimed at him. We dove in a mock engagement, popping our blades to distract whatever hidden enemy were so successfully engaging the ANA. It temporarily seemed to work, and ANA sprung up and ran around buildings and corners for more effective cover. One ANA soldier stumbled backwards and fell on his ass, sitting in the road blinking hard and frozen in momentary shock. He raised his AK over his head and held it sideways, swinging it left to right while letting a long burst of unaimed automatic fire fly. He then managed to get up and run the way his comrades had gone.

The skirmish ended, and to our knowledge, no ANA were seriously injured. We nearly gave up trying to figure out the status of the insurgents in town after receiving confused and incomplete reports. Finally, all we saw were ANA casually walking around the village, smoking and talking with locals as if nothing had happened. A few prisoners were loaded onto some ANA vehicles that had shown up in an un-briefed convoy. The Mi-17 helicopters never returned, and Raven called us up to thank us and inform us that the mission was successful. The fighters in the farm field had wisely been instructed to stand down, and a few even remained to actually farm while the remainder had dispersed with most heading back over the ridgeline and out of sight. We were asked to tail a small white van for a bit that potentially held some of the men, but nothing came of it as it drove far away into the distance and out of our AO.

With the mission deemed complete, we refueled at a remote FARP and had a little time remaining to explore. I took a few pictures of the unique area with its sizable lake and decent sized mountains. It was a refreshing change of scenery from our normal brown nothingness around KAF. We finally reached our fill of poking the hornet's nest for the day and moved back into more known and controlled terrain. After sorting out some confusion with our TOC, we returned to KAF and shut down for the day. I got back to the room late once again, tired as hell and knowing that I'd have to get back up and do it all again in the morning. The Air Assault was only the first component in a much larger operation, and for the next few days our same team covered the ODA team and ANA while more areas of interest were searched and investigated. The operational impact on the enemy was reported as exceeding our best expectations. In the end, it was an interesting experience overall, and I was glad that I had been chosen to be a part of it. There wasn't much to be proud of in my mind while we were in Kandahar, but getting selected for something important was a needed morale booster for me. I had liked the team, and the change of pace and style of mission was certainly a bonus since I'd never done anything exactly like it before.

Ford Ranger with Soviet-made DShk machine gun, Afghan National Army (ANA).

The maze that is your average Afghan village.

Suspect military aged males take a tea break. As long as you smile and pretend not to be bad, maybe the Americans will fall for it.

An Afghan policeman pulling security becomes exhausted from texting and sleeps on his AK-47 pillow.

CHAPTER 24

"If it wasn't for taking a break and drinking this tea in our room,
I would probably lose my shit." -CW3 Matt Vaccaro

S oon after the ANA mission, it was once again weather day. We sat in our
troop area shooting the breeze, also killing flies... lots of them. We had
recently been invaded by black flies; they were all over the area. I must've killed
nearly 20 on that day alone, in addition to every other pilot in the troop doing
the same. We hung crazy amounts of fly paper from the ceiling, creating a vast
swath of fly paper stalactites that caught the little bastards as they streaked
across high above. The ceiling seemed to buzz and wriggle with their constant
sound and activity.

Rumors about what would become of us continued to swirl around and mess
with our heads by late February. Matt said it best regarding our return home:
"Expect September, plan for December, appreciate August or earlier." That's
really all that we knew. At least, by the end of the month, we were told that an
official briefing would be held so that everyone could finally know the realities
about what units were being affected, if at all, by the Afghanistan withdrawal
plans. The sequester business may also have something to do with it, many of
us guessed. We continued to feel the tightening of our budget in anticipation of
a drawback in funds, even though it hadn't officially happened yet. Pet projects
of Generals at the top were being fought over for funds, so sustainment of
those fighting on the ground would be the first area where corners were cut.

I understood it as corruption at the top in the U.S. Department of Defense in the worst way, and at the expense of front-line units still fighting a war—all so lofty contracts could be held.

Since I had recently admitted my desire to separate from the Army upon completion of my contract, I was beginning to experience some strange consequences as a result. When someone admits their intent to get out and pursue other ventures, regardless if it's in the spirit of doing what's best for their family and situation, the act is invariably misconstrued as a defiant stance of "I don't give a damn anymore." I had been trying to counterbalance this by letting the leadership know that they shouldn't discount me yet, as I was still fighting in Afghanistan with them and would remain willing to fight until we returned home. Luckily, I'd been in the squadron for a while, and I'd been making some headway on ensuring that everyone who'd listen understood that I was not mentally checking out while still deployed.

After convincing those I cared most about that I was still in the fight with them, I knew that I would still need a plan for my exit. I finally got clarification from our personnel office about when my Additional Duty Service Obligation (ADSO) of six years officially began and when it officially ended. To my understanding, I needed to begin my official notification paperwork at 18 months to go since everything in the military moves so slowly. With an end goal in sight, Matt and I spoke of our respective exit strategies outside the room along with several other pilots researching their own paths out.

*

The first week of March marked a serious spike in both temperature and activity, and the severity of the temperature shift was truly impressive. The weather in KAF was so strange; occurrences of freak dust storms or foggy thunderstorms when everything appeared to be normal not long before were commonplace. I did not expect however to be wearing a jacket one day and literally sweating the next. It was only March 7th, and I hoped that the scorching heat wouldn't be entirely permanent. What was permanent, however, was how I became the accidental hero of the troop in regards to our van that day.

While shuttling some folks to the flight line, I attempted to avoid a literal quicksand pit as I was forced to move dangerously close. I gave the throttle a quick boost and my right tire began to catch the loose gravel. Another boost of the throttle and the van fishtailed, which I over-corrected with a fast counter-wheel turn.

My front left tire hit the corner of a concrete barrier head on, launching the van with a sickening crack. I managed to continue forward and gassed it past the quicksand, knowing that I was dragging some part of our van along the way. After a tire change, I managed to limp it out to the flight line and turned the keys over to the next driver. Our commander couldn't believe that I wrecked the thing, smirking and shaking his head as we explained what had happened. The impending death of our van had already been clear, and everyone joked that I had only tried to put it out of its misery.

A plan for a replacement vehicle was hatched, and little did I know, Team Brown was given an opportunity to work their magic behind the scenes. Our supply representative on Team Brown had made an unusual discovery: Peaches could be used as a currency. He was able to secure many, many five-pound cans of peaches and secretly stored them. I did not realize that my killing of the van was only part of the story, as Team Brown had been actively trying to kill the damn thing for weeks. It was how the condition had deteriorated, but the thing had stubbornly stayed alive. Team Brown had been taking clandestine operations with our van in order to drive it at max speed and then shift it into reverse to destroy the transmission. They tried jumping the thing like *Dukes of Hazzard* over shit. Although battered and bruised, the van only succumbed to its injuries after I had bent a rim right off the axle.

"Operation Peaches" could now commence. A Team Brown representative went over to the Al-Hadi local van mechanics on Kandahar and attempted to make the deal in the standard way. Al-Hadi mechanics weren't too keen, that much he expected. Team Brown sweetened the pot. Five large cans of peaches later, they had reached a deal. Shortly thereafter, a suspiciously new van appeared on Kandahar. It was sanitized, and plates and paperwork were transferred over. As much as the ones in charge hated to admit it, my act of destroying our van provided us with a better model. One man on Team Brown drove it with pride, even decorating the interior with glow sticks and playing loud techno music as he broke the Kandahar speed limit everywhere he drove.

Team Brown were the real heroes behind the scenes meeting our troop needs. They were instrumental in fixing our computer situation as well. After several visits to a supply point known as the Free Yard on Kandahar, one of the troopers isolated a contractor that had a problem that he may be able to help with. This contractor desperately needed a hat because his head was burning to a crisp in the Afghan sun. Team Brown had thankfully secured a large box of boonie hats to also use as trade currency in addition to the peaches. A few handshakes and two hats later, our troop suddenly had three new Dell computer monitors that we desperately needed.

Through a few more contacts, unimaginably one of our Team Brown members became the only person on KAF that was able to obtain tropical fruit on a regular basis. These included pineapples and papayas, which gave even more bargaining power. Most noteworthy outside of our own Charlie Troop benefits to having Team Brown in our corner was that they were with us, and not against us.

A secret war was being waged on KAF via water balloons, thanks to them. Team Brown obtained a rather impressively large water balloon sling-shot, which was used on various occasions to conduct drive-bys on other NATO partner forces. Their actions prompted a water balloon retaliation by the British soldiers. In an escalation, a second long range water balloon launcher was obtained. Once the war with the British resulted in the United States winning, Team Brown focused inward. Indirect fires amongst our own forces began, and Team Brown, in addition with their "favorite guest gringo," held nightly mock battles utilizing the launchers. One evening, while coordinated balloon fire exercises were being conducted, the Afghan Coffee Shop on the south side of the RLBs was hit. The patrons thought they were taking actual indirect fire from the noise of at least three hits to the roof, and they subsequently emptied from the coffee shop and ran to the bunkers for cover. Team Brown couldn't have ever been more amused or proud.

*

A lot of our guys had taken to growing mustaches and smoking cigars. We were beginning the month of "Mustache March," and usually, soldiers would grow a mustache in an attempt to boost morale and give a little jab to leaders who hated to see mustaches on their soldiers. My mustache was hideous, which was the point of the competition; who could grow the worst one? No matter what, I couldn't shave it until the honorable mustache picture was taken at the end of March.

I found myself back on the flight schedule for more Pink Team missions. We flew high and close to each other while transitioning over a desolate area. I looked over to the Apache flying right alongside us and I began to laugh. Brian asked me what was so funny, so I handed him a pair of binoculars and told him I would take control of the aircraft for a minute. He relinquished the controls and took the binoculars. He pulled the binos up to his face and said, "Alright, what am I looking for?"

I pointed to our wingman and said, "Look at that cockpit. Tell me what looks crazy." He nodded and began to peer through the binoculars. After a few seconds, I saw his shoulders start to bounce up and down, and his laughter grew more and more. Brian keyed the radio on our team internal frequency and asked, "Hey dude, what size is your helmet? Your noggin is enormous!" We all started laughing, and the guy in the front seat of the Apache flipped us off. It was all in good fun, so I moved closer, told them to smile, and took a picture. He had the biggest flight helmet I had or still have ever seen, and we likened him to "Lord Helmet" from the movie *Spaceballs*.

Myself and several other pilots ate in the chow hall late in the afternoon, and we suddenly heard the tell-tale "whoosh-whoosh-whoosh!" and whistle of incoming rockets. The sound to impact ratio was only a few seconds, and usually didn't leave much time to react. The earth shook as we all bowed our heads and cringed. One of the rockets had landed very close. Filth and dust fell slightly from the ceiling in a silent, yet packed chow hall. Then, the resulting reaction of the entire chow hall made us start laughing our asses off.

The migrant workers and civilians literally dove under the tables around us.

Soldiers followed suit shortly, and the next thing I knew everyone in the entire chow hall was under tables as the sirens for the attack rang out. We five pilots sat in our seats cracking up in shocked wonder from the whole scene.

Someone yelled at us to take cover, breaking the silence in the chow hall. We laughed even harder and struggled to catch our breath, while another of our pilots jeered at the man.

"It's already over, dumbass! Don't yell at us; why don't you get off the floor instead and finish your food!" A little while later, a senior officer came over and had strong words for us, but we held our ground and had a solid case, so he finally gave up and walked away. We weren't trying to be tough guys; the fact was we hadn't gotten killed, the attack was over, and we had somewhere to be, so we didn't have time to hide under furniture. It was pretty cut and dry to us.

On March 9th, I flew with our task force commander again, along with an Apache as our wingman. The Pink Team made sense in certain tactical situations, and in fact given where and how we were operating it probably had made more sense than a Kiowa-Kiowa team, anyway. Despite having operational experience in the past conducting business like this, it was still strange sometimes. Both the Scout and Attack communities had their own little idiosyncrasies, and it could take some getting used to working with each other in such a manner as a two-aircraft team. They did things one way and had their reasoning, and we had our own ways. As long as we briefed an agreeable compromise before we went out to fly and ensured that both aircraft were on the same page, no serious issues were really ever encountered, thankfully.

I was ever-increasingly ready to be done overseas. My goal was to just protect our guys on the ground and in our teams until we were finally allowed to end the madness and return home. There was no doubt that I wasn't the only one who would like to leave Afghanistan; it was more accurate to say almost everyone would drop everything they were doing and leave in a heartbeat if they could. The realization that we were going to be receiving a vast cut in budget and flying hours once we returned home was chipping away at those banking on being able to add flight time and experience to their log books. To get out of the Army and still be able to find a helicopter flying job, the civilian companies were only hiring those pilots with over 1,500 hours of flight experience. The average new guy in our squadron at the time had maybe 350 combined hours of training back home, and only roughly 50-80 hours of combat. Our line pilots were flying very little, with our squadron and troop opting instead to bend over backwards and give our mission time to staff officers and other non-troop aviators.

With no additional war on the horizon and a vast cut back in training, I had no clue how any of our guys would ever rack up the additional hours required to meet the hiring minimum demands of helicopter flying jobs outside of the Army. Most would face the tough choice to stay in for their total 20 years and try, or get out of the Army and do another job unrelated to aviation.

There had been a lot of people talking more about home recently. I knew that I would be much more excited when I returned home this time than I was last time, despite the duration of my current deployment being three months shorter than before. I felt that the two-week break for leave during deployment being taken away would have a lot to do with it, but I was also so happy at what all I had to look forward to. I could not wait to sit in the backyard with Lindsey and play fetch with our dog. I wanted to grill out and have a beer, and use the smoker more often. I also wanted to go hunting again so badly; I had a few magazines that were sent to me and I knew that I probably shouldn't look at them anymore. It made me realize how much more I wanted to be back out in the woods and enjoying myself. For whatever reason, we had the busiest training schedule in our unit's history the year before the deployment, so I never had the time to get out and enjoy what I wanted to. Lindsey and I traveled, but I also wished that we could do so much more. I kept reminding myself, all in due time. War first, then back home to reclaim freedom and live out the rest of my life in peace, as Lindsey and I saw fit.

CHAPTER 25

The second week of March began, and our task force's spiral effect continued downward and out of control. The past week had been very, very difficult on us. First, the Afghan president appeared on the news and (shockingly) accused the U.S. of working with insurgents and the Taliban to destabilize the country in order to justify our presence. He called us liars and insinuated that we worked directly with the enemy. Even the Taliban went on record by saying that they hadn't had formal talks with the U.S. for over a year. They didn't want to be accused of working with us any more than we wanted to be accused of working with them.

Shortly afterward, we tragically lost an aircraft. A Blackhawk helicopter from our task force with a total crew of five on board crashed close to midnight. It was the Trail ship, so when the Lead aircraft lost communications with them, they asked our Kiowas if they could find the Blackhawk. It all happened fast; one of the Kiowas nearby saw a flash and moved instinctively towards it. The aircraft lay on the ground in pieces and on fire. The Kiowa landed right next to it and one pilot immediately jumped out and ran to the burning aircraft to see if he could pull anyone from the wreckage. The fire was too great and all that our pilot could do was stand there, alone and in the dark, and watch the aircraft burn, along with one of his friends up front in the cockpit.

Our TOC received the call, and shockingly, the first question asked was if the sensitive items were secured, not if the crew was okay. An additional Blackhawk with the Armed Response Force (ARF) team requested to scramble with fire extinguishers to try to quickly put out the fire. In the chaos, the resulting miscommunication, or ineptitude, led to the firefighting ARF request being denied.

A QRF team from another FOB was called up and arrived 30 minutes after the reported time of the crash. At least eight air assets were finally stacked over the crash site. The Kiowa that had initially responded was still present along with their wingman, pulling close security, angrily and helplessly forced to watch as the aircraft continued to burn. One IP, one pilot in progression training, and three enlisted crew members were aboard the Blackhawk.

Aircraft continued to rotate through the night to secure the crash scene. The recovery effort moved into the morning and news spread of the crash. Individuals from all affected units were selected for the ceremony to move the deceased crew members in their caskets from vehicles onto the awaiting C-17 to bring the bodies home.

At 1000, another 3-17 CAV pilot and I joined with others from across the task force, volunteering to assist the Bravo 4-3 unit who had lost their aircraft. We moved to COMKAF Headquarters to be trained in the ceremonial process and await the remaining recovery efforts. Each MRAP armored vehicle would sit idling, and five total vehicles would each carry one metal casket in the back. There were eight man details assigned to each casket, with three teams being from our task force. Training was conducted for us to know how to properly remove the caskets and carry them to the waiting cargo transport plane back to the U.S.

Regardless of the reason, we had lost five great people that many of us knew.

Without any jackets, we stood out in a pouring thunderstorm, cold and soaking wet, moving caskets as precisely and ceremoniously as we could with our numb hands. Not a single person complained or even seemed to wince at the frigid rain drenching us. The only words spoken for hours concerned the proper movement of the caskets.

Hours later, everyone had it all down and were prepared to move to the airfield for the ceremony. Just then, a bus arrived with seven soldiers from Bravo 4-3, the unit most affected by the crash. They wanted to help and honor their dead by carrying their friends to the airplane. I bowed out, along with six others, to make room for them, as I was not about to take one of their places if they wanted to be involved instead. We left the area and tried to find a ride back to the airfield.

The ceremony for loading the caskets onto the airplane did not begin for another 12 hours after I left, finally beginning around 2300 that night. Our Charlie Troop pilot that had been the first one to land and try to pull the crew out was sent to the airfield with bags packed to accompany the body of his friend home. Other soldiers, those who knew and cared for the deceased individuals the most, were sent with their bags, also acting as the escorts. At approximately 30 minutes past midnight, the ceremony was complete, and the bodies had been loaded aboard the C-17. The soldiers acting as escorts waited aboard the plane, and the airfield had emptied of those who had attended the ceremony.

What followed was the most shameful, despicable thing that could ever happen. The true shame should never fade from those who were responsible.

At 0100, some officials boarded the C-17 and the escorts for those who had fallen were taken, without warning, quickly off of the plane and onto the flight line ramp. They were told to hurry up and retrieve their bags. The escorts were then even kicked off of the ramp, out of the fence line, and literally put on the street. In complete shock, no one knew what had just happened.

Words can barely describe what this action caused to our pilot. The devastating additional blow after watching that Blackhawk burn was horrible. The situation became yet another reason why so many passionately despised our higher command and their warped decision-making processes. The incident further and rapidly degraded morale, and solidified many in a very real hatred.

A few days later, we had the memorial ceremony in one of our hangars. The pictures of those that had perished were framed and our ALSE shop provided five flight helmets to place out on display to represent them. The hangar was packed with hundreds of people. We listened to the commanders and platoon sergeants who were in charge of those lost. Their words and accounts served as a respectful and professional account of each one of our lost crew members. Each fallen crew member also had someone speak on behalf of their life and character as their friend and comrade.

Our Charlie Troop pilot spoke for one of the Blackhawk pilots, and it was heartbreaking to hear him speak so fondly of his neighbor from Louisiana who left behind a daughter and a wife. Their kids had played while they grilled out together. Silent tears rolled down still and transfixed faces in the audience, including my own, from hearing such heartfelt speeches. Rather than be able to pay his final respects at the funeral for his friend and comfort that family, our pilot was forced to stay back with us. At least we had somehow managed to ensure that he was allowed to speak on the Blackhawk pilot's behalf.

Our task force commander did open the memorial with a few comments as well, being well spoken and non-robotic. Unfortunately, nearly everyone in attendance of a rank higher than him was clearly only there for the cameras. The commander that was in charge of our whole Combat Aviation Brigade did not say a word. These were ultimately his crew members, but he chose to remain silent when he finally had the rare occasion to address all of us together in the same place.

The "VIPs" in attendance were the first up to the stage after all the remarks were complete, to stiffly walk from picture to picture and lay their symbolic coin at the feet of the fallen. The hangar was dead silent despite the hundreds of soldiers in attendance. While the "VIPs" were up front playing their game, the distinctive rapid fire of flash strobes and camera shutters broke the silence. I had no doubt that they, and the other probably 50 "important people" who made us all stand in the heat to watch and wait our turn, had very little emotion over the event at all. They had no true connection to these soldiers except in some cases on paper, and others didn't even have that.

I was convinced it was a politically motivated event for most of the "VIPs" to even show up. All the soldiers eventually trickled out the back of the tent after watching this all go on for more than 30 minutes and realizing that there would still be a very long lapse before we underlings would be able to actually go up there and pay any respect we wanted to give. One of our senior pilots apparently saw this coming and had slipped out much earlier. He knew what was about to happen and didn't want to see the shameless display by people pretending to care. I really wished that I had slipped out with him and missed that, too.

That same day in our AO, an Afghan policeman jumped into the back of a truck and manned a heavy machine gun. He gunned down two U.S. soldiers and wounded many others in the police compound before being killed. A couple days later, two U.S. Special Operations personnel were shot in the back by the very Afghan Army soldiers that they were actually attempting to help. When I would write home about these things, I always gained a complex about it all, feeling like a downer or ashamed. I knew most times that such a feeling was irrational because all that I was doing was writing as I had promised: to tell the truth about what was happening and delivering facts that would otherwise be unknown. I spent an average of four hours writing per account, and sometimes more. It was important for me to know that those that I wrote to and cared about could understand what we dealt with.

At the time, I felt that for the 12,309 wounded and 2,189 killed U.S. soldiers sacrificed for Afghanistan, the public wasn't very concerned. Most people were not directly affected, and there really wasn't anything on the news, so why would the average person even know to keep track? For those that read my words, and those that truly supported us overseas, I pleaded that they take the average American out of their comfort zone by talking to them about such taboo subjects as our dirty little war. I knew that it wasn't necessarily malicious on the average person's part; many would be outraged if only they were enlightened to what the truth really was. This was easy to remedy by explaining to people that despite talks of some "pull back" by whatever arbitrary date was spouted by politicians, the fight we were in was not over.

I asked that everything I was writing be kept in mind when our citizens were told of the "progress" and "great things" that we were accomplishing in Afghanistan. I listened to an account of an Afghan policeman who dragged a few people out onto the street and shot them in the head. That was all that the Afghan people appeared to know: extreme violence. The country of Afghanistan and the Department of Defense contractors was where the tax dollars were going, not to the U.S. soldiers or main war effort in terms of our equipment. It was hard to see past the ugly truth. We were being put in harm's way and dying to assist Islamic drug lords in an unstable tribal warfare region. The Afghans had a black market of over $100 billion of yearly raw opium trade mostly marked for heroin production. It was one of the only things supporting their economy, other than the billions of dollars that we would also give the Afghan government. The black market dollars were not factored into official reports of their economic success because it was ours and the international communities' money that had brought some charted percentiles of poverty down and yearly wages up.

I didn't believe the government, police, and military of Afghanistan had any interest in stopping an industry that was the heart and soul of their economy. We were not truly eradicating the Afghan poppy fields; that would upset them and destroy their economy, so we would "help" them instead, so that they'd still be our "friends." We had America's sons and daughters literally dying and it was heartbreaking to know that another year of your life would be devoted to helping it along. Or that you may lose your own life and leave behind your grieving family for such perverted reasons. The only thing that kept me and several others fighting was a sense of loyalty and defense to one another, not the cause we were to embrace and believe in.

To my understanding, there were already non-aggression pacts being established between insurgent groups, police, and the locals. These were being declared the second we pulled our forces out of contested villages and regions. A non-aggression pact meant that the insurgents and Taliban forces could move along freely through those zones without fear of being hindered by Afghan military, police, or civilians. In exchange, the hope was that the bad guys would leave the locals and ANA/ANP alone and focus on the outside aggressors, being the U.S. and other coalition forces.

The money from the drug trade was more than enough to pay anyone off in an economy where the average working male was believed to make the equivalent of $5,000—10,000 U.S. dollars, per year. Imagine being offered your yearly salary, or even part of it, in return for your cooperation with militants. Would the average person not think, "*Not only am I going to not get murdered, but I'll even get paid?*" I guess it's not hard to understand why many said, "Sign me up."

Kandahar once was, and would once again become, an insurgent and Taliban stronghold. We'd already shown our cards, and they knew that we were setting up to leave. We were slowly shutting down bases and pulling back, but it was taking a painful amount of time to conduct the "retrograde." The enemy didn't know why, and frankly, neither did the average soldier. We joked around amongst ourselves, jabbing at our leadership for seeming to think as long as we were pulling out really, really slowly, it would somehow look less like we had "lost."

CHAPTER 26

A large complement of cigars were sent to one of our guys by a company back home. They sent probably a hundred different ones to him to pass out and enjoy with our troop. We had increasingly taken to sitting outside for a few hours and smoking cigars and drinking non-alcoholic "near beer." Very few of us were cigar connoisseurs, and I was also not too big of a fan near beer. Despite this, it was good for us to all sit around joking and talking, as the camaraderie was what we all needed by then. Our pilot who had lost his friend in the Blackhawk crash had come out the last few times, which I was silently glad to see because he needed the companionship most of all.

One of our pilots was good at playing the guitar, as was one of the crew chiefs. Two guys from an Apache company came by and hung out with us, one of them toting a small cooler that he had turned into a harmonica case. He taught himself the basics of how to play the harmonica during an Iraq deployment and had gotten deeply into it. He selected from a dozen different-keyed harmonicas, and the trio began to jam while we all listened in contented wonder.

Despite our consistent kicks in the nuts, we kept moving ahead. We had to lean on each other, and although even that had become hard for some to do, we attempted to hold each other up and keep tabs on those struggling the most. The support of our family and friends back home was also an unmentionable source of strength and resolve to press on until that one day that we could put all the deployments behind us.

Just as things were getting back to normal, and our attempts at bringing up our spirits were showing positive results, we experienced another horrible tragedy. On St. Patrick's Day, March 17th, we lost another helicopter. This time it was not only one from our task force, but this one was also a Kiowa.

The alert for a communications blackout was issued just before dinner, letting us know that something terribly serious had occurred. Not more than 15 minutes later, we had confirmation that it was a downed Kiowa. Another 20 minutes later, we knew that it was one of Bravo Troop's birds. Speculation didn't take long to confirm which bird and crew that it was, and all that we knew then was that one pilot was deceased, and one was in very bad shape. The accident occurred right near KAF in the area where we usually conducted our test firing and basic combat maneuvering training.

An hour and a half after the initial notification, the crew and conditions were confirmed. Lead had conducted a gun run and broke out to the right as briefed, moving far out of the way for the next training engagement by the Trail ship. Trail moved inbound, shot, and then broke right. Suddenly, the Trail ship called on the radio that they were going down. Response to a downed aircraft training had been briefed before the flight, so the Lead ship took an extra few seconds to process that this was a real life emergency and not part of the briefed training.

The Kiowa that crashed had experienced a mechanical failure so severe and so fast that there was nothing that could have been done outside of what the crew attempted in their last moments of flight. It could have happened to any of us.

Just as the initial distress calls were being made over the radios, a Canadian civilian contractor Huey helicopter was coming over the ridge and saw the scene below. The Huey landed immediately and the pilots friction locked their controls. All three crew aboard jumped out and sprinted to the downed aircraft to see if they could pull anyone out. The Lead Kiowa circled close overhead trying to assume the duties they needed to undertake in order to facilitate the quickest possible emergency response.

Minutes after the crash, a Blackhawk sat on its parking pad in KAF about to undertake an entirely separate mission when they heard the radio traffic. Without bothering to ask for permission, they launched directly from their pad and continued at max airspeed directly towards the crash site. They landed close to the wreckage and dismounted soldiers to join the Canadians working to pull the pilots from the wreckage. One pilot was successfully pulled out and immediately flown to the hospital pad where anxiously waiting medical personnel stood ready to receive the wounded man. Despite the best efforts of so many, the other pilot, Bravo Troop's SP, could not be saved.

Later on, it was noted from the remaining Kiowa that if the Blackhawk and its crew hadn't taken such lightning fast and decisive action, then the pilot that they recovered would have surely perished. He remained in critical condition and after a long night of emergency surgery and being stabilized enough, he was evacuated to Germany for further emergency surgeries and treatment. We had a hospital in Germany that had been taking in the wounded from both of our wars in the Middle East for 12 years thus far, and it was one of the best in the world. The supreme level of quality combat medical care came from an unfortunately high degree of experience.

The following morning, we had a ramp ceremony to once again load a fallen pilot onto a waiting C-17 aircraft. It was very heart-wrenching to stand out on the flight line while the American flag-draped casket was carried by his closest friends and troop-mates.

The loss hit our squadron very hard. The man that we lost was an experienced standardization pilot, and likely the best pilot we had. Having been in our unit for seven years, he was one of the longest serving members of 3-17 Cavalry. A consummate professional, he cared deeply for his pilots and was known for his humor and expertise with our aircraft and demanding missions. Upon his return to the states, Bravo's SP was set to retire. Now, he left behind a family in total shock and despair, as well as a troop without their most senior warrant officer and mentor.

Not even a week earlier, in response to the Blackhawk crash, Bravo's SP had called for the arrangement of a donation drive for flowers and cards for the families of the fallen Blackhawk crew. One of the Bravo Troop pilots had set up an account and had just begun taking donations. Bravo's SP had also desired to have a troop cookout on the deck during St. Patrick's Day, so a setting for him was placed at the head of the table, complete with his Stetson and a near beer. The troop commenced their lunch cookout in his memory and there were many, many emotions running across our squadron. No one could believe what had just happened, and the surreal feeling of shock and sadness was ever present.

It was the first time that I had seen anyone wear their Stetsons in a long time, and they said that he would have wanted it that way. I hoped that our troops may bring the Stetson back in his honor, being a welcome sign of Cavalry spirit and unity. We had been stripped of so much tradition and motivation lately that any sign of unity, even if it was just the wearing of a hat, was extremely encouraging.

We received word that the other Kiowa pilot from the crash was listed in Germany as critical, but thankfully, stable. We were very grateful for the efforts of those that responded so quickly to the crash and their attempts to save the crew. Fortunately, after the injured Kiowa pilot was stabilized, he was able to begin a long road of recovery and still had a chance of life ahead of him.

Losing two aircraft and many lives in the span of only a week had been incomprehensibly difficult for us. The struggle to make sense of it all cannot be understated. We'd barely been able to catch our breaths from the last crash, and then, this came along. I was saddened by the fact that we were getting better at memorial ceremonies through experience. We all continued to lean on each other, and the strengthening bond and closeness with one another helped immensely. Our little fellowship porch evenings with cigars, near beer, and civilian clothes would continue, as they were now needed more than ever.

Not long after the cookout day, I flew well over five hours and stayed quite busy supporting ground units. Sudden missions and intense situations got our heads back in the game, helping us remember that there were still ground guys outside the wire going through their own slice of hell that we needed to protect. An endearing quality of our enemy was discussed as we began to set up for an engagement.

"You guys ever notice how much these dickheads favor the use of graveyards when they wanna start some shit?" Our wingman casually asked.

A man with an AK-47 ran from a pile of rubble to a large tree among the graves. A second fighter was reported, and I scanned with our sight, hoping for my quarry to make a mistake. Hadji continued ducking and weaving between graves, believing it gave him a better opportunity to hide and maneuver. It was marginally true, I supposed, better than hammering away with his AK-47 while standing out in the open and shouting. I pulled up my binoculars so that I could make out colors, and described the individuals that I was seeing to the ground forces. We had to confirm that they were the same duo who had engaged them earlier. We all knew that it was, but once again, we had to be able to defend ourselves in court. The enemy's expected lifespan was shortening, and I suddenly recalled the TV shows that depict a focused hunter, shaking with anticipation as he lines up his shot on a trophy deer. My own rush was intensifying. It was because of these savages that we were even deployed and lost great people in the first place. Sadness over our week of loss had cemented into further determined and focused hatred.

I finally replied to the other aircraft, "You see, Hadji really is only being courteous. This way, his buddies don't have nearly as far a distance to carry his body."

"Yeah. That makes sense," the other crew replied. "Well, except for the whole courteous Hadji part." I guess they had me there, but at any rate, two more insurgents were removed from the battlefield.

Once we got back and debriefed, I shared pictures that I had taken with the Bravo Troop guys of the lighter times from their cookout. I moved around as unobtrusively as I could while they smoked cigars and played poker, trying to stay upbeat and relax to honor their SP's memory just as they knew that he would have wanted.

The continuous hits that we'd been receiving had culminated in this one, and it knocked us down for a while. I hoped that we could bounce back, and the events would shrink to just a horrible memory in the back of everyone's minds. The memory of when we lost so much in so short a time.

I wrote home and told everyone that I sincerely hoped that they had a better holiday. I was not intending to be sarcastic; I truly meant that. I wanted everyone back home to be able to enjoy their freedoms and hold their loved ones close. I implored everyone to not take anything for granted. We were learning more and more that anything could be taken in an instant. I vowed to continue to fight my ass off, and hoped the rest of us would come home, put everything behind us, and live the rest of our days with a brighter future. I wanted to live a good life; my attempt to do good would hopefully honor those who no longer could. Lindsey and I spoke about what we wanted to do almost every time we talked. It was rough knowing that we still had six more months of the deployment to go, but at least we had each other.

*

On March 22nd, I completed reversing out through an uncharacteristically cold and rainy day. I hadn't realized until then just how much I missed it. When on nights, the chances of being wrangled in for dumb stuff that the day-walker staff folks dreamt up was far less likely. Other perks included cooler temperatures, generally calmer weather, and Hadji was usually up to things that were not as focused on us. The ground guys weren't interested in going out and doing stuff at night anymore, either. They'd officially let the ANA and ANP undertake that dangerous task. It was about damn time—let Afghans blow up Afghans if they wished; I was perfectly content sitting on the sidelines until our brass could see how pointless it was to keep us deployed for that madness.

My last flight on days before my transition to the night schedule encompassed a rather odd, but funny event. As Matt and I flew, we were not encountering much excitement. The locals were going about their business and the enemy had taken a recent vacation. I was in the left seat, so I snapped a few photos out of curiosity and idle boredom. I saw a man standing outside of what looked like a cave mouth or entrance to an underground storage area near a structure. I snapped a few photos, then pulled them up on my camera display screen and enlarged the image. I had begun this method of recon early in my previous deployment, as it gave me a close-up and still picture to study when trying to find a weapon or other clue that something wasn't right. The picture that I now stared at was not right, not at all. I began cursing and told Matt to double back the way we'd come. He banked hard and called Trail, letting them know that we found something and were moving in for a closer look.

"What was it man? What did you see?" Matt asked.

"Fucking Hadji just mooned me, and right as I was taking a picture of him, too," I angrily spat. Matt stared blankly at me for a moment.

"No way. There's not a guy down there mooning you," he said. I then thrust the camera screen at him and took the flight controls. Matt looked hard at the screen, mouth half open, then he began laughing. "I'll show that son of a bitch how great of an idea it is to show me his ass," I growled, as I took a smoke grenade off the dash.

"Don't be butt-hurt that Hadji just hurt you with his butt!" Matt exclaimed, laughing uncontrollably. He then told Trail what happened, and they laughed hard and jeered at me for getting mooned by Hadji, too. Jackals. We flew low right back by the area, but the guy must've seen us turn back and had ducked inside somewhere. I cursed and threw the smoke grenade anyway, just missing the opening to the underground area I figured he may have gone into.

My following cycle into green world was the first time that I was impartial to gaining the strangely sought-after specialty NVG flight time. The accumulation of NVG time is special and necessary in the pursuit of a helicopter job once you get out of the Army and seek employment in certain niche positions. I didn't necessarily need any more NVG time than I already had, but, hell, I'd still take it.

*

Later in March, we assembled in the hangar for the memorial ceremony honoring Bravo Troop's SP. The memorial ceremony transpired much like the previous one for the Blackhawk crew. The higher-ups, however, weren't as numerous as they had been the last time. One "foreign dignitary" even had the balls to make a fuss about where his assigned seat was. Rather than tell him to kindly go fuck himself, we instead capitulated and a bunch of seats were shifted around at the last minute. The foreign dignitary just wanted to have as much exposure with our dignitaries as possible, and he didn't give two shits about why we were all there. It infuriated me.

Despite that shameful lack of respect, we banded together and sent the pilot off the right way, so some took solace in that. Bravo Troop surrounded the stage, almost all wearing their Stetsons in his honor. My gut wrenched, and a lump rose in my throat as I watched a few pilots tearfully embracing and comforting each other. The loss continued to devastate our entire squadron.

The rest of that day we had a "tactical pause"—basically, a day to take a break en masse. We were afforded the opportunity to take the time that we needed to talk with one another and catch up on anything we needed to do. We were positioned to launch at a moment's notice though, and I was on the QRF team due to my experience of that being the bread-and-butter mission of my time in Fox Troop. Sitting QRF while on a de-facto off day was a welcome move amidst such a short supply of good decisions as of late.

I reverted back to nocturnal life once more. A call to Lindsey let me know that we had just hit our six-month anniversary. No, I did not know that was a thing. We'd already had a great start, and I knew that the deployment would bring us closer than most couples could ever dream of becoming. There was something to be said for grueling hardships and mutually endured sacrifice. We both knew that we would be better for it in the end. With the recent events, it sure was great to talk to her.

I had come to better terms with the tragedies of the previous two weeks, but I still thought about it. It was not any true hardship in how we were living day-to-day, but had rather become a mental ordeal. That's what made it even more difficult, I think—we weren't living a completely austere existence, yet I felt so miserable despite it all. Our rooms were nicer than anyone had ever had it, and we almost always had a steady stream of hot water for showers and enough chow hall food to grow someone out of way too many pants sizes.

The lack of belief in a cause is what plagued us. When I bitched and moaned, it was not because I was living in squalor or anything. I only knew of serious problems and challenges that our nation was facing, and giving billions of dollars over to a corrupt government in Afghanistan and the Muslim Brotherhood ruling Egypt was not what we needed to be doing with our money. There was no point in me standing atop a soap box for any of that; almost everyone reading my words or that I was physically around were like-minded, so I'd only be preaching to the choir.

I ended up doing some night flying and making my way through the following week more or less on our Afghan normal-type schedule. We had a few (thankfully) uneventful convoy escorts, as well as escorting some Blackhawks in and out of some areas unmolested by enemy activity. Things were returning to normal, and I welcomed the decrease in enemy activity at the moment. It was finally the last day of what had been an agonizing month, and also the end of our Mustache March competition. It was also confirmed that I was not a sexy mustache man. I had continued to get laughed at by those around me just by looking at my face. There's nothing more disheartening than having a group of males and females walk by you and receive only the sour-apple face. The mean ones would even point directly and laugh unapologetically. I can't complain—I did it to others, too.

I made it up to the troop to wrangle up the guys remaining with their 'staches so that we may get a photo while sporting our Stetsons in front of a Kiowa. I had several photos taken of us, and it was a fun time to get it all down for the pages of shameful history before we said goodbye to our furry-lipped friends.

In my mind, I had decided that the ceremony of shaving the mustache off would also symbolize my relief that the month was finally over. As I shaved my mustache, my mood turned somber as I thought of the tragedy that had struck one final time towards the end of March.

Another pilot, a very senior member of our task force, experienced a catastrophic heart attack and was unable to be revived. Ironically enough, he had also been directly responsible for the recovery efforts and securing the crash site of the Blackhawk that had gone down just a few weeks prior. He'd been extremely upset and broken up about it, as we all had. Again, an American flag-draped casket was ceremoniously loaded onto a waiting C-17 while we sadly watched. His memorial service was soon to follow. Lindsey once mentioned the common conception that bad things happen in threes. I couldn't deny that she was right, and hoped like hell for the cycle of tragedy to end.

U.S. vehicles proceed down the highway, remaining as vigilant as possible for IEDs.

Lead getting aggressive.

Making it rain .50 caliber brass.

Smoke marks a hasty PZ for a MEDEVAC Blackhawk.

PART FOUR

FIGHT FOR HOME

CHAPTER 27

Dear Soldier,
You are sweet. I am 7 years old.
Please save the world for us please.
We love you so much so just be careful.
Love, Hayden

There were a lot of changes going on. The draw-down and sequestration were becoming more evident with the rapid shuffle of personnel and equipment from out in the AO. Some flying was getting a bit more interesting in certain spots. As our ground forces vacated an area, the enemy naturally moved back in. It seemed like a simple and obvious concept to me, and I could not fathom how it still seemed to surprise some.

I flew much less in March because we had way too many people on our books to share the flying. We also had a disproportionate amount of staff aviators outside our troop to support, and they seemed to get a lot more attention and flight time than I'd imagined. The whole backrub system on that wasn't too surprising, however.

My flights on the new night shift had been decent. The sky had been nice and clear and the area was relatively quiet. The night sky was breathtaking since there wasn't any light pollution once we ventured outside the Kandahar city area and our airfield. The NVG's ability to amplify the smallest amount of light by over a thousand times continued to provide an unreal view of the celestial world above. Millions of small points of light glowing under varying degrees of intensity blinked and sparkled wildly while vying for our attention. It really was beautiful.

My night schedule continued forwards in a very calm manner. I looked forward to hopefully better days in April. I wanted to eat right, work out, get my head back on straight, and be better overall. I'd needed a goal, any kind of purpose, really. The decision to better myself as a whole exactly met that need.

We were informed that, at the end of April, we would see a large scale back in the food services offered to us. I wasn't sure what would be taken away. There were four different meals served on KAF per day since the base ran 24-hour operations, but two of those meals would be cut out. A 50 percent cut in rations, because of further budgetary constraints. That would really, really suck for some of the work shifts. In the remaining two meals served, I supposed that they'd be scaling back on selections. We seemed to take the whole sequestration idea of "we're poor now" to heart; meat and potatoes only... no tacos and ice cream for the fat kids.

We began to experience a fuel shortage for KAF's many vehicles. Diesel, which our van ran on, became a hot commodity. Lines for the fuel could take hours, and a specified allotment was assigned after the issuance of special memorandums proving a real need were furnished. We frankly didn't have time for that shit, and had a serious need, so we began stealing. Our FARP had JP-8 jet fuel for our helicopters, which would coincidentally work in our van. During aircraft refueling stops, clandestine movements of our van and jerry cans were made to skim extra desperately needed JP-8. It was ridiculous that we even had to do it.

More and more, I realized how much myself and a few others around me were done playing the Army's games. It was a natural progression. I think I exuded that hostile attitude more and more each day towards those policies that I saw as an annoyance or, to a small degree, even threatening. In all honesty, there was so much subjective leeway built into the interpretation of many of our "standards" and "regulations" that I (and many others) didn't feel like we were bad soldiers or rogues one bit for acting on what we believed the interpretation should be in our own minds.

We had an unusually high percentage of soft soldiers in our ranks, and I blamed our watered-down, touchy-feely social engineering that began trickling into our military. If some of the soldiers on KAF could not get on the internet because of whatever technical difficulty, you'd think someone had just slapped them in the face and kicked their dog. Checking Facebook had somehow become an inalienable right in our society, and it had spilled over into our military.

A very rapid and nasty dust storm descended upon us. I was not sure how long it would last, but this one looked like it wasn't in any hurry to leave. The winds had really kicked up and the gritty feeling between my teeth, watering eyes, and dirt-caked hair all reminded me of why I would never live in a stupid desert. Wiping the grime from my body as best I could with wet wipes and paper towels, I plopped onto the couch once again after being told that there were zero productive tasks available for me to help with. I drank my protein powder and scowled. What would cheer me up at present would be fighting insurgents and Taliban, but unfortunately, that was not in the cards at the moment.

*

During the last half of April, I began to shut down and had only written a few sentences home the entire month. Having only flown an abysmal total of seven hours in April, there wasn't anything interesting for me to say. Despite it all, I finally decided to give it a try at the end of the month. I started with the present, and then tried to work backwards as I recalled things.

I had just reversed back out to nights, and since the 25th, had even done the night-to-day-back-to-nights swap. It was a tough turn on my body and mind, which was already operating on a ragged margin to begin with. I managed to stay up most of the night on the 29th and woke up about when I was supposed to on the 30th. I figured we could say that I was reversed out once again and call it good. Whatever I was, it wasn't really that pleasant.

I was thrilled to be back on nights already after having such a rapid and temporary stint on days. The stupidity around inconceivably had continued to grow. Being a night-walker rather than a day-walker continued to have outshining perks and insulated myself and a few others from the madness. Mainly, it was the benefit of generally being forgotten all day. There always existed the guilty concept of wanting to "be a team player" and help where needed, but that had somehow and unnecessarily morphed into allowing yourself to become a target of opportunity for people with power that were bored and would get "good ideas" for their pawns to carry out.

Our aircraft were experiencing continuous and massive maintenance issues, so further large scale reductions in flight time had also contributed to some of the turmoil. Aside from maintenance, the weather in the second half of April had also been plain bad. We'd endured thunderstorms, hail, dust, and sandstorms with up to nearly 80mph wind gusts. A freak hail storm wreaked havoc among the entire fleet of aircraft that our task force had, resulting in a multi-million-dollar disaster. Two young soldiers were crushed by a roof that was ripped from a building in the wind and pummeled their asses while they scrambled to get to a shelter. Luckily, they survived.

In the past, sitting around on a deployment wasn't necessarily a bad thing. We could catch up on a book, watch a movie, whatever we wanted to pass the time. Video games? *Super Mario Brothers* and *Punch Out!!* were like crack for us. This time around, though, for whatever reason, if we were observed "sitting around doing nothing" then we were somehow asking for trouble. As a result, creative ways to appear busy had to be invented and rediscovered while on days. On nights, no one important was awake and we were usually spared from most of the craziness.

I found that the best way for me to deal with all the targeting was to simply withdraw into my world on the iPad while wearing noise-canceling headphones. I could study, read, and work on whatever was needed. With my silence and focus dialed into the device in my lap, I was often left to my own affairs. Hopefully, that could continue for the rest of the deployment, but I held my breath secretly in hopes that even this benign action would not be seen to finally offend someone. Never in my life had I appeared to be such an introvert, but the deployment was causing me to shift—not only my mentality, but also my very personality in order to adapt and overcome. I hoped that I could reverse these changes later after returning home, and that too much change would not end up being irreversible.

I needed to catch up on some studying. We were all held to the same standard of core knowledge in order to safely operate the aircraft and respond appropriately in the time of an emergency. Those procedures were essential knowledge, and no one had any issues with knowing that stuff cold. There were a litany of other subject areas that were pretty ridiculous, however, and some were even just plain laughable. Distance Estimation and Depth Perception, with subtopics like Increasing and Decreasing Size, Geometric Perspective, and Linear Perspective. You may struggle with some of the concepts because of over-analyzation, but as long as you just think about it like a six-year-old child, you'll do just fine.

*

The enemy announced that they were ramping up their attacks on Afghan military units, as well as attacks against us. We had begun the war by kicking the enemy assholes into the dirt with vicious and unrelenting precision and authority. About midway, we began to bend to international sentiment and also began to feel a bit more "humane," forgetting what our savage enemies were like or stood for. Finally, 12 years later, we were most concerned with chow hall closures, wearing PT reflective belts and eye protection at all times, money tightening up, and "area beautification."

All the while, insurgents were rearming and regrouping while we had provided tons of leeway and opportunity because of inaction. Insurgent fighters were emboldened—they increasingly believed that they could lay IEDs and attack anyone they pleased. We were too afraid to accidentally damage property or injure someone "innocent." We had crippled ourselves into being an inept force led by those who appeared motivated foremost with covering their own asses and staying out of trouble.

I was convinced that I knew the answer to the question why a lot of our people would return from the Middle East wracked with PTSD. Up front, it must be acknowledged that Afghanistan provides the wholesale mind-fuck package of asymmetrical warfare—where literally everyone around you may be an enemy, but they're dressed as civilians, and a few even smile and wave. Even still, many times, it was not combat itself, seeing dead bodies, rocket attacks, or any of that. I believed much of the PTSD and/or intense anger issues arose from the mind-bending ridiculousness that was brought to bear upon the soldiers from higher officials sitting in their swivel chairs, dreaming up more elaborate and "great" ideas in their air-conditioned offices while fantasizing of the next promotion. It was unfathomable and so despicable that we couldn't be trusted to use our best judgement and training to intervene in fights while attempting to save our ground forces. Even a "show of force" by harmlessly shooting into the dirt if only to make noise, with no possibility of danger to friendlies, civilians, or structures wasn't allowed. Sometimes, my mind would nearly vapor-lock or act as if it were a computer stuttering incoherently after receiving bad code when I replayed the events of my day.

There was a survey created and passed down that was designed to bring all of this nonsense to light. Upon receiving the orders and instructions on what the survey was and how to complete it, we did as instructed. We completed the survey, which was supposed to be anonymous, and turned it in. Not only did we get a two-hour lecture and intimidation session once our results were identified and read, but the survey which was supposed to be Department of the Army high and untouchable was somehow swept under the rug. Nothing surprised me anymore.

*

The last week of April had been a very difficult one for my family and I personally, and it had taken me a while to even write about it. My grandmother, Virginia Robicheaux, who had just survived a stroke and was still in the hospital experienced a catastrophic blood clot that gave her a relatively short time remaining to live. My father and aunt made it to the hospital to be with her during her last moments and we were very fortunate that they could be together at the end. My uncle was driving down from Maryland and didn't make it in time, but could at least get a few last words in via cell phone.

It was tough on my father, and it had also been tough on me. Thankfully, I had called her now and then during my deployments. She was a great and wise person and was my last surviving grandparent. Despite my grandmother's age and dwindling health, she was always on top of the news and what was going on in the world. She was tied in with current events and knew several Congressmen and Senators, having served as a reporter on Capitol Hill in Washington D.C. from the 1950s to 2000. She had interviewed everyone from President Nixon all the way to Willy Nelson (and later contributed to a book on Willy).

My grandmother's constant concern over the safety of both my brother and I while deployed was very genuine and real. One of the last times I had talked to her in Kandahar, she and I discussed my writing to friends and family back home. She had read everything from my year in Bagram, and had been keeping up with the events in Kandahar. At that point, I still had no intention of ever publishing any of it. She assured me that the things I was writing about and experiencing were far from common knowledge, including the government officials she knew. No one would ever hear of what was really happening unless those like myself took what were essentially dated journals and created an account of what we saw and experienced.

The final time we talked, she had seen how bad things were affecting not only me, but also those I wrote about around me. She told me again that she wanted me to publish everything, and that she would help me when I returned home. I finally caved, and I promised that I would do it. Not long after that conversation, she had her stroke, and I received the devastating news.

I never even got a Red Cross message, nor was I ever asked if I desired to return to the states to attend her funeral, although we were grossly over-staffed. I could have easily been spared for the week that it would have taken. In shock and still processing it all, I sat in my room. Matt made us tea, and put his hand on my shoulder, saying, "I'm so sorry, man. Are you all right?"

I sighed and sipped on the beverage before me, and finally said, "Yes, I'll be okay. I'll just take a day or two, let it sink in and process it all, you know? I'm glad that I just spoke to her recently." Matt nodded.

"Yeah, it's fortunate you were able to have a good conversation."

"You know how I've been writing everything down in journals?" Matt nodded again. "Well, she made me promise to publish it all one day." Matt straightened up and said emphatically, "She's right. You definitely should. People back home need to know this stuff. In the meantime, I'll make sure you get the time you need, brother."

Matt spoke to our commander and troop SP, resulting in me being left to my own devices until I was ready. A few days later, I rejoined the fight.

CHAPTER 28

My brother had watched over the past few months and could see that I wasn't doing so well, so he began sending me links to job opportunities outside of the Army. When I was feeling hopeless and depressed, it helped to have an older brother that was in the industry and knew how to motivate me and give me something to look forward to professionally. Combat in the streets of Baghdad had changed him, too. He was always simple and to the point, essentially telling me to power through and keep my eye on the prize. He wanted me to see that I was the opposite of hopeless, as I had much to look forward to and be hopeful for instead. My parents continued to try to keep my spirits and motivation up, while Lindsey and Scout gave me the strength to drive on emotionally. Recently, I had also made a purchase to give myself something to look forward to working on when I got home. A few inexpensive, Korean-War era Mosin Nagant carbine rifles slathered in a foul axle-grease-like cosmoline preservative awaited my return. The wood stocks were coated in decades of grime. After returning home from the previous deployment, many of us bought old WWII rifles. We spent days removing the preservative gunk and bringing them back into shootable and serviceable condition. The time spent quietly undertaking the task alone in my garage had been therapeutic, giving my mind something to focus on. There were stranger hobbies out there, I assured myself.

I ceased feeling rotten. We still had a war to fight, and men depending on us. I dragged Matt out of our room with me to the coffee shop down the alley and ordered an Afghan Shir Chai tea. It was always made out of sunsets and angel tears.

"I'm tired of feeling like crap. Today is my day, and I'm determined to climb out of the rut," I told Matt. He squinted at me and took a gulp of tea.

"Well, Robo, it's about fucking time."

To mark the occasion, I contacted the Henry Rifle company after surveying several interested soldiers about doing a group buy. Henry had hooked us up with beautiful rifles and custom serial numbers on our previous deployment, and it thrilled me that we would receive another deep discount on them. It gave me a positive project to work on the side, and everyone appreciated my efforts, which also felt great.

*

The beginning of May had clipped along at a decent pace. On a recent night flight, I had flown in some of the crappiest dust and visibility that I could ever recall. Adding to the difficulty was the moonless night, and I relied heavily on my NVGs. The highly concentrated dust particles clogged up the air and diffused what light was available. Vehicle headlights and other light sources caused a very bright green, blurry, and washed-out picture to try and pilot the aircraft with. Mountains became the dark spots which loomed out of the distorted picture an inch from my eyes like shadowy ghosts, ready to offer a destructive embrace to those who ventured too close.

The reason for our flight in such bad conditions was sobering. A giant IED had annihilated one of the ground force armored personnel carriers and claimed five lives. The crater itself was enormous, taking out a vast amount of highway. Vehicles moved around the destruction while U.S. and Afghan forces kept the area as secure as they could. The soldiers who were hit had zero chance of survival. That same day, two more soldiers were killed in another "insider attack," whereby our "Afghan allies" kept deciding to go ahead and shoot up some of our people. Seven deaths in one day, for no goddamn reason.

The propaganda network that we had (Armed Forces Network, or AFN) continued to show stories attempting to convince our forces we were doing something worthwhile, but even they seemed to be running out of misdirection to impart upon the viewers. Most of the AFN broadcasts and news focused on programs that the Navy and Air Force were trying to keep alive during the sequester. There was an incredible amount of self-serving news stories to benefit those who were training various African nations, and attempts to justify the various European posts that we had to support NATO and other American commands. There was barely any more news relating to the combat deaths of our forces in Afghanistan. Most combat loss reporting came from unauthorized leaks delivered to the standard civilian news agencies such as Fox, CNN, etc., back home. The events that could no longer be denied were quickly reported, then dismissed and swept aside as hastily as possible.

The poppy harvest was coming to an end, so Hadji declared that it was time to play again. I was sure that the month of May would continue to get more and more interesting and violent. Our forces out in remote and outlying areas likely did not feel much safer in the comfort that they were now surrounded only by "friendly Afghan allied forces." I worried a lot about the guys that remained in bad-guy country because they were becoming increasingly cut off. I was sure that worries could be assuaged and denied by at least 15 PowerPoint presentations explaining the strategies in an attempt to make sense of the senseless. The busy slides, along with a dizzying array of colors and graphics, always substantiated next to nothing as far as I ever saw. As long as a PowerPoint presentation looked important and impressive, however, I don't think the message contained within was really as concerning. It was amazing.

*

I gathered my things in our troop as we prepared to fly a standard security zone patrol, and then moved out to the aircraft. Our AMC had to return to the squadron to clarify a few things, so he said he'd meet us by the aircraft and update us just before takeoff. Right as we were finishing up our preflight, our AMC came jogging up to my aircraft.

"Robo, fire this bitch up, we gotta roll!" He said from the left side as he handed over a sheet of paper to the left seater. I instinctively began flipping switches as the AMC wheeled around to face his bird parked next to ours, raising his hand above his head to get his right seater's attention. The right seater was already in their cockpit, and the AMC emphatically whirled his hand over his head, signing to start spinning the rotor blades up immediately. He then turned back to us.

"Bravo Troop is working up an engagement near Dorzi, but they're nearing bingo fuel and the end of their mission block. We gotta go do a battle handover with them, like yesterday!" He exclaimed. I gave a thumbs up, shouted "clear," and cracked the throttle to bring our turbine to life. Fast paced chaos, this was what I'd been needing and where we all thrived. We hauled ass through our checklists as the grids, freqs, and callsigns were entered and reviewed. Both aircraft in our SWT lifted off the parking pads in unison and cut in line at the FARP to get quickly topped off and armed up. We called the team from Bravo Troop just as we cleared the wire on KAF. Coalition forces had been receiving harassment fire and a few squads were split up in a labyrinth of deserted and dilapidated structures. It quickly dawned on me that we were headed toward the same spot in which I had gotten into a motorcycle chase on my very first mission flight after arriving in Kandahar.

"That area sucks, lots of places for the shitheads to hide," I remarked to our team. As we approached at maximum speed to relieve Bravo Troop's SWT, the ground force net that we were monitoring came to life.

"Contact, contact!" Men yelled and shot in the background, the snapping sounds of bullets broke the squelch of the radio. "We're taking fire from our north. Wrath, you're clear to re-engage, runs south to north, over!" Bravo Troop's SWT had already worked up the clearance to fire earlier, and began another gun run. We circled like sharks in a pattern nearby, waiting for our turn and watched as the dirt kicked up in a string of destruction from both aircraft gun runs. They circled back, immediately re-engaging with a short burst of .50 cal followed by two satisfying rocket explosions each.

"Hell yeah! That'll get their attention," called Trail. Bravo Troop finished conducting the battle handover with us, then signed off with the ground force,

Hammer 46. We immediately checked in on their frequency, asking for an update.

"Wrath 61, Hammer 46. That last run stopped the incoming fire, Predator UAV reports that three military aged males are quickly moving north from the vicinity of that last engagement. Request you get eyes on and see if they have weapons or display hostile intent, over."

"Roger, Hammer 46, moving there now."

We quickly spotted the trio, who appeared to be covering up weapons under their clothing and entering the outskirts of a small cluster of inhabited qalats. They were attempting to escape into the populace, and we only had partial descriptions or confirmation that the trio we watched were the same that had fired upon Hammer elements. I suddenly dove low and fast directly at them, trying to spook them into action. *Do it,* I mentally urged. *Please try to shoot me!* I desperately wanted one or all to present their weapons and try to engage us. Instead, they took off running and split up.

"Shit! They're running! Two moving west towards the first structure on the southwest corner, the third is moving into the center of a courtyard to the north!" As my left seater relayed this, we both dropped our jaws as one fighter grabbed a young boy who stood frozen in fear in the courtyard. He half-dragged the kid along with him, looking up at us as he made his way to a red motorcycle. He roughly maneuvered himself onto the bike, pulling the stunned kid onto the back. The boy's parents exited a qalat, arms outstretched and screaming in distress. The insurgent quickly started the motorcycle and screamed out of the courtyard with his terrified kidnapped human shield on the back.

"Hammer 46, Wrath 61, be advised, two men ducked into a qalat to your north, grid to follow, break—" my left seater shuddered in anger. "Additionally, the third man grabbed a kid from the village and is now on a motorcycle proceeding east, about to join the highway!"

We dropped down low, and I put the motorcycle right outside my left seater's door. He pulled up his rifle and tried to motion for the man to pull off and kill the engine, but the enemy fighter was unfazed. When we attempted to photograph the man, the fighter held a scarf up over his face with his left hand and full throttled the motorcycle with his right. We watched the petrified boy on the back. His head darted back and forth between his captor and our helicopter, his face registering sheer terror. We were helpless to stop it, so we coordinated UAV and other assets to continue to follow the man on the motorcycle to see where he would end up once he thought he'd escaped. I could only hope that the abducted child on the back would survive, but there was a very real chance that the fighter may murder him once he outlived his usefulness.

We returned to supporting Hammer 46 as he and his men moved through their patrol, finally ending up back in their vehicles with thankfully no casualties or injuries to report. After the remaining hours spent supporting them, we slowly flew back toward KAF. Bravo Troop had stopped the fight and we had continued to support and keep Hammer 46 safe, so the mission was technically a success. Despite that knowledge, I still could not shake that terrified, pleading gaze and my curiosity about whether or not the child lived or died.

*

I begrudgingly took another PT test, and as per usual it wasn't my favorite thing in the world. I made it through the events, coughing and choking hard on the dusty road during the two-mile run made worse by a convoy lumbering slowly by. It was unpleasant, but I refused to fail and found the internal motivation to pass without issue. After my PT test, I sat shirtless in the room, propped in front of the air conditioner doing nothing more than breathing hard. The next day, my chest diligently tried to rid itself of all of the crap that I'd ingested. Sitting outside, smelling the putrid rank air of raw sewage from the poo pond did not help.

The ability to fly quality missions and give effective coverage opportunities for our forces continued to deteriorate. A palpable tension could be felt growing both in and out of the cockpit. There began an unrealistic strive for total perfection, and I don't mean in the positive, "you should always try to be perfect" mantra. The strange perfectionist attitude and expectations created even more compound stress. When someone acted like a human and missed something small, it wouldn't be considered a big deal back home. If that same situation were to happen to us on KAF, it was taken way too seriously. It could be as simple as a forgotten flip of a switch, or a mis-tuned radio frequency, an incorrect or improper radio call, or slight deviation from a checklist—they had all become much more serious of an offense, thanks mostly to the stress build-up.

The defeated attitude amongst our pilots was plain as day to see. Issue after issue with our operations and command had really taken a lot larger and more serious toll on us this time around than it ever had last time. Many men who should have been chomping at the bit to get as many hours as possible, men who should be gung-ho about progressing up the ladder of military status and responsibility, they just didn't have the drive that we all once had when I was junior in the squadron. The lack of drive in many of our junior guys was an unfortunate consequence stemming from our fracturing organization, and while I was sad to see it, I also knew that it was a mirror shining back on my own psyche at the moment.

I spoke to Lindsey and vowed to stay as positive as I could, despite all that we were enduring. I tried to focus on more things that would keep me going, rather than the mountain of negativity that loomed ever larger. My doubts were mounting. *Is it just me? Am I fucked up and misreading the situation? No, no...you've been deployed before. This is all as real as it gets, but you've got no choice but to persevere through protecting your ground guys and team. You must carry on.* It was imperative to keep that perspective, as well as the light at the end of the tunnel in view, lest I fall from the path and into a darkness with no escape. *Three more months dude, just three more months.*

I needed to clear my head, so I spent two hours wandering the bazaar and enjoyed being alone, not having realized until then how much I was in need of actual solo time. As I was walking down the aisle, I caught sight of several pieces of lapis. The merchant and I had done business in the past, and I had also brought a buddy to him the last time I was in the bazaar. The merchant saw me.

"Hey man, you my homeboy! Come see what I have, nice lapis for my friend, hell yeah homie!" I'll be damned if he didn't have one of the nicest pieces of blue lapis lazuli stone I'd seen to date. It was giant and, of course, he wanted way too much money for it. We began to haggle, at times ripping on each other for trying to screw one another over. He finally remained set on his price, and I told him maybe next time.

"Come on, dog, you my homeboy, I give you best price for best customer! Why you no like this piece, I give you best price ever, business slow today and I barely make profit! Come on!"

I laughed at him and said that he'd have to sweeten the deal. We settled on another smaller piece of lapis for free, so I agreed to pay him. Our next issue with the deal of course was part of my deliberate bazaar tactic. I maintained that 50Af (Afghani) equals $1.00 USD, despite the minutely fluctuating exchange rate. The day of this bazaar visit, the USD just happened to be a little weaker against the Afghani than usual. When it came to final payment, I reverted to Afghani on him and he remembered me even more.

"You only carry Afghani?! Shit! Why you no have American money, American?!" He exclaimed.

I smirked at him and said, "You better take it, homeboy, it's all I've got and I would like to bring you back some business another day."

He shook his head but smiled a bit at my uncharacteristic ability to win one over on him, and accepted my offer. Part of their culture is bartering and pageantry. They seem to really enjoy it and engaging in it with them appears to earn a degree of respect in their eyes. After the pleasantries (if that's what you can call them) were over though, you could tell when they were finally ready to settle.

I moved on to an old man sitting in the dirt with piles of obsolete Afghan currency. A contractor had come over and squatted down next to us, waiting for his turn. The old man finally caved to my haggling and I received three stacks of old, worthless Afghan currency. The contractor muttered to his other civilian buddy that I had just gotten the good ones, and proceeded to not be nearly as decent to the old man as I had been.

I didn't generally like contractors, especially the sheer number of them that we had bloating the place, so I abruptly stood and left. Contractors made two or three times more money than the average soldier on base, and they appeared in many cases to do just as proportionately less work. They also easily outnumbered us. I wanted nothing to do with them. Perhaps it was jealousy for their salary-to-work ratio, or maybe I was just an asshole by that point. I hated everyone equally as far as I saw it, and I had a lot of cause for justifying it as far as I could plainly see.

Some kids had begun to show up in the past few weeks, all hawking piles of worthless little trinkets, bracelets, and other junk. They were like a stereotype in a movie, shouting, "Mister, mister, one dollar! One dollar, is good, all good!" The little freaks would mob someone and the only way to clear them out was to wave them off like swatting at flies and raising your voice.

Once I was almost outside the bazaar, a merchant caught me checking out his stone tea sets and stone goblets. *How can they see my eyes through my damn Ray-Bans?* I thought, a bit annoyed. The merchant stopped me as I tried to leave, and I reiterated that I did not have any more money. I asked him if I could take a picture, so that I could show my wife and ask her if she'd like me to buy any of his goods on my next bazaar visit. He opened his arms and said, "Of course, my friend, you take pictures, is okay, very nice things and I give you good deals, is all good business." I snapped two photos and thanked him, informing him that I'd be back and we'd talk next time. He then surprised me with an odd proposition.

"You take picture of me here, and when you come back, you give to me, huh?"

"You want a print out or something?" I asked. "We only have computer paper, it wouldn't be like getting it from a photography processing lab or anything." He waved the limitations off, agreeing that printing it on a printer would be fine. He then informed me that if I did this for him, he would give me extra special deals when I returned. It dawned on me that most Afghans don't have ready access to establishments such as Walgreens to print family photos, so I shrugged and told him it was a deal. He posed and I quickly snapped a shot, taking care to avoid any of the Air Force blue armband-wearing numb nuts from seeing me and approaching to confiscate my camera.

I was satisfied that I had gotten away with it successfully and the merchant and I shook hands. I often walked away wondering if I'd just shaken hands with an enemy sympathizer, financier, or actual fighter.

*

We were getting a new commander, and it would be a few more days before we could coordinate all of us to have a proper introduction or meeting with him. The change of command ceremony was a formality, and none of us had had any real time to even see our new boss. Changing command in the middle of a combat deployment seemed asinine to me, but it was yet another common practice in an increasingly asinine Army. The next morning would be a rehearsal, and then the live ceremony would immediately follow. Many of us ended up going to the Boardwalk in the evening, enjoying our last night hanging out with our current commander while he was still technically the boss. I knew that he was truly going to miss us, and he would probably hate his new job working in the circus that he was about to join. I was so glad to be a warrant officer and not nearly as at risk for a desk job as a commissioned officer. The thought of all-day-office-desk-sitting or, even worse, a cubicle, gave me goosebumps. Exchanging fire with bad guys was better than that in my mind, which was a bit humorous to me as I came to realize that about myself.

The next morning's ceremony was mercifully short. It was hot in the hangar and thankfully, no one got long-winded and basked in their importance while having the microphone. Most of us had missed a critical piece of info until we were standing in the formation about 10 minutes before the ceremony began. The Army, like all branches of the military, has an official song that all soldiers must learn. The funny part was that the already clunky song had changed, and a new verse had been added. Not only that, we were expected to know and sing it out, loud and proud. We all laughed hard as we were reminded of this, and to the dismay of the lieutenants, no one present knew what in the hell they were talking about. A few tried to quickly learn it, but no one even knew the tempo and the words were horribly convoluted and stupid. The attempts in singing it had us almost pissing ourselves laughing over how bad we sounded.

When it came time to sing during the ceremony, we, along with every other soldier in the hangar, sounded like total shit. The gap we heard where the new verse had been inserted was painful. Everyone tried to lip sync and pretend that they knew it, but a bunch of us were stifling fits of laughter and I was among the ones finally and loudly singing random silliness amidst the madness.

Eclectic and exotic trinkets in the bazaar.

A bazaar merchant ready to provide his very best deals.

Piles of obsolete Afghan currency.

The locally crafted lapis lazuli chess set I obtained as a gift for my father.

CHAPTER 29

Dear Soldier,
I am 8 years old. We want America to win.
Thank you for fighting for our country.
We appreciate you for that.
Love, Trey

The end of May was already fast approaching. I was asked by a few pilots why I even studied or worried about anything since I was getting out of the Army. The question of why I even cared anymore had been my biggest enemy and fallout from the "I'm getting out of the Army" statement I had made. Although I was someone who would have 12 years of their life and two deployments personally invested with the Army, I would be in no way thanked for that. Instead, myself and others separating from the ranks at the time would be seen as strange dissenters. The questions I got essentially amounted to, "Why aren't you giving up more?" and the decision and subsequent stigma from it was also essentially a branding. Anyone who had decided to leave before their 20-year retirement date was not understood. We joked amongst ourselves that many of our higher military leaders had risen to the top simply because the smart ones had gotten out. It was inconceivable by those remaining as to why someone would want to leave our institution. To them, the regular world was *actually* referred to as "The Outside," as if we were in some sort of prison system.

Despite my personal feelings, I was still currently serving in the system and had even volunteered to do so. As such, I was not going to stop caring about everything altogether like some expected me to do. Many who were separating from the Army were so intensely burned out that they ended up being quite worthless in their last year. While I awaited my separation date, I didn't want to be worthless. It was imperative that I suck it up and find the drive to continue on.

The temperatures during the day had been well exceeding the 100-degree mark. It was all complemented by a hot, dry, dusty wind that hit you in the face and baked your skin. Locals wore those signature scarves of theirs for a reason. We were not allowed to wear anything like that because it wouldn't look professional. We did so while flying in lieu of the face shield occasionally because, again, who really gives a shit about that sort of thing? Our crew chiefs could not even wear the light moisture-wicking combat shirts we pilots wore while we flew. When the crew chiefs worked on aircraft in the dead heat, they couldn't wear the combat shirts because it didn't "appear professional." They couldn't even take off their uniform tops. We'd rather lose crew chiefs as heat casualties than to allow them to use an issued and approved garment designed to protect them, all because someone thought it didn't look the same as what their cognitively challenged brain believed was the professional appearing "standard." Dehydration had become our number one enemy as we acclimatized to the new and ever-enduring heat wave that would remain until we left the country.

*

By May 30th, operations had picked back up and we'd been busy. We were not necessarily flying any more or any less, but it did seem that we had been busier out in the AO. I'd flown the last three mornings in a row, and the lull we'd experienced as of late was over. Along with Hadji's morning cup of tea, he liked to greet the day with IEDs and attacks on patrols. Luckily, by this point in the war, we had plenty of overhead surveillance eyes out there. What would then ensue was a game of cat and mouse.

Our team flew in a pattern attempting to not let Hadji know what we were seeing. Our Lead aircraft remarked, "Trail, we've got this fucker digging to emplace an IED. Time to send his sorry ass to Allah to be with his 72 male virgins. Grid to follow." We laughed in my aircraft. Before I hit "record" on the MMS for a potential engagement, my aircraft responded with, "You do know that such a prospect is exciting to them, right? Okay, time to be politically correct though, because we're going Hollywood."

"Roger, Hollywood," they responded with acknowledgement of the key phrase for recording, also hitting record on their MMS as well. Once again, the horrible rules of engagement web had to be traversed. Multiple gates, considerations, transmissions, permissions, and lists had to be carefully navigated. If any of the restrictions even so much as hinted at raising a concern or warning flag, our war for the day was put on pause. The mouse won again, as we had plainly seen him bury an IED and be hostile, yet a few technicalities that remain secret were frustratingly in our way of killing him. There's no doubt that we really, really wanted to kill him, too. However, I really, really didn't want to eat sloppy shitty government food in a giant military prison due to an investigation ruling against us, either.

IEDs are a terrible thing, and the hostility that I was feeling was due in part to the previous day where I witnessed a little girl about the age of six that was cut in half by an IED. I suppose she weighed just enough to set the thing off, like a giant land mine. We flew immediately towards the smoking cloud billowing up into the sky and had been so close that we felt the concussion of the blast. Villagers came pouring out of nowhere, sprinting across fields and roads to converge on the small dirt path where the little girl lay in contorted bloody pieces. The horrific scene seared into my brain, but at present, I couldn't afford to get upset. It was amazing how fast they had the body covered up and into the back of a vehicle.

The body was transported to a village only a few hundred meters away. Multiple elders stood around the back of the vehicle, animated and gesturing wildly. They then pulled the remains out of the vehicle and quickly moved into the village and out of sight. It appeared that a local villager who moonlighted as an insurgent was trying to get one of our guys or an Afghan patrol and had instead nailed one of theirs.

This was the real side of our war.

What I was witnessing was just the way that the country was, is, and will continue to be. Once our coalition forces finally departed, the battle for the area below would continue until the Taliban and/or insurgency groups became inevitably victorious. The local Afghan military and police forces didn't stand a chance. It actually seemed that most of them were only trying to survive and go through the motions, waiting for us to leave so that they could turn it all over peacefully and avoid any sort of further danger or confrontation.

Recently, a documentary was posted online by Vice Media Group called *This is What Winning Looks Like,* and word spread quickly. Much of the content shown was the stuff that was held under wraps and not talked about. It was important, and I was passionate about urging every single American to watch it and to start asking a lot of questions. It had been filmed close to us during part of our current deployment, and it proved successful in validating and confirming what we knew and witnessed in our own area. They showed the truth about what was going on, a key vantage point being provided by their reporter embedded with a group of Marines trying to train and assist Afghans in taking over operations in and around their villages.

Across our AO, FOBs and COPs continued to slowly be either turned over to the Afghans, or simply dismantled and leveled to leave only a giant patch of dirt where they once stood. The Afghans were being forced to finally settle their own affairs without using the United States Treasury and its military to solve their problems. As welcome as the idea appeared on paper, reality could be quite different.

It was well known by those fighting outside the wire that our Afghan National Police and National Army allies should only receive the most cautious or tenuous trust. Aside from Taliban infiltrators and insider attacks against our soldiers and other government personnel helping to train and assist the Afghans, the Afghan forces would also occasionally turn on their own people.

This was most disturbingly true when it came to those who lusted after and abused local young boys. The kids were known as "Chai Boys," and most had been abducted from nearby villages and forced into sexual and physical slavery in outlying Afghan outposts and bases. The practice was widespread, and appeared more normal and harmless than taboo. In the aforementioned documentary, a conversation between Marines and a senior Afghan police official demonstrated the attitude towards the practice perfectly after the Marines voiced their concerns. Children were raped, abused, and some were even murdered in their course of being Chai Boys, and there was nothing that U.S. forces could really do to stop it.

Several uniformed Afghan Police and Military were also routinely high. Sometimes, it was not only marijuana in their systems, which is unsurprising considering Afghanistan's chief export appeared to be opium marked for heroin or other illicit drug production. Back when I flew in the Tagab Valley, stoned Afghan police wildly shot machine guns into the air one evening. I saw the police stumbling about, obviously having one hell of a party as their tracers arc'd up into the sky. That's where we were, so we didn't appreciate the light show. After many attempts to have them stop over their obviously unmonitored radio, we were told to just stay out of the way.

Flying one night in Kandahar, my team experienced the exact same thing. The difference in the KAF AO was that we would also get hit by lasers. A laser to the eyes of a pilot is a Felony offense in the U.S. and much of the civilized world, but our idiot Afghan allies would laze us just for kicks occasionally. We called up to our TOC, reporting the events while being pissed off and contesting that it was a hostile act, but not a thing was ever actually done about it.

It was a hard situation. Among the ranks of ANA and ANP, there were soldiers and police who were actually trying to do the right thing. Their country was a dangerous mess, and some fought as best they could with the poor resources and support available to them. Interpreters, or "terps," living and fighting with our forces faced earned scrutiny because of the high rate of double agents. That being said, many terps risked their lives to help take back Afghanistan alongside their U.S. counterparts. Especially loyal and helpful ones could be rewarded through a program to resettle themselves and their families to the United States, which was a life-and-death important step should the enemy figure out where they lived.

The problem was, it was nearly impossible to tell who was truly good or bad.

We began to see further evidence of the Afghan forces slowly taking over operations as our U.S. forces disappeared almost altogether from some areas. Of course, this was a good thing and needed to happen, but in the interim while some of us were still deployed, the situation presented a unique challenge. Our visually confirmed withdrawal was a sure propaganda win for an emboldened enemy. As our forces shrank, we were sure that attacks on the remainder would get more frequent and intense. Rather than sit by and bide their time like smart tacticians would do, the local dumbasses would rather keep up or even increase their attacks.

✶

Lately, I'd seen a lot of rounds fly. Until a few days prior, I'd never seen a Mark-19 automatic grenade launcher exchanging fire with heavy, Soviet-made machine guns from ruins and tree lines. That all kicks up a ton of dust, by the way, and it was an incredible sight to behold. We had actually stumbled upon the fighting. The battle was taking place very far to the west of our AO—so far, in fact, that the ones below were Marines on the extreme eastern side of their area. The nearest FARP was actually quite far away, and we had no communications with the Marines fighting. Because of the lack of communications, all that we could do about it was "observe and report" to our TOC. The possibility of killing a Marine by not understanding where all of their men were located was too great a risk for us to engage from the air, ROE concerns or not.

Below, the Marines had taken note of our presence and used the opportunity from our minimal coverage to run fast around the small grouping of qalats and reset their formation. It was a small compound surrounded by low walls and ruins, with a patch of tree line and vegetation close to the north abutting the beginnings of a steep high ground. It was obvious that insurgents were hiding in there, taking advantage of the cover and, in all probability, using an unseen cave system. I felt helpless and angry; inter-service rivalries are bullshit when rounds are flying and Marine infantrymen are just as important to us as any other U.S. force out there. Our TOC was unfortunately unable to give us any definitive information.

The turret atop one of the vehicles stopped shooting grenades, and the Marine disappeared momentarily into the vehicle interior. Dirt kicked up on the sides of a few vehicles as enemy rounds thumped and ricocheted away from the armor plating. The thick glass from the turret gunners' windows was spider-web cracked and opaque from stopping bullets. The front of a vehicle facing the tree line took a severe string of rounds, and I hoped that none penetrated the windshields or managed to damage the engine compartment. Apparently out of grenades, the Marine I had seen in the turret popped back up, surprisingly boosting himself over the protection of his armored paneling and firing his rifle while exposed to the incoming enemy rounds. *God, I love these guys,* I thought with swelled pride over their display of bravery. The Marines were not retreating; they were inching towards the tree line instead. I wanted to help so badly, but even throwing a smoke grenade into the tree line would only confuse the Marines, who may mistake it for a marker of an enemy position. Since we couldn't pinpoint the enemy fighters yet, all we could do was aggressively dance above in an attempt to fool the enemy into thinking we may soon take action against them. We'd learned to use Hadji's doubt and uncertainty from American helicopters overhead at every possible moment it was advantageous. We couldn't shoot, but the enemy didn't know that yet.

Marines made a mad dash to the next set of cover, a low ditch and crumbling wall closer to the tree line. They were bounding, using part of the platoon and vehicles to lay cover fire while others surged forward when the enemy heads were down.

"Whoa dude, they're gonna advance right into those trees!" Trail remarked. A vehicle lurched and then began moving forward toward the trees, grenades flying and shredding timber and foliage. A Marine waved and more men ran forwards. Two men crouching behind a vehicle were on a radio, looking up at us. *I know guys, I wish I could hear you, too!* I thought. Their faces showed an intensity, like they were saying the same to me in return. Another wave of covering fire began, and more Marines bounded forwards.

"*Bong!*" We looked at our fuel gauge. Although we'd previously noted our fuel and briefed a bingo or low-fuel strategy, this was very inopportune given the situation.

"Damnit! Trail, Lead. We got a bit sidetracked and we just started bonging. We gotta get to a FARP, ASAP." Trail cursed and said that they had just noted that they only had under bingo fuel themselves, but my aircraft was definitely the low bird. It was unfathomable to think that in the most critical moment, we would have to leave the overhead position we'd taken for the Marines. We swooped down low by the vehicles, and I tried to sign to a few men that we were low on gas and had to fly away. They looked confused, and I tried again, doing my damndest to figure out how to best display the most critical bit of charades signing I'd ever have to do in my life. More Marines charged towards the tree line, and more rounds flew. *"Bong, bong!"* We had no choice—we had to go, and go now!

Our aircraft panicked and bonged as we tried to fly at economy settings as best we could to conserve our precious remaining fuel. There were no friendlies anywhere near. A desert loomed to our south, and brown nothingness spanned to the horizon ahead.

"This is gonna be close," I remarked, and we discussed our plan in the event our engine began to flame out. After flying what seemed like forever, a small FARP was finally nearby and we still miraculously had a chance of making it. We flew on, sweating bullets and talking to Trail.

We landed right on the FARP pad, and I didn't even want to look at our fuel gauge. We'd made it, and I took on more gas than usual. We radioed our TOC and asked them for an update on the Marines we'd been supporting. They'd just had a shift change apparently.

"What Marines?"

Like most times we'd get ourselves involved in such things, I was rarely able to learn how the event ended. I had long ago learned to accept living with a lack of closure, and I could only hope that they all made it out okay.

⋆

It was more and more evident that Hadji was figuring out when to conduct his activities, and, more importantly, how to do so while keeping our hands tied from engaging. I suppose we had to "save face" with the media and international community, though, and couldn't afford any kind of bad press, choosing instead to sacrifice a few of us pawns here and there. Of course, besides the Vice media guys who created the earlier mentioned documentary, what we were doing felt pretty much disregarded. No one would know of the heroic charge against an unseen enemy I had just witnessed, in a forgotten battle, in a forgotten war.

I supposed we were too busy focusing on arming Syrian rebels who had ties to Hezbollah and other wide-reaching terrorism networks. Those assholes were basically training themselves and executing their guerrilla tactics with improvements and our backing. *History not learned from is doomed to repeat itself.* Some of the ones that we fought in Afghanistan were trained by us during their fight with the Soviets during war in the 1980s. We seemed to have overlooked that fact, and the "freedom fighters" would almost surely set up a nice sanctuary in Syria once their official government was toppled. Was the current Syrian government a better alternative? Russia thought so; we appeared not to think so. The proper answer in my eyes was who in the hell cares, let them annihilate each other. We had enough to worry about at home. Why we believed that Middle Eastern conflicts were our responsibility continued to perplex me. I was of the opinion to get our military the hell out of the region, a region that was painted red by the blood of Americans fighting for a hopeless cause. I realized once after talking to Matt that we didn't know what our "official mission" statement was anymore. We would ask, "Why in the hell are we still here?!" The vague reply was usually, "You're supporting the Government of the Islamic Republic of Afghanistan (GIRoA) and assisting it in transitioning itself to being able to operate and exist in its own sovereignty."

Every life that we lost in pursuit of that goal upset me further and further, and it was becoming very hard to bear the thought that it would continue.

We were six months into our nine-month deployment with intensifying operations and temperatures. Although I had previously spent 12 months in Afghanistan in another area doing the same things, we had reached a different level in Kandahar. My give-a-shit factor had reached dangerously low levels for who I offended or upset by that point. Like a 90-year-old man, my verbal filter was all but broken. What raw truth we spoke was sometimes as abrasive as a cheese grater across the skin followed by salt. I got that. What was so hard to deal with was that the military was where we were because of our government's inability to properly function. We were not keeping our citizens safe at home, because we were on loan by our government more than 8,000 miles away assisting another government. Unlike the immediate post-9/11 years where we were kicking ass, taking names, and killing those networks responsible, we had a massive shift in focus and rules occur somewhere down the line. The only people we were keeping safe were each other, and that would continue to be the case until it all one day hopefully ended. In our current day, a strong and resilient portrait of the American military was painted on the surface. I maintained that if one were to peel back a little of that paint and ask soldiers to tell the truth about what was really going on, the combat arms ones especially would paint a very different and unexpected picture.

I wrote all of those things home furiously in an effort to both get it off my chest and also with the belief that the American reader was entitled to know more of the truth about what was going on with their government and its forces. Almost all of my squadron-mates appeared to insulate their loved ones, preferring to keep these sorts of things from their families and friends. Even if I disagreed with their silence, I still wholeheartedly respected their wishes. I kept my writing home quiet for a reason.

CHAPTER 30

"It took me 20 minutes to get approval to put my shoes on this morning."

-CW2 Brian Fullen

I was set to fly on a "Hunter-Killer Team," which was a non-politically correct, yet often-used synonym for Pink Team. Early in our mission window, I received what could be called an "honorable mention" from our Apache as I wailed away at a target with my M4 out the left side of the helicopter. We were a decent distance away, but I'd gotten pretty good with the thing. A lot of ballistic factors had to be taken into account and calculated on the fly when you were firing a rifle while hanging out of the cockpit of a helicopter. The Apache saw the bullet impacts with his super sensors and complimented my shooting. It felt good to know that at least my bullets were still working right.

That was just enough to cheer me up a bit. The upcoming month was discussed at chow, and it was going to be special. "Jacked June" was beginning, and it would be celebrated by copious amounts of working out. The goal was to gain as much strength and attain the highest level of whatever your personal physical fitness goals may be. I was personally striving to cut down a little more weight (despite losing 15 pounds in the past several months) and to gain quite a bit more of my former strength back. I had already been working out for two hours after completing my long 12-hour days. When I returned back to the room, I would feel like I'd gotten my ass kicked.

Fatigued mentally and physically, I had been on a "Sleep, Wake, Prep, Fly, Debrief, Workout, Eat, Sleep, Repeat" schedule. I would get a snack here and there throughout the day, but a proper meal was impossible with the current schedule, so I did what I could. When I tried to stay up and make dinner chow, I learned the hard way that I was just screwing myself out of a few hours of precious sleep.

Despite how unappealing that schedule sounds, it was actually the best one I'd been on yet. Life was simple, and we were left entirely alone and to our own devices. That was all. No games and no stupidity, because we were sleeping or off shift by the time any nonsense would start up.

I made the long climb (only because I was so sore) from my desk under my bunk to the topside with my bed. It was like the Siren's call of an awaiting reward for enduring yet another daunting day.

"Quit bitching, you sound pathetic," mumbled Matt from his desk a few feet across the room.

"Screw you, old man!" I retorted and then let out a very real sigh of relief as I plopped down in my bunk. I cursed once more, rolled out and hit the floor hard in a practiced maneuver to simultaneously don my shower shoes while contacting the ground. Matt knew that I had forgotten to pee and laughed hard at me as I flipped him off and made the walk to the bathroom. I then repeated the climb into my bunk with the same sounds, eliciting the same back and forth jabs.

Right before drifting off to sleep, I pulled my headphones off my ears as I saw Matt standing up from his desk to climb the bed. He moaned and groaned, and I laughed at him weakly from my dark corner.

"Who's the bitch now?" I chided him between yawns. Matt hinted at an apology for laughing at me in the first place, because the climb was a lot more painful than he had anticipated. We then both fell asleep in under a minute.

The second week of June began with a temperature of 108°F. We swore that things were seconds away from melting. The sun had been completely unobscured and beat down on us, doing so with a ferocity that you'd think only existed in movies and cartoons. "No wonder this is the birthplace of the

Taliban," one of our crew chiefs remarked. "This place would turn *anyone* into a psychotic asshole bent on destruction."

We were doing maintenance a favor by starting and running one of the helicopters to ensure that a few repaired systems were functioning properly. I looked out towards the horizon for no real reason, and I noted that it was suddenly dark and very brown-looking in the distance. I'd seen this before, and became a little more alert.

I was standing outside the helicopter with my helmet on and connected to chat with the guy actually starting the helicopter on this particular check and run-up. I mentioned to him that it looked bad on the horizon, and may be getting worse. We both got a bad feeling and began speeding the checks up, as bad weather could possibly be coming and we didn't want to be outside anymore. There was also the damage that could be done to helicopter blades as they spun through an air mass filled with tiny rocks.

Just then, one of our maintenance pilots came running down the line, waving like a maniac at me. Laughing at how ridiculous he looked, I unplugged from the helicopter, letting the right seater know that I was going to intercept him and see what in the world was going on.

He pointed briefly to the rapidly growing darkness in the distance. He then only had to yell one word while cupping his hands and shouting from half a football field away.

"HAAA-BOOOOOOB!"

Just then, I watched in frozen awe as a mountain range a few miles behind him was hit and engulfed by a sudden tidal wave of sand and dust. A haboob is a type of violent dust storm that's carried on an atmospheric gravity current. It looks apocalyptic and can cause significant damage. Thank goodness they are so enormous that you can see them coming. I spun around and ran back to our idling Kiowa. The right seater was staring wide at the sight of the enormous brown mass moving towards us. I plugged my helmet in, and my buddy exclaimed excitedly, "That whole mountain range is gone, did you see that?!"

He still didn't fully appreciate the situation yet. I responded, "YES! Now, shut this thing down before that haboob whoops our asses! I'll get the doors and covers!"

He nodded in agreement, chopped the throttle to idle, and began the required two-minute countdown. I ran to the aircraft plywood storage boxes on the parking pad and grabbed the doors and coverings. I put his door on and ran around to my side, tossing my helmet into the seat. I watched as more of the mountains closest to us were silhouetted by the oncoming wave. The helicopter's engine immediately ceased with an emergency shutdown. We did not have time for two minutes of cool down. The pilot yanked up hard on the controls in an effort to slow down the rotor blades now free spinning with no engine providing power. By pulling up on the collective control, the blades could twist to bite into more air, which in turn caused more air resistance to slow them faster.

I grabbed the weapon and air filter coverings and began to frantically fasten them all, looking back over my shoulder just in time to see the tidal wave consume the last mountain and swallow the entire horizon in a maelstrom of brown and darkness. We both snapped out of our pause from what we'd just witnessed, and my maintenance buddy yelled excitedly, "We gotta get the hell outta here, dude!"

Still wearing my gloves and with the rotors spinning rather fast, I jumped up and thrust my hand towards the leading edge of the nearest spinning blade, getting the hell knocked out of my hand. I did this again and again until my beaten and bruised hand and arm acted as a rotor stop. The right seater gathered our stuff from inside the cockpit as me and the maintenance pilot quickly tied down the two forward rotor blades. The storm was bearing down on us, and there was no time to do anything else. The other pilot had just cleared the cockpit and thrust my helmet into my hands, and then, we started running.

It was a quarter mile from our helicopter parking area to the indoor safety of our troop, dodging in between concrete barricades and braving thousands of large, ankle snapping rocks between the taxi rows. We watched in disbelief as the landing strip only a few hundred yards away disappeared. The sun was blotted out and the day turned to an ominous dusk. I ran into the troop, followed by the other two. We choked, panted, and coughed.

About 30 seconds after we entered the troop, the full force of the storm hit. Strangely, the wind could not be heard, and someone unwisely opened the door to peer outside. The poor decision was met by a face full of dust and sand. He shut the door hard and came away coughing. I was too close and got gritty teeth as I tried to cough away the awful mess. Thirty minutes later, the bulk of the storm had passed, and everything outside was coated in a layer of grit and grime. It's how the desert says "hi."

*

A few days later while out flying, we had cause to visit one of our lesser traveled U.S.-operated FARPs to the north. We landed to refuel and rearm at FOB Frontenac's FARP, and the FARP personnel were feeling a bit froggy, so they began messing with me. I was in the left seat, and a few of them approached with too many rockets. I waved them off, and they nodded, then retreated back to the ammo storage to put the remainder away. All except for one guy. The young specialist kept acting like he understood, then would turn back around and run towards the Kiowa with his rocket, grinning. Finally I got him to go back to the others, looking a bit dejected that we didn't feel quite as playful as they were. The FARP guys were our lifelines and critical support lynchpin in keeping a battle going, and we all appreciated the hell out of them. This particular crew was located in a rather desolate and forgotten area, nestled near a large and nice-looking lake, which they never got to see. Little did they know, I was hiding my cards that I could play, too.

There existed a stupid and crude "Circle Game," adapted from a movie and widely played just for fun. It was simple: Make a circle with your thumb and pointer finger. Get someone to look at said circle, and they were crassly vilified and you got to kick them in the ass, or at least make fun of them. I understood that the FARP guys knew the game well, but they didn't expect that a pilot would participate.

Just as we began to pick up to a hover, I quickly signaled for the FARP crew's attention. I had five eager sets of eyes on me, ready to see what we needed.

We pedal turned the aircraft at a three-foot hover so that the FARP crew was outside the rotor disk and on the left side, looking intently and spring-loaded right at me. I pulled off my maxillofacial shield and raised my visor so that they could see my full face. I then pulled my hand quickly to my face, making the peace symbol and pointing to my eyes in the universal tactical signal for "Look!" They were following my every move now, and suddenly I thrust my hand low to my side, making a perfect circle with my thumb and pointer finger.

Their mouths all dropped. I had circled all five of them. I pulled my fist to my face, acting as if I was shoving an object down my throat and pointed to each of them and mouthed obscene remarks. They lost their minds laughing, throwing their arms up into the air. I smirked, flipped them off, and we buzzed past in a quick takeoff as one fell to his knees with hands outstretched to the sky screaming and laughing. At least out in our element, we managed to entertain ourselves despite the crushing blows we received from higher all of the time. A few days later, I had cause to once again land at that FARP, and I was given a high five and treated like a hero. I had gotten them good.

At the point where we were, the war felt like it was nearly over. One of my coping mechanisms for just how horrible it had all gotten was to continue my focus on something that I enjoyed. If I was not gainfully employed trying to protect or save ground guys, then I was going to be practicing photography. I came to the conclusion that this was the best way to keep myself from going crazy, so I bought a book on the operation of and best uses for my specific camera.

The way that I saw it, I was on what would be my last combat deployment and the last time that I would truly get to shoot photos from the vantage point that I currently had. I wanted to continue to take advantage of the unique photographic platform before it was gone for good. It was no secret that I had been taking pictures from helicopters for years, but I had just decided recently to really try hard to appreciate what a unique opportunity it was and relish it until the end. If anything, it helped me attempt positivity when all hell was happening around me and continuing to threaten my and everyone else's sanity.

I felt as though I had been drinking water bottles by the minute. In all reality, within the previous 48 hours, I had possibly drank 48 water bottles. The cotton-mouth feeling that remained from such hot desert temperatures only left me needing more. At least I was one of the half not suffering from headaches and pains due to dehydration and my pee was remarkably clear. All were good signs for sure.

Back home, Lindsey continued to video chat with me. Scout had gotten a new raccoon plush toy and I was enjoying the videos that Lindsey had been sending of Scout fighting the raccoon. It was fun to talk to Scout and watch her cock her head and nose the iPad. It did make me a little sad when she began to run around looking for me, but I knew that she was wagging her tail because she heard me and I didn't want her to forget my voice.

I looked on as a few people departed early for home. I was jealous, but that light at the end of the tunnel was at least off in the distance somewhere. Hadji was still blowing people up and we were still blowing him up, but it all had an expiration date approaching—for our unit, at least. Our replacements would be showing up before we knew it. I would be very happy once June was over and July had started, since that would mark a significant milestone in our preparations to go home, and the reality of it all would really take hold.

*

June trudged onwards, and I became a lot more busy. Temperatures hovered in the 110°F+ range. I had flown 12 hours in the previous three days, and I was also looking at a heavy flying schedule through the end of the week.

I snapped back to the present when our Apache wingman asked, "You're gonna do what?"

We were getting shot at by something heavy, buried deep in a twisting maze of dense foliage and earthen ruins. An older, partially destroyed compound was reported to have fire emanating from the courtyard. Hammer 46 had been working the area for a while, and they knew the hotbeds well. Each time we flew over their position and subsequently began taking contact, Hammer elements listened to the gunfire and tried to narrow down the possible locations of origin. We flew fast, low, and with varied flight paths. This was the perfect scenario to be operating our Pink Team—one Kiowa down low hunting and drawing fire (and generally stirring things up), while one Apache covered us from way up high.

"I said we're gonna fly over the compound that keeps shooting at us, and I'm gonna drop a smoke grenade into the courtyard so you can work up the engagement," I replied. There were too many similar structures and compounds clustered together, and I wasn't able to verbally describe the precise area in which the Apaches would potentially need to engage.

"Okay, just let us know when you're about to drop it," the Apache replied. "Please be careful!"

Our aircraft whirled around and ducked low, heading straight for the compound. Tree tops zipped by mere feet below our skids. A winding maze of irrigation canals and foliage-dense clusters blurred by. Green, healthy plants clustered tightly to their tiny life-source of water, obscuring the narrow canals and earthen channeling walls almost completely. I held tight to a smoke grenade in my left hand and pulled the pin with my right once I had the grenade out the door with my outstretched arm. I heard the snaps and taps from missed rounds coming from a different concealed position somewhere close below. We hurried forward.

"Yellow smoke, in 3-2-1!" I tossed it and we pulled up hard and away. The firing stopped; the enemy realized that they'd just been marked and were no doubt scurrying to hide. I couldn't have been more proud of my toss, observing a yellow plume of smoke billowing up from the center of the small courtyard, right where I'd wanted it to land. The Apache grumbled about my tactic, but congratulated the successful smoke toss. They saw brief movement, and then nothing.

"Wrath 53, Hammer 46. We don't hear any more shooting. You must've scared them into hiding. The shooting from our west along the canals has also stopped. Nice work, guys!"

Unfortunately, the stalemate only lasted 30 minutes, and I soon found our team marking a hasty PZ for a MEDEVAC. An ANA soldier had taken a round to the chest, and his condition was rapidly worsening. We wanted to shoot into the dirt and make noise in an area devoid of any collateral damage concerns or possibility of injuries to friendlies or civilians, but the request was denied. Our team orbited and then closely covered the MEDEVAC, which fortunately swooped in and out of the field in what felt like under a minute. Hammer elements were on their way out of the area and had no further requests for coverage, so we stuck with the MEDEVAC bird as it raced to the hospital. Fortunately for the ANA soldier, despite suffering a tension pneumothorax, he was stabilized by the medics and given a positive prognosis after they relieved the pressure in his chest cavity. Even though the AO was "calming down," more thanks to our slow withdrawal and turnover of the fight, we still had some interesting days ahead. We continued onward with our standard cat-and-mouse game with the enemy, and escorted convoys and MEDEVACs where necessary.

On my following flight, we briefed, and then went out to fly a standard patrol. I watched an insurgent-held town that was otherwise abandoned get blown to hell, and then bulldozed to dust. It was literally suitable as a dirt parking lot afterwards. As cool as that was, a lot of blood had to be shed before it came to that. . . too much, in my opinion.

This was not the first time that this had happened, either. As we continued our draw down and turned over certain areas, the enemy continued to gain strength and territory. It was becoming indisputably evident that our presence was more and more pointless. New restrictions had forced us to operate in the least effective manner than I had ever flown the Kiowa helicopter. We were not sure if anything else could happen that would really surprise us or make matters worse, but we found that we should never say never.

We'd become so hands-tied that we spent much of our time only wasting taxpayer money on jet fuel. The only consolation for our continued flying was that, albeit few, Americans remained on the ground. These unfortunate souls were still slogging it out with the enemy down there, and they managed to find solace in our presence above, so that kept me happy to help them. We might not have been able to do nearly as much as we used to in order to assist them, but oftentimes, just our presence overhead was enough to keep them safe. Our protective instincts and love for those we protected remained fierce. That was probably the only reason we hadn't all gone completely nuts. At least we still meant a lot to a small percentage of people that I trusted loved us just as much in return.

*

Before I knew it, another 10 days had passed. Jacked June had sped by like mad. I managed to get another three days of flying in, but just barely, thanks to the weather. Conditions outside had turned very dusty and affected the required visibility. The temperatures were also still averaging about 110°F in the day with practically no wind.

A few days prior, we had conducted a cookout behind the troop. This came about from a bet between Charlie and Bravo Troop regarding a large scavenger hunt. Both of our troop commanders had picked out 40 different sites in the various areas that we flew. We got little flip books containing only pictures of what we were looking for. The object was to find the different buildings, objects, etc., on the cards and then take a picture and get a grid location on the map. Once you returned from a mission, if you'd seen any of the points and gathered the proper proof, you were to bring it to the opposing troop commander to prove that you'd found it.

We were tasked with some easy ones to find, and some very odd and incredibly difficult things to find. There were many district centers, odd structures, strange markers and statues, you name it. The search area was incredibly vast, but it also gave us something fun and encouraging to do. I was impressed by the stroke of genius in creating the scavenger hunt, providing a friendly, yet heated, competition between the two line troops. The added benefit was that scouting for things was our bread and butter, so finding a way to exercise and hone those skills was also welcome.

Unfortunately, the way that our teams were stacked (and probably because Bravo Troop cheated somehow), we lost by only a few points. The losing troop had to cook for the winning troop, but we ended up with an insane amount of food and fed anyone in the entire area that wanted our fantastically grilled and seasoned goodies. I couldn't recall how many wings and ribs that we had seasoned and grilled that afternoon, but the event was a big hit and I didn't care whether or not we had won or lost. I looked around, and saw a rarity: Everyone was smiling. I recalled our higher leadership once remarking that soldiers smiling and joking was a sign of poor unit discipline. What a crock— that couldn't have been further from the truth. We all laughed and ate well, appreciating the extremely rare occasion of good food and fun. I applauded the ingenious strategy employed by both Bravo and Charlie Troop's commanders to contrive the much-needed, morale-boosting event.

Just after our BBQ, I received surprisingly good news out of the blue. American Eagle, a commuter wing of American Airlines, was looking at assisting former military helicopter pilots in making the transition to flying for the airlines. This was fantastic news—I could use all of the help that I could get. The details, in a nutshell, were that they would be relaxing a few of the more stringent requirements that made such a transition unattainable for most. In my case, already having some airplane time, I would be well lined up and hoped to take full advantage of what they were offering. Ironically, I had also recently spent 45 minutes sitting in a turbo-prop Army C-12 airplane, known to the rest of the world as a King Air. I was up in the cockpit with a very senior pilot who showed me around and talked me through an entire mock flight. It was awesome and very motivating for me. Just the smell of the airplane made me happy. Turbine airplanes seemed to have a certain smell to me, and growing up around them had made me acutely aware. I was drawn to it; there is a dead tie between the two best smells on earth: jet exhaust and gunpowder. Honorable mentions go to triple-smoked jerky and single-malt scotch. When I could experience all four in one day, there was no greater happiness.

CHAPTER 31

The Crash of Jay and Stu

June 2013, Kandahar Airfield, Afghanistan
Security Zone: Scout Weapons Team, Shift 5
Narrative by CW2 Jay Amarillo (Member, Team Brown)

The day started off like any other. It was about 115°F, and the ride to Mustang Ramp felt like I was sitting in a pizza oven. I was scheduled to fly on a standard SWT and was paired with CW4 Stuart Crews. Our Trail ship was crewed by 1LT Mathew Palange and CW2 Caleb Sharpe. After meeting up in Charlie Troop at about 1230, we prepped all of our flight gear and additional equipment for the mission. After signing out all required equipment, it was time to receive our mission brief before launching. Both crews walked over to the TOC to receive our mission brief and mission products. The brief began with an overview of climatology for our flight period. The mission for the day was to provide overhead security for any ground forces that may be outside the wire in the "Horn of Panjwai."

The Panjwai was a current, and historic, IED hotbed for insurgent activity. The fact that two U.S. outposts had shut down in the previous week had allowed for increased Taliban activity within the horn. Our mission brief also consisted of a group of Taliban operators that had been operating in a nearby village. Men had been spotted by a UAV while planting IEDs along routes utilized by U.S. Special Forces. There were also reports of IEDs that had been struck by ANA and ANP vehicles. The final part of the brief consisted of our ROE guidelines, as well as other pertinent data and info for the day.

After the mission brief, we grabbed some food in the chow hall on Mustang Ramp. We all sat down to eat, and our spirits were high. We were joking around as usual, making light of any situation just to break up the monotony. After finishing our meal, we walked back to Charlie Troop and grabbed our gear. We walked out to the aircraft with about 30 minutes left until launch and conducted our preflight checks.

I climbed into the aircraft and strapped into my position as the left seater for that day. Our aircraft, tail number 569, had been outfitted with one K2A Hellfire Missile on the right side and the .50 cal M3P machine gun in the standard position on the left side. The Trail ship, 328, had been outfitted with a .50 cal on the left and a rocket pod on the right. After completing all of the required-before-takeoff checks, we air taxied to the FARP in order to load up the weapon systems. Once armed, we lined up for departure from KAF to head out to our initially assigned grid out in the Security Zone and the Panjwai area.

After departing KAF, we entered the AO and checked in with the controlling ground forces. No significant activities were reported, but they mentioned that an SF team was in enemy contact out in a neighboring area. We proceeded southwest towards the Registan Desert and checked in with the area where the SF team was located. Three separate SF teams were currently taking enemy fire. Upon receiving the information, I navigated our team towards the fight in order to establish communication and support Panther 09.

The three teams were primarily located on top of three separate mud hut roofs, with additional elements also within the courtyards. We began to fly left orbits over each position in an effort to identify the insurgents and their firing positions. As we orbited, I noticed plumes of dust, as if IEDs were exploding. The plumes seemed to follow our ground track. I asked Stu to begin right orbits to see if fire was being directed to us. The plumes continued to follow our ground track, and then I noticed a military-aged male (MAM) in the grape rows to the south with a recoilless rifle. He was attempting to shoot down our aircraft.

An instant later, I noticed a motorcycle on the north side of the southernmost SF team's position. As we flew over the position, the motorcycle suddenly exploded. The IED had been planted for Panther 09, but instead, the insurgents attempted to use it to destroy our aircraft.

While conducting our aerial reconnaissance, I was also speaking with the teams on the ground. They described so many different locations where the enemy fire was coming from that it seemed like we were going to run out of letter identifiers for each target. We got a request from Panther 09 for immediate attack on a MAM riding a motorcycle towards the west. The MAM had just fired at the SF team using a PKM machine gun. Unfortunately, one of his rounds had also just grazed one of the rooftop-positioned SF snipers. Panther 09 relayed the grid location of the MAM, and also notified us that a Predator UAV had visual confirmation of the target. The MAM was immediately labeled "Target Golf," and he was being tracked by the UAV, callsign Osprey 11.

We maneuvered south into the Registan Desert again. This was in an effort to obtain standoff distance so that the UAV could develop the movement pattern of the target. After flying west and just south of Target Golf, our window of opportunity to eliminate the threat opened up. I began to coordinate the clearance of fires through Panther 09. As he worked out the ROE clearance, our team maneuvered to set up an east-to-west engagement. Meanwhile, Target Golf continued westbound.

I was receiving updates from Osprey 11 as to the location of the target. Our team was currently west of the main village on the western side of the horn of Panjwai. We were flying about 130 feet above the ground, maneuvering tactically so that the target would not get spooked. We began to turn towards our target and get visual confirmation. At that time, I received clearance of fires from Panther 09 for our gun run. Our Hellfire missile and the rockets aboard the other aircraft could be used for escalation of force, if required.

As we rolled out on a westerly heading, I spotted the motorcycle, as well as the MAM and the PKM machine gun he carried. He was right off the nose of our helicopter, about 400 meters away as he continued westbound. I reconfirmed the target's position was north of a Bedouin village, and he was traveling westbound. Panther 09 acknowledged, and re-cleared us with, "You are cleared inbound hot for the east-to-west gun run away from friendlies."

He also reiterated that Osprey 11 was monitoring everything via the UAV situated far overhead. Our team coordinated the engagement between cockpits and started maneuvering in order to begin the engagement. Stu began to slow our aircraft back, pitching our nose up so that we may momentarily "bump" up in attitude in order to start the diving fire engagement. As we slowed, the aircraft climbed about 250 feet. We leveled off at 600 feet, and then began a shallow dive towards the insurgent. When we reached 900 meters away, Stu began to fire the .50 cal. The rounds landed around the target as Stu refined his shot groups. Our gun was unloading smoothly as I felt each concussion in the fillings of my molars.

As we encroached on the target, we gained back the airspeed we had bled off earlier. We had also descended down from 600 feet. The rounds continued to impact around the moving target, and a bead of rounds crossed over the target and appeared to have hit the insurgent. As was the procedure for the left seater, I proceeded to wave off the engagement for Stu so that we could begin the dive recovery. By this time, we were approaching an altitude of 150 feet and 90 knots of airspeed.

Stu placed the helicopter into a right bank and slightly raised the nose. The aircraft began to shudder and suddenly seemed squirrelly. The controls felt sloppy, and they had no effect on helicopter control as we continued to descend in the recovery profile. The aircraft was experiencing a dangerous aerodynamic phenomenon known as "mushing," and we needed to level off our descent in order to stop it. I instinctively grabbed the controls in order to make emergency inputs just as Stu began to do the same. With the aircraft now level, I then realized that we were going to impact the ground.

I looked down at the instrument panel and saw 93 knots and 80 feet. As we impacted the ground in a level attitude, the cyclic violently moved forward and left, then aft and right, hitting my right thumb and forearm. It felt like a baseball bat had hit my arm, and it went instantly numb. I placed my numb arm across my chest and held it back by crossing over it with the other arm.

I grabbed the shoulder straps and pulled my feet towards me, away from the floor-mounted trim pedals. I was now along for the ride.

In my peripheral vision, I could see the skids collapse beneath us, and explode off of the aircraft. The Kiowa's belly dragged along the dirt for about 15 feet. My seat stroked down as the helicopter rebounded back into the air. Everything seemed to slow down, then the vibrations began.

As soon as we were airborne again, the helicopter began to vibrate and shudder violently. The first thing that came to my mind was the tail rotor. The tail boom had been bent with the impact, and the tail rotor was now destroying itself. The vibrations and shuddering got so violent that I was unable to see anything clearly. A sound like crackling cellophane could be heard very clearly all around the cockpit. It was the aircraft structure beginning to crumble and crack as it ripped itself apart. The vibrations reached a point where they felt almost unbearable. Then, as the tail rotor broke away from the aircraft, the vibrations and shuddering abruptly stopped. We then began to spin clockwise very rapidly. We were about 40 feet in the air, and travelled a distance of about 120 feet before impacting the ground again. During this excursion, the aircraft spun clockwise seven full turns within four seconds.

We then hit the ground again. The aft section of the helicopter impacted the ground and changed our motion. We bounced back into the air once again. As the transmission section hit the ground, the aircraft abruptly stopped spinning clockwise, and then began a series of longitudinal rolls. The helicopter rolled three times in the air, then came to a crashing stop on the left side. I was seated in the left seat, and as I looked out the door, all that I could see was the dirt coming at me.

As we fell back to earth, I rolled my shoulders towards Stu, in an effort to distance myself from the door opening. The helicopter crashed so violently that my left shoulder impacted the armor side panel and threw it open. My left arm also came in contact with the collective flight control. Had it not been for the collective being all the way up, I would have been ejected out the door.

My legs shot forward and impacted the bottom of the instrument panel. Both legs immediately began to go numb with an accompanying stinging sensation. I thought I had broken my shins. My head and neck whiplashed to the left, and my nose impacted the sun visor on my helmet and lacerated. Blood shot out everywhere.

Once my vision came into focus again, I could see that we had come to rest facing east, and the helicopter was lying on its side. It was perpendicular to the ground. I looked out through the pilot windscreen and saw the MAM that we had just engaged, lying motionless with a PKM machine gun close by. We were about 75 feet away from the insurgent. I looked up at Stu, and he was still frozen on the controls from the shock of the crash. I quickly accomplished a limb check to verify everything was still attached and functioning. I then released my seatbelt and climbed out of the cockpit through the pilot windscreen.

Once I was out of the cockpit, I immediately pulled out my Beretta 9mm, and began to pull security. I kept looking back into the cockpit, and saw that Stu was shutting the aircraft down. The engine was still running, and it was making a high-pitched whining noise. Stu then handed me a smoke grenade, and I noticed that my rifle was stuck. The impact from the accident was so hard that the left side of the cockpit had been crushed, pinning my rifle to the ground.

As I stood holding my pistol, I spotted some individuals in the Bedouin village to the south beginning to come out of their hooches. I fired a few rounds towards them from my 9mm so that they would go back inside. Hearing this, Stu handed me his rifle while I looked down and noticed that I was straddling the Hellfire missile that had been ripped off of the aircraft during the crash. I began to rush Stu out of the aircraft because the status of the missile was unknown and could very well explode.

After shutting down the aircraft, Stu pulled on my rifle until he freed it from the crumbled instrument panel. Reunited with both of our rifles, and as Stu crawled out of the wreckage, I began to initiate the communications procedures for recovery. We both moved to the north side of the helicopter once Stu had successfully crawled out. I took his survival radio and tried to communicate with our sister ship that was still flying overhead.

As I attempted to talk to the Trail aircraft, the air filters for the engine on our aircraft began to smoke. Stu and I then decided to move to a hay pile that was about 75 meters to our northeast. We ran to the hay pile and took cover within it so that we were concealed from the enemy. There, we continued with our recovery and communications procedures, and began to devise a plan of evasion in case we had to move again.

I had an orange metal Hydroflask drink container that turned into a rotini after we crashed. I remembered running by it as I'd made way towards the hay pile for cover from Hadji. In the hay pile, I was so damn thirsty that all that I could think of was the flask and my Gatorade that was in front of the Hellfire missile. I told Stu that I was super thirsty, and he suggested I go retrieve my Gatorade. He didn't know that it had been destroyed and lay there in a mangled wreck. He then felt bad about it and told me that he'd buy me another one. No sooner did he say this that we started taking fire from the enemy. Needless to say, I never got my Gatorade. It was lemon-lime...my favorite one, too.

As we discussed our evasion plan further, gun fire could be heard in the distance. It was coming from the northeast of our position, and was aimed at the Trail aircraft circling above. I told them that fire was being directed towards their aircraft, and that they should vary their flight profile to avoid being shot down and ending up in our hay pile, too. I then moved to the south side of the hay in order to cover our position to the south and east. Stu remained on the north side and agreed to cover us to the north and west. As we moved into position, we began to take direct fire right into the hay pile. The enemy knew where we were, and they were maneuvering to the northwest to get a better angle on us. As I laid on the south side of the hay pile, I listened to Stu firing his M4 towards the enemy. Soon, the firing interval started slowing down, and I was afraid that Stu had been hit. After not seeing any movement to the south and east, I joined Stu on the north side.

When I touched Stu's shoulder to let him know that I was next to him, he turned and looked at me with giant eyes that I will never forget.

"There are about forty jibs in that tree line to the north!"

We relayed that information back to the helicopter circling above. By now, two more Kiowas had rushed in and joined the fight, and were providing overhead suppression for us. Stu directed them to suppress the tree line to the north, just shy of a cemetery. Meanwhile, we were taking an enormous amount of direct fire from the enemy. I could hear the whizzing crackle, and feel the concussion of the bullets as they flew past our heads and through the hay. I sat shoulder to shoulder with Stu as we continued to fire our rifles towards the enemy while the helicopters overhead suppressed the growing enemy presence.

After fighting for 25 minutes, we realized that our situation on the ground was getting much worse. Without notice, one of the Kiowas began what appeared to be a gun run approach in our direction. In reality, they had decided to land behind the hay pile to pick us up. I would have never thought that I would end up having to "spur ride" on a Kiowa during my aviation career, nonetheless during combat. I didn't have time to feel a sense of relief—I just instinctively knew what was about to happen.

As the helicopter landed and the dust settled, I realized that it was our sister ship that had come in to save us. We sprinted towards it, and I climbed onto the outside of the aircraft and strapped onto their left weapon's pylon. Stu had run to the right, straddling the rocket pod pylon and had his back against the helicopter. I realized that the .50 cal still had a few rounds left in the chute, and I was leaning right on it. I prayed that the pilot wouldn't have to fire that thing. The helicopter began to take off, and dust kicked up everywhere. I could still hear the bullets whizzing by the helicopter as we attempted our evacuation.

Once we broke out of the dust, I could clearly see the enemy. They were continuing to fire, and I fired my rifle back at them. As we gained altitude, I could see the wreckage of our aircraft more clearly. Additionally I saw the enemy positions, and the devastation left behind from the suppression that had been provided for us. I continued to fire my M4 until we were out of sight from the enemy.

A sense of relief began to set in, but it still all felt too surreal. I was riding the weapons pylon of a Kiowa Warrior, bloodied and bruised after surviving a helicopter crash and fighting for our lives. I could tell that we were flying towards FOB Pasab. All that I could think about was the overwhelming relief, and the loud noise that the wind was making as it rushed into my ears. I looked over at the other helicopter that was escorting us, and all that I could see was the glare off of the windscreen and the desert backdrop. I could see the Bravo Troop pilot sitting in the right seat, glancing over periodically at us.

Once we reached FOB Pasab, I could see our landing area, as well as the ground personnel that were tasked with refueling and reloading our aircraft that we affectionately referred to as the "farpies." The closer we got, the more it became clear to the farpies that this was no ordinary FARP turn. As we landed, the farpies saw me and Stu hanging on for dear life from the weapons pylons, along with my bloodied face. They then proceeded to run away. I assumed that they were frightened by my appearance, and ran to the medic station to alert them.

A Blackhawk transported us back to KAF. Still bloody and in pain, we had to immediately go see our brigade commander (the one in charge of all of our task forces). His first words to us were:

"Thank God you two didn't die, because that's two less letters I have to write for family members back home. Do you think that the target was worth six million dollars?" He then told us that we were an example of what not to do, and that we should be embarrassed. We would be investigated, and I was in shocked disbelief. Stu was informed that he would have to forfeit two months of pay before he would be allowed to leave KAF for home. Fortunately, he appealed and fought that asinine prospect and won. We had tried to do the right thing and take an enemy combatant off the battlefield, and after surviving our ordeal, we ended up fighting our own command, as well.

CHAPTER 32

We received word back on KAF that Jay and Stu had actually pulled themselves out of their aircraft and fought their way to safety. They only sustained cuts, bruises, and a few strained muscles. The bird was a total loss. Since that crash, our leadership's aversions to scary war stuff shot to the moon and we had gone into full knee-jerk reaction mode.

Our flying toward the end of June reached the point of near uselessness—there were significantly less ground forces to support any longer. Additionally, we also had other new restrictions, to most importantly include a "hard deck altitude" forbidding us to descend any less than 1,000 feet above the ground. Where we once flew as we needed in order to accomplish our mission, we were instead being relentlessly micromanaged. In order to descend any lower, we had to go through a series of "mother may I" requests and be able to justify said request to the TOC. To make it even more annoying, there were individuals assigned to closely watch our altitude and progress on laptops. By far and away, this was the most effective means to kill almost every single one of our capabilities, to include removing the ability of seasoned crews to make decisions. The guilt of flying high and not doing anything but burn gas seemed to get to us all quite a bit.

The risk aversion was so severe that we were actually prohibited in late June from dropping down to give some thirsty SF guys a water resupply. They were stuck out on a ridgeline with a bunch of Afghan soldiers, and the entire group was almost completely out of water. We were advised that a few of the Afghans were nearing the point of becoming a medical issue.

Despite our recently imposed hard deck, our SF brothers were in serious need. Our plan was simple. We could land at a relatively nearby FOB, grab as much water as we could carry, and then fly low and close by the ground forces in order to air drop it to them. The procedure of dropping critically needed supplies to ground guys was known as a "Speed-Ball" and was nothing out of the ordinary. Being plastic water bottles, we figured a 50-foot drop or so would allow most or all of the water to survive the fall and remain useful. We briefed the plan to ensure all four pilots agreed it was both necessary and worth the very slight risk it may pose to us. The ground units were nowhere near any known hostiles, and even in the unlikely event we did come under fire, we had reliable fighters covering us.

We called the TOC, and briefed the plan.

Denied. This was where we arrived in our higher command levels with our cowardice and disgrace. A few years earlier, Charlie Troop had flown out of Jalalabad and delivered critically needed supplies to ground forces during intense and direct combat. Ammunition was dropped, and an aircraft even landed near the trucks getting shot up in order for a pilot to dismount the aircraft, running into the fight to hand deliver the precious ammo and supplies needed to survive. The crew was awarded a high commendation, and they saved a lot of lives while being so selfless and courageous.

Now, we couldn't even descend below 1,000 feet to deliver water to guys in no other danger than heat strokes and dehydration. I was incredibly upset, apologizing very sincerely to the man on the radio who stood thirsty and hopeful that the Kiowas above would be able to help them out, just like we always had. Words could not describe how ashamed I was. We could have safely and quickly gotten them what they needed without any issues, but the decision was ripped from our control. All other requests that they made also could not be fulfilled.

The small amount of solace that I gained was that they understood that it was not we pilots making the decisions to screw them, but I was still party to it nonetheless and couldn't shake how terrible I felt. After an unacceptable amount of time had passed, we finally coordinated two Blackhawks in an attempt to fly in low and drop some water to them. We relayed a grid for the drop area and triple checked to make sure that it was close to the ground force location. We briefed the Blackhawks on where it was, and even the best direction to approach from.

Our team widened our circles out and made room for the Blackhawks. We watched as the two aircraft approached, and then shouted in disbelief as they kicked the water out onto a completely different ridgeline. The Blackhawks then proceeded to depart the area.

"Those dumb motherfuckers!" One of our pilots angrily shouted. I was so mad that I was almost speechless, along with the other crew members in our team. The SF guy came on the radio, asking if they were expected to move at least two or three kilometers across the jagged terrain, down a steep walled ridge, and then up another one to receive their water. They were really starting to suffer from heat cramps and the effects of dehydration. We were too mad to be mad.

I'd never felt so small, so absolutely failed to be relied upon by the ground forces. I had always felt so much pride and responsibility towards protecting them, and our task force couldn't have failed them any worse.

It was all over, as far as I was concerned. We were at the final point of failure that I'd hoped that we may never arrive in my lifetime in the Cavalry. Back on KAF, I began to inventory and pack some of my gear. The good news was that we were literally weeks away from starting to see a few new faces from our relieving units' advance party. They would come in and begin to take things over, learning about the area and our operations just as we had in order to set up and prepare for their own handoff. By August, we'd start to see more and more new faces, as well as increasingly transfer more flying and operational responsibility over as their forces showed up. The proper dates were still being decided, and I tried to ignore the rumors since I viewed it as both a fool's game and unnecessary speculation. Suffice it to say that once July was up, we would be in "pack up and prepare to head out" mode for the entirety of August.

Another sign that it was time to leave was once again getting into my least favorite activity: driving the bus for a week with a shift beginning at midnight. At least I'd been flying on the night shift, so I was relatively set up for nocturnal living. There may never be words available in the dictionary to convey how much we all hated bus duty. The ironically hilarious part was how far such actions pushed the airlines and civilian light on so many people who would have never even considered it.

Would an Army "pilot," who was forecast to spend maybe only 70 hours of their next *six months* actually flying want to stick with the bullshit that we were suffering? Would they want to continue with their multiple and ever-increasing additional duties load? Duties such as acting as a Supply Clerk, a Night Vision Goggle custodian, an Armorer, a Pubs guy (ordering manuals and being a pilot librarian), a Safety guy making PowerPoints and maintaining various programs, a Tactical Operations Officer, planning for missions that were seldom actually enacted and dealing with computers and programs that were far past their expiration dates, or the litany of other increasingly ridiculous duties assigned to pilots that were never intended for us to deal with in the beginning? Some of the above were perfectly congruent and acceptable with normal operations, but throw in a period of below-minimum missions and flying, and the whole thing became too stupid to endure.

The worst part was that the 70 hours in six months was also waiverable in certain instances as deemed by the higher command. Essentially, if it was inconvenient to the Army and leadership, the regulation could be ignored with a simple memorandum containing the proper buzz words and signatures. Any pilot out there can barely remain true recency of experience and proficiency in an aircraft with 20-30 hours a month. Imagine less than ten hours in a month. It would be a constant game of catch-up and learning from failure due to being out of the saddle, all while hoping that mistakes made were minor and not leading to anything major or disastrous.

It was becoming more apparent that our operational funds were being reduced. At FOB Pasab, they had always served the best chow. No one ever faulted this, as it was honest due compensation for their location. Unfortunately, the past few weeks had seen a decline in their once superior food supply. Sometimes, on rare occasions, I had actually found a banana out there. That always used to make my day—I'm not kidding. A banana where we were in Afghanistan was like finding gold at the end of the rainbow. They also used to get breakfast pizza, and I'd starve myself in the morning because I knew when I went out there to get bullets and gas, I could get a slice of that goodness. It was a shame that the only perk that they enjoyed was taken away.

Recently, we had a cockpit conversation about first-world vs. third-world problems and all decided that we'd rather always have first-world problems for the rest of our lives. An example of this would be in a third-world country, you wake up and in order to not die or allow your family to die, you must find water in order to survive the next 24 hours. Across the world at that exact moment, a first-world problem was occurring with a man on the couch watching reality TV, and he tragically realizes that he cannot get his hand all the way into the Pringles can to get those last remaining chips (son of a bitch!). Both people had an issue, but one was certainly less dire than the other.

We came up with multiple scenarios and concluded that in the grand scheme of things, third-world survivors definitely beat our soft asses. I hoped that I would be able to return home and live a life where I was fortunate enough to only experience first-world problems. I would, however, never forget to compare my woes with the alternatives that I'd witnessed in Afghanistan in order to give myself some perspective. Plus, it would hopefully help me to not sweat the small stuff.

*

The stress of the deployment by this point had made our squadron turn inward, and we were gnawing away at even our own. Case in point, I had been up at the troop waiting for a ride back to the room at noon. Pilots were sitting around "idle," not having anything to actually do. That equalled the prime target opportunity for bored instructors. Suddenly a No-Notice written exam, 100 percent passing score required, word-for-word renditions of all listed limitations and emergency procedures was passed out. Miss one word, one number, or jumble up one step (even if still correct but not word-for-word from the manual), and you fail. Failure in one of these No-Notice written tests was a severe offense in our world.

Technically, a failure resulting from this sort of test could immediately knock a pilot back down to the lowest level possible, that being to the level on paper of a new guy arriving at the unit fresh out of flight school. They would be required to do multiple training flights with an instructor to prove that they were once again mission capable and competent. Imagine the mind-fuck of one minute joking with friends, and then suddenly a career-altering, high-stakes test was in front your face the next.

Lucky for me, I had spent a considerable time recently going over everything with such a fine-tooth comb that there was no way that I could say anything without quoting it straight from the book. I had counted those that I may have gotten leeway on while studying as honest and hard failures, determined to settle for nothing less than what had become our expected form of perfection. My psychological state for this was a drive from pure anger and disgust—that was my high-octane and extremely powerful fuel, along with the coffee and determination to get the hell out of the situation without a further need to prolong it.

I took the test and gave it back to the IP, who had his red pen out and was marking up a test from one of the more junior pilots in our troop. The IP looked my test over while one of the crew chiefs sat there screwing with me, asking if I'd messed it up or what may happen if I failed. I explained the process to him while mine was graded on the spot in front of us. I said frankly that I better get an A+ or my day was about to become a pretty big pain in the ass. The IP looked up from mine finally and said, "Well, A+ then. Good job, dude."

I slumped in my chair and let out a hard sigh. One of the pilots had just heard some intel about some fat monkeys by the TOC hoarding a tin full of doughnuts. He was on his way to steal some and asked if any of us wanted any. I gave an enthusiastic, "Hell yes!" Usually, I didn't eat things like that, but I savored it on this particular occasion. I soon learned one of our PCs was not so lucky. Despite having just returned from a long and difficult mission, their test was administered anyway just after the debrief, and unfortunately, the less-than 100 percent score was harshly dealt with.

*

Our packing situation was briefed, and the money-tight situation was not the brightest beam of sunshine. I looked at the pile before me, and knew that it was a pretty serious undertaking. As we were told, in order to cut costs, or who knows whatever other reason, we were limited on what we could take back with us.

Furthermore, even though we had each personally carried our carry-on bag, rucksack, and duffle, we were now prohibited from bringing the large duffle along on the trip back home. Once again, we were scrambling to find room to put all of our duffle bags into some sort of container going home. As I understood it, our containers would also be taking the, shall we say, "economy" route home. They would most likely get pilfered and robbed by not one but TWO of our allied Middle Eastern countries on their trip back home.

I had seen what happens to a container that took this route home from the previous trip to Afghanistan. On the way back from the previous deployment, a few containers had been tampered with in those "allied" countries that we trusted so much. One had even been so expertly robbed that the military and Customs individuals of the burglar country had weighed it, emptied it of all of the contents, and then filled it with sand to weigh the exact same weight that it had been originally logged. They also then re-secured the container with the proper seals.

On Hunter Army Airfield, Delta Troop (3-17's maintenance and armament support unit) sent personnel outside to receive their shipping container. When the brand-new, proper tamper-proof guaranteed seal was broken, the Delta Troopers opened their container to find nothing but sand and a few pieces of scattered metal and debris rather than their equipment. I ran outside to see after I got a text about it, and laughed my ass off like some of the other pilots standing around taking pictures of what happens when we trust our Middle Eastern allies to handle our stuff. My buddy from Delta Troop started to enter the container and I hastily stopped him, asking if he really thought that was wise. Upon further talks and head scratching, I learned that an Explosive Ordnance Disposal bomb unit was called in to make sure no booby traps or other surprises were set. What great friends the Pakistanis were.

Poor weather in the beginning of July caused me to only fly once out of four times scheduled. Unfortunately, our Independence Day consisted of a squadron pilots' class, in which we were briefed about the latest Kiowa crash that had occurred a few weeks prior. The pilots were all belittled by numerous individuals for being "cowboys" and/or unsafe, and we were briefed on the newest round of restrictions imposed upon us. Furthermore, I learned that our command had effectively put a price on how much soldiers were worth. I had always joked about this sort of day coming, but it was very ironic to hear a dollar value associated with our lives on the 4th of July.

$6.8 million dollars.

That's how much an American soldier's life is worth. That needs to be divided in half actually, so I suppose it's really $3.4 million. Explaining how this came about is rather simple. That was the cost of our Kiowa, and it was made pretty clear that our leadership was more concerned with the cost of the bird we had just lost than they were about those who piloted it. At least, that's how many of us took the briefing. Simply put, we were told that oftentimes, engaging the enemy was just not worth it. The enemy should be allowed to escape, rather than us taking any risks in stopping them. Our risk aversion had gotten to the point that we'd rather let insurgents get away, undoubtedly to come back at a later time and lay more IEDs that would kill more of our soldiers, than risk getting into a gun battle with them and have the chance to stop that individual for good.

The briefing (or scolding) destroyed any remaining vestiges of support for our leadership as far as I could tell. It was downright shameful, and I believed that the American people had a right to know that this was how we were now conducting business. Thanks to higher headquarters directives, those who left the wire to do the fighting were forced to remain on the defensive at all times, just waiting to get blown up or shot at. It felt wrong and twisted. So, rather than a "Happy 4th of July" BBQ, we took a square kick in the nuts. I'd never forgive it and never forget it.

A few days later on July 8th, I was taking a break from driving around on KAF. I drank coffee and read a magazine on a rather unremarkable morning. There was suddenly gunfire, emanating from a heavy machine gun in one of our guard towers on the base. Instead of shooting out towards an oncoming enemy or suicide bomber in a vehicle, the ANA soldier trained his weapon suddenly inward. A convoy slowly moving down the road on KAF was taken completely by surprise, and in seconds, at least one man lost his life and several others were injured. Word spread very quickly, and I wondered if this was the kickoff of something larger. It was the perfect way for Hadji to officially mark the first day of the nearly month-long religious holiday of Ramadan. Insider attacks had become rampant in recent times (almost 50 in 2012 alone), and events such as these only worked to continue our correctly placed distrust in our Afghan military and police "allies." I was surprisingly numb to the news—not from a lack of caring, but it was instead just a common theme and threat that we all knew too well to be shocked from the violence.

*

We were going to see some new faces in a few weeks, and that was all that I could keep counting towards. The guys coming in would certainly have one hell of a road ahead. It may be the most uneventful, boring year of their lives. On the flip side, the enemy might see the withdrawals around them as weakness and step up their attacks. I genuinely felt sorry for our replacements, and saw why the Hawaii guys that we replaced had felt sorry for us. As time went on, government financial support and public support continued to diminish. I still found that there were many back home who were surprised to learn that we were even still on deployment in Afghanistan, swearing that they had heard on the news that we'd left.

Some of the guys in our squadron had endured too many deployments, and I was seriously worried about a few of them. They were very jaded, very cynical, and I sincerely hoped that some time back home could help them mentally get put back together, and they may one day find peace. Our forces were tired, and further troubled from the news when our officials boldly talked of new conflicts in Syria, Egypt, Iran, North Korea, Africa, and other hopeless places.

We were still receiving new military members just out of training, but notably the seasoned lower– and mid-level leaders were flocking towards the exits. We were experiencing a push from higher commands to address the "very alarming exodus of junior officers" from the military. Basically, never-before-seen numbers of officers from the rank of captain and below had openly indicated that they had no desire to continue their career in the military. The old saying that the smart ones get out was really beginning to become a stronger reality.

The day after the Afghan soldier saw it fit to fire upon a bunch of folks on KAF, I had my first day off of the month. I needed it. Matt and I chatted and grinned as we packed some of our belongings. It was symbolic that it was all almost over for us and that the light at the end of the tunnel was getting a little more distinct.

By the 16th, we were still in our original rooms but making sure that we finished up packing. The weather remained hot and dusty, so flight operations had continued to be sparse. Operations and missions to cover were a lot fewer and far between. Apparently, neither friendly nor enemy forces felt like doing much for the time being. It was smart of the enemy to lie in wait, if that was the tactic that they were actually employing. It could also be a mere coincidence of them being lazy in reality.

Kandahar was purported to be the capital of the Taliban and possibly the heroin capital of the world. The smart ones knew that they only needed to wait us out and then they may resume their operations. Thanks to us helping arm the rebels to overthrow the Libyan government, coupled with their ability to empty that country's arsenals during the pandemonium, there were reportedly a lot more updated and better-serviced weapons in the hands of extremists beginning to circulate throughout the Middle East. I really hoped that our forces got out of the area before the enemy networks were able to successfully turn better-quality and updated weapons back on us.

In our troop, I sat at our table with a former SF support guy who had been out of the Kiowa flying game for a few years. Recently, he'd been flying with us to get himself back up to speed as a pilot after his hiatus from flying to act as an aviation advisor to some bearded badasses. The stories that he told us about his adventures helping the Afghans pretty much mirrored what the documentary *This is What Winning Looks Like* portrayed. He had also seen that film recently, and he affirmed that there was not any better way to show or describe the reality of what working with the Afghans was like.

The pilot and I hit it off, especially once we realized our mutual hobby of photography. He looked at me incredulously and said, "What, just because I'm Asian, you think I know about photography?! Well, it's true." He then took a lot of time explaining to me how to get the best shots out of my camera. He had civilian buddies back home who were professional action photographers and worked for companies such as Red Bull, notably having much of their work aired on a visually stunning snowboarding documentary called *The Art of Flight*. He wanted to set up some sort of photography clinic for those interested once we returned home and if he pulled it off, then I told him to sign me up.

In a few weeks, August would begin and we'd all become significantly busier. I also had my APART coming up, which always required many, many hours of studying and preparation. Just when I was red-lined on my patience and showing an empty fuel light on motivation, I had my yearly proficiency evaluation to show off how good I was.

I hoped to be shuffled through and it wouldn't be made an extra pain-in-the-ass than it already was. I was banking on the IPs being burned out, too. Still, I set about doing my best to pull out one last feat of mental strength before turning my brain off for a while. I cannot convey how absolutely sickened I was to think about poring through worthless Army doctrinal manuals at that time. The knowledge that I would be discussing potential fantasy combat scenarios unlike anything I had seen in my two deployments was laughable. The sheer amount of filler that we were expected to maintain knowledge about between the few things that actually mattered was crazy.

I closed my eyes and daydreamed again. Airline life would beat hearing the whistle and hiss of a 107mm rocket or 82mm mortar just before feeling the earth shake from its impact, with shards of metal tearing through tents, equipment, and worst of all, people. Airline life would beat launching into bad weather while talking to a scared man on the radio with bullets making snapping sounds through the static as he fights for his life, or watching soldiers and children ripped apart by roadside bombs. Airline life would beat getting chewed out after you'd just landed for not shaving, all the while having just returned from hours of direct combat and calling in MEDEVACs to stop the bleeding. I'd take an airport sandwich, hard hotel mattress, and a late crew bus any day of the week.

My Apache wingman passes near a surveillance balloon in the security zone.

A shell casing flies as I engage in a practice known as "M4 out the door."

Ground forces take a break between skirmishes.

MEDEVAC Blackhawks stand ready to launch from FOB Pasab.

CHAPTER 33

"I want two pistols. One to shoot you in the face,
and another one to also shoot you in the face!"

-An angry retort, by CW2 Frank Norbury

July 19-21st had been very busy for me, and it didn't look like my schedule would lighten up any time soon. Over the previous three days, we had worked on packing up and sealing the ALSE container. Bravo Troop's ALSE guy and I formulated the best warrant officer type of plan that one could expect since we didn't have a surplus of time. Rather than find out the proper way to get the wooden pallets and bracing materials for the interior of our shipping container (paperwork, approval letters), we'd just take what we needed instead. We located the supply yard, and I found a lieutenant mostly in charge. We told her that we planned to run around and grab whatever we needed, we didn't have paperwork, and that we were in a hurry. She was smart enough to know that it's a losing battle to try to thwart a group of determined Kiowa pilots. The female lieutenant sighed and said, "Sure, whatever. Go ahead," and that was that. We nabbed someone who knew how to drive a forklift, and I commandeered a vehicle. The whole process took us maybe an hour, but if we'd have done it properly it would've taken all day, at a minimum. This was one of the times that I was glad to be a warrant officer, since generally no one asked what we may be up to because they figured it was none of their business or worse, they were probably better off not knowing.

I woke up at midnight to get ready for my shift and made my way to the troop. The laptop that served as our aircraft logbook was not functioning right, so I spent 15 minutes pounding on it and cursing its existence. My method worked and it finally pulled up what I needed. Once we moved out towards the aircraft, we could already tell that visibility would be an issue. There was a hazy halo effect around all of the dim lights in the area, and the moon was a big blurry orb. That sort of thing always spelled trouble for us being able to see anything while flying. We proceeded to preflight our birds and then made our way into the mission briefing.

One of my favorite Apache pilots ever was scheduled to be our wingman. He was a funny, yet pessimistic and jaded guy, and despite being around my age, he had spent far too many years of his life deployed. He was also a prior medic, and saved guys in the most horrific situations imaginable.

In the early morning hours that we met, he was pissed off, pacing the room like an angry tiger does at the zoo. We asked him what was wrong, and it basically boiled down to the same old situation that we'd encountered the entire deployment: An aircrew was getting screwed because higher headquarters weren't talking to each other and no one knew what was going on. I felt bad for him, but even when super-pissed, he never failed to always be a funny character. I knew right off the bat that it would be an interesting flight.

We received a legal weather brief by our (often wrong) Air Force weather guesser. We told him to go outside and not to screw us, but he insisted with the same line always used, "This is what our sensors are showing."

After our briefing was over and we were walking back to the troop area, one of the teams that had just landed came up and gave us the real weather situation. The team had taken off, returned immediately, and reported how bad it was. Soon afterward, they had taken off again, and returned again, just to report how bad it was. For whatever reason, these sorts of pilot reports were not trusted over the Air Force sacred sensors, so we had to take off at our normal time and go through the motions.

We departed the airfield and headed towards our test fire area, visibility being two miles at the most. In some spots, I was convinced that it may have been half that. We fought over the radio with our weather guy, who had the balls to assure us that a civilian helicopter had just reported three or four miles, so everything was okay. This was over the radio, to us, while we were flying.

Our mission AMC was the other Kiowa pilot with me. He called back with, "Roger, understand that we're just full of shit, then." and changed the frequency. Our Apache keyed the radio, laughing, "Dude, yes! As soon as I'm able to stop cracking up, I'll be ready to continue."

We test fired our weapons, and our gun was gummed up with carbon and sand, shooting very slowly and shaking the whole helicopter as it struggled. We managed to call it good and proceeded out into the security zones. As we made it farther and farther out, our visibility held at just the legal amount.

We landed at FOB Pasab's FARP for gas, ammo, and to get some breakfast and discuss our plans. The Apache pilot began discussing a rumor that he'd tried to start about us having to do organized PT early in the mornings right after we returned home while we were going through reintegration training. The AMC and I laughed and told him that it was a pretty good rumor and we'd help him spread it, but then he blew our minds. He informed us that even though he'd thought this preposterous idea up on his own, his commander had overheard him spreading it in their building. Their commander then told him, "An hour of PT in the mornings isn't going to kill you..."

That's when it dawned on him: He'd imagined one of the dumbest things that he conceived that could possibly happen, and it turned out that it was to come true. We told him that we didn't believe him, but he challenged us to find out for ourselves. Later, we were shocked to discover that he was right. As if being away from our families for so long wasn't enough, we were expected to show up before sunrise to work out for an hour on base rather than spend those special mornings with our loved ones.

Before departing Pasab's FARP and after hearing about the PT that was to begin immediately after we returned to the states, our AMC began to mock our division by bombastically singing our official "Dog Face Soldier" song over the radio. This elicited a primal yell over the radio in response, and I looked to my right just in time to see an Apache gunship with an already pissed off man at the controls hovering and pointing menacingly at us. This drew gales of laughter from us and we completed the whole song, just for him. He settled with a simple, "I hate you both," over the radio rather than shooting us. The AMC then wrote the entire song down on the forward airbag module of our cockpit. Our false motivation grew day by day.

We took off from the FOB after our breakfast and began to talk to what very few U.S. forces remained out in the security zones. Not much was going on, and the visibility was beginning to drop again. At one point, we even received a confused radio call from a ground force higher headquarters because they didn't expect us to be flying at all. We told them that we didn't think that we should be, either. We always played lip service to "safety," rather than actually exercising safe and sound decision making when it pertained to weather. Endless and beautiful PowerPoint slides were even created about our dedication to safety, just for good measure.

We managed to support some ground guys for a short period of time, but then Mr. Sun hit us full blast. When I turned back toward the east, the full sunrise coupled with the haze and dust blanked everything out. It was bad, and I could no longer see the mountains. I cursed how ridiculous it was to be put in such a predicament, and our AMC agreed. We informed our TOC that we were returning to KAF, and thanked them for putting us in such a dangerous situation that we would literally only make it by having to follow the Apache back. The Apache had an optical sensing system that could see through a lot more obscured air than we could, so I stacked behind him and to his left. We told him that we'd have to stay very close to maintain visual contact with him, and we agreed upon a fixed airspeed.

On the way back to KAF, a small, white civilian contractor helicopter suddenly streaked out of the dusty loom ahead of us. He missed our aircraft by diving just below us and flew fast in the opposite direction. Any closer would have potentially created a mid-air collision.

"Woah, did you guys see that?! Are you okay?" The Apache called to us.

"Son of a bitch. That was too close for comfort, but we're okay," I called back.

Thankfully, we made it back to our ramp, where we quickly refueled and then shut it down. A quick call to the TOC was made to tell them that we had encountered bad weather, just like we'd expected, and that they needed to pass that information on to the next crew. Shortly thereafter, we ran into another crew who'd just briefed and had been given legal weather to fly. They were wondering if they should go and sought us out. Talk about deja vu.

⋆

It was July 27th, and I had been flying every day for the last six days. For whatever reason, I had been rediscovered and placed heavily into the flight schedule. It had been good to fly so much again, and it most certainly made the time pass by a lot faster. I needed to get my ass out of bed. It wasn't very often that we conducted Air Assaults anymore, but one had been assigned and it was going out nice and early. A complement of soldiers would be inserted by air to look for enemy and weapons caches up in a dusty and remote mountainous area. My team of one Kiowa and one Apache would check their landing zone and protect both the ground forces, as well as the two large Chinooks bringing them in.

We departed on time and flew fast through the twilight sky. My team pushed ahead of the Chinooks and scanned the still-sleeping village and the landing zone we intended to use. The LZ didn't appear to harbor any threats, so I called back to the Chinooks.

"LZ appears clear, proceed from west to east. We will be covering the insertion and monitoring the village."

"Roger, understand LZ appears clear. We're two minutes out and will approach from the west."

We watched the Chinooks land together in a tight formation, kicking up large plumes of dust in the LZ. Soldiers poured out of the aircraft with amazing speed and ran into the village. A few locals had just begun to peek out doorways and wander into the road when they were met with a large group of Americans. Intel had pointed to the village, and our forces were looking for the Taliban and/or other insurgents that they were harboring. The sun began to rise just as the village was declared secure.

I witnessed one man turn a 180 and begin quickly walking in the opposite direction near the village edge.

"Gotcha, bitch! Trail, you see that guy thinking about getting away to the south?" I asked.

"You mean the man walking like he's suddenly gotta take a shit? Yeah, I see him."

I radioed the ground unit, "Viper 11, Wrath 63. We've got a potential squirter making his way south away from your platoon near building three. He's wearing dark man-jams and has a white scarf and grey hat. He doesn't appear to be carrying a weapon, but he does appear to be trying to get far away from y'all. How copy?"

"Roger, Wrath 63. Viper 56, you copy that?" Viper 56 was a squad near another numbered building indicated in our intel packet, and they stopped what they were doing and keyed back directly to me. "Wrath, you say he doesn't have a weapon and is moving south towards us?" I abandoned looking through our MMS and again picked up my binoculars to get a better look as we moved closer. The man quickened his stride, and looked up at me. He had a cell phone to his ear, no doubt attempting to warn his terrorist buddies that the Americans had surprised them in town. I then saw the motorcycle in the shade that he was about to jump on and take off.

"Viper, I'll bet he's trying to get to that motorcycle less than 50 meters from him, it's near building..." I flipped through the intel packet, scrambling as I knew that time was of the essence. Suddenly, I watched a few of the Viper elements sprint towards the motorcycle while others ran towards the building I was trying to indicate. They'd seen him and it was all in their hands now. A few soldiers ran around a nearby structure and met up with the suspect just as he turned a corner. One soldier looked up at me, smiling and giving a thumbs up while the man shoved and shouted at the soldiers. He found himself on the ground with flex-cuffed hands for his conduct.

"That's what I'm talking about!" Yelled Trail triumphantly. I smiled and congratulated Viper for making it to the man and swiftly apprehending him before he had a chance to flee. "Wrath, we appreciate it. This guy is pissed and I'll bet once we run him through our system he'll turn up as one of the guys we've been looking for." Viper 11 congratulated his men while they all continued through the streets.

The remainder of the assault was quiet and proceeded like clockwork. Viper did their jobs well, and put a dent into a surprised enemy operations cell that had probably gotten a bit overconfident and complacent with the slow down of U.S. operations. Viper elements and a few prisoners waited in the LZ as the massive Chinooks swooped back in and created another mini dust storm. It had been a very successful raid, and those on my team had needed the morale boost and solid win for the USA.

After that was complete, we once again stopped for breakfast at Pasab and hung out for a bit. The AO was eerily quiet, which I figured was mostly due to Ramadan continuing to affect the overall patterns of life. There were still plenty of acts of violence being committed, just not quite as many as we were used to. I believed that was because many of the locals would fast all day for Ramadan and I didn't even think that they were allowed to drink water. In the evenings was when they seemed to be able to indulge in all of those life-sustaining activities, but then they seemed to be busy just surviving by that point, so they wouldn't attack as much then, either. It felt like a strange Ramadan, to me at least. My rather motivating day was drawing to a close, but then ended with a bang.

On the way back to KAF, our Apache suddenly called out from his position behind us.

"Explosion, nine o'clock," and our heads immediately slewed that way. A giant mushroom cloud of dirt and dust went up and debris fell from the sky. It was close, and I banked hard in that direction, hoping that I wouldn't find a burning U.S. vehicle down there. It was quickly confirmed over the radio as we moved at max speed towards the blast that no friendly troops were in the area. We couldn't believe it.

We all shouted with sheer joy and glee, singing happily about how Hadji had just gotten blown up by his own IED.

Just recently, I had convinced one of our intelligence soldiers responsible for briefing us in the mornings to put a special little happy sun graphic on the AO map for every time this sort of thing happened. I couldn't wait to tell them when we got home to put up another little sun. The graphic chosen looked like the little dude off of a popular cereal box; watching Hadji blow himself up while attempting to kill us was like the happiness brought with two scoops of sunshine! I wanted his soul to be celebrated for heading downward to hell.

We were on top of the area very quickly, just in time to see villagers pouring out of their houses and running. The blast had occurred on a dirt road in between some fields, and we saw the local markers out identifying that there were IEDs in the area. The villagers halted at the intersection in the road and a few women dropped to their knees, hands outstretched and wailing. My joy instantly turned to numb neutrality as another horrific image embedded itself forever into my brain. I slowly shook my head, trying not to let my emotions engage with what my eyes were recording.

About 50 meters down the road from the villagers was a charred hole in the earth with a child's body torn in half next to it. Chunks of human flesh lie in the dirt, and blood stained more of Afghanistan's soil. Our thermal sight indifferently and silently recorded the hot blood pool slowly emanating from the remnants of the small, mangled body. Another innocent young life abruptly ended before it had truly begun, cut short in the cruelest of ways.

The Apache behind us had a different crew than normal and the scene below seemed to really disturb one of their guys. He was older, and I imagined that maybe he'd never seen this sort of thing before. He probably had kids of his own.

A few villagers worked up the courage to move along a wall and ended up standing over the area, dropping a sheet over the body. It was obvious that they knew more IEDs were around and they weren't willing to risk getting on that stretch of road. Afghan forces from a nearby outpost drove up in their Humvee and moved to the intersection carefully, also not willing to push forward any further. It occurred to me that all of these bastards, the Afghan forces included, must've known that there was a trap laid on one or more parts of the road. Now one of their children lay in a dismantled, oozing heap because their plan had backfired on them and killed one of their own instead. *Way to go, you fucking savages. Way to go.*

I reported the incident as matter of factly and professionally as I could. A very tired and weary sounding ground force radio operator who obviously recorded this kind of stuff all of the time took down our report. We then went about our business and proceeded back towards our base. I'm still concerned about the frequent, unavoidable, and often wild emotional swings we all experienced. We snapped so rapidly between numbness and anger.

I couldn't have hated the Taliban or insurgent groups any more than I did; my attempted path to not hate the enemy had ultimately failed. I still couldn't believe that they had an office in Qatar—you could just call a Taliban representative up. "Oh, lunch and afternoon tea with the Taliban? Splendid! Put me down for 2:30, please."

It was reprehensible what courtesy we extended to them, not only negotiating with them as if they were actually humans, but also as if they were an organization worthy of recognition and true decorum. Brutalizing, raping, and murdering your own citizens is not exactly an acceptable practice, in my humble opinion. I will concede that my hatred may not have allowed me to grasp "the big picture" well enough, though.

Our team landed back at KAF and shut everything down, then walked into our troop after our debrief at the squadron. I found Matt sitting at a table, scowling at me.

"How many days in a row have you worked?" Matt asked.

I pondered the question a moment, then replied, "A lot. By the look on your face, it was probably more than I should have." He was our Safety Officer, so he nodded.

"You are red on the tracker, and you must absolutely take a day off tomorrow. No excuses."

I felt relieved, knowing that there was no way it could be argued now that I had the mandate from the troop Safety Officer. It was official that I would get a day off. Of course, my relief was somewhat shattered less than five minutes later when my platoon leader informed me that our troop photo was the following day. EVERYONE, no matter if they were off and also to include the guys who were flying, would be mandated to be on the flight line at noon sharp. It was "just a photo," so although mandatory attendance was required, it wasn't counted as "working" for everyone to attend.

I realized that I was pretty exhausted. I hadn't been sleeping as much as I should and I hadn't taken a day off in 15 days. My diet had also not been as good as it should be. Basically, I recognized it after my roommate pointed out that I was a ragged fool. He and I both knew that I needed to drink more water, and get some more sleep. When I did try to sleep, haunting thoughts and images did not make it very pleasant or restful.

CHAPTER 34

Dear Soldier,
How are you doing in Afghanistan? I am proud of you for being brave.
Thank you. We love you.
Love, Destiny

At the end of July, a few new faces appeared with the proper patch of our replacement unit on their arm. Over the previous week, new units had begun pouring in and sending those whom they were replacing on their journey home. On this day, it was the first time I'd actually seen ours. They were the "advance party," and the rest of their unit would be along very shortly. The group was tasked to learn the area and get everything set up for their guys. Every unit wanted their arrival and integration at the beginning of a deployment to go as smoothly as possible. Our troop wasted zero time, sitting down with them and passing over pre-prepared information we'd put together for their arrival. The pilots were integrated into our flight schedule in order to start flying immediately. We had a limited amount of time to get them an orientation and learn how to operate in the Kandahar environment from our instructors.

My current shift required me to go to sleep shortly after lunch; however, I would sometimes not actually get to sleep until around dinner time. The resulting shortness of hours in REM sleep affected me greatly, so I took naps where I could. Despite the sleep issues, I still preferred my schedule, since it was so odd. Our team was generally left alone to do our job. We were the early night-crawlers that existed out of sight and out of mind when all of the "great ideas" and tasks occurred around lunchtime and afterwards each day. Still, woe betide you at night, always and no matter what, if you were observed outside not wearing your clear safety glasses as well as a specifically colored fluorescent reflective PT belt. You had better wear it as prescribed, too: Draped over the right shoulder and angled down across your torso to the left. Uniformity in child-like safety mandating is key for the modern soldier!

I wanted my last few weeks in Afghanistan to be as painless as possible. Somehow, I recognized that, inconceivably, a small part of me would miss it. The country had a certain familiarity to me with the sights, experiences, missions and combat, the picture-taking and reporting back home, all of it. It would be strange no longer having anything to do with those sorts of things, and the absence of deployment operations meant big changes were coming in my life. Still, I thought of the most recent horrific images and stressful recounts as they fluttered into my mind's eye and then vanished. *We'll be home soon,* I told myself.

On the last day of July, Matt and I moved around the room making fun of each other while tripping over crap as we packed. We had been finally told that once the very early morning sunrise of August 1st came, we all had to be completely done with packing and ready to move out within 15 minutes or less prior notice. Moving to transient group living quarters at the end of deployment kind of sucks while still having a month to go, but it was nonetheless a welcome milestone. We would be living out of our large rucksacks and deployment roller bags, dealing with all of the chaos that was only going to continue to intensify as we got closer to departure. We would watch as more and more replacements arrived, but we still did not know our actual departure date.

The roller coaster ride of frustration versus elation at the prospect of finally returning home continued. My excitement and anticipation grew. Lindsey was an excellent cook, and told me how excited she was to try out some of the recipes that she'd gathered since I'd been gone. Her phenomenal crawfish étouffée had always been a crowd favorite. I hoped that once I returned home and got over the first month or so readjusting to my normal surroundings, I would return back to normal. I felt like I was beginning to get too excited about coming home, however, so I quickly stopped myself and crammed it all back into the box in my mind. There were still enemy fighters out there that may pick my number, and I couldn't yet afford to become complacent.

The tragic losses that we had experienced and witnessed were real, and in no way did I want to add my name to that list because I was daydreaming about home. I had to continue to remain vigilant for myself, our teams, and most importantly, those others on the ground that still depended upon us. I felt as though I had done a good job thus far about suppressing my emotions regarding thoughts of home. When we were in the air, I had to master pushing the pleasant thoughts of the future out of my mind so that I could focus on the assholes trying to shoot me at present.

Our job as Kiowa pilots had included us literally hunting humans and gathering intelligence in Afghanistan. In my case, I had experienced this for almost two full years of my life, while some of our guys had done it for even *far* longer. There was no doubt that hunting the most dangerous game in the world (an armed enemy and motivated human) would be an activity missed by myself as well as most other combatant veterans. Whether that was good, bad, tragic, or other, I couldn't even really say. In any case, it didn't matter; the fact remained that it was true.

Our next living area would be a large building complex housing thousands of bunks and serving as the KAF transient barracks. Right next door was a USO, which stayed pretty busy. My future plan was to utilize a quiet corner of the USO as often as possible to study for my fast-approaching APART evaluation. I really needed to get on the ball and continue to scan and highlight the multiple study guides and flashcards that I had. That was my last and final standing goal, to get the APART over successfully, painlessly, and forever done with.

Given my luck, it could end up happening in a week or less. The mere thought of the APART made me frown and could instantly get me depressed, but I was fighting hard to put the negativity out of my head and just focus. I knew what to look at, and knew what I had to do. It was time to get after it one last time.

*

August had arrived with a vengeance, and we moved out of our rooms right as it began. I had unfortunately been tasked with a gym guard shift early that morning and the order to quickly vacate had come completely out of the blue. That left my roommate to move both of our stuff all by himself, which was pretty lame. At least I had all of my stuff packed for the most part, and he hadn't really needed to do much with my gear but transport it. Everything ended up at our new transient living quarters, the aforementioned-complex known as the RSOI. What it stood for, I hadn't the foggiest clue. It had a foot-and-a-half thick concrete walls, so it was the only real fortress on KAF that I knew of.

Just as I expected, it was a building composed of giant, 80-man bays filled with nothing but bunk beds. Not only bunk beds, but exceptionally rickety, squeaky, and uncomfortable ones. My mattress liked to slide off of the springs, but at least I was on the bottom. Our bay had air conditioning, and due to the fact that there were 80 people in there with different work and rest cycles, it always remained pitch black and dead silent (save the creaking bed frames). All that could be seen 24 hours a day in there was the dim glow of laptops and tablets, and the occasional headlamp beam as one attempted to navigate the maze of beds and luggage on the floor to make it to the exit. I busted my shin pretty good on a homemade wooden night stand when I neglected to bring my headlamp with me on a bathroom run. When initially entering from the incredibly bright and sandy conditions of Kandahar outside, our eyes seemed to take forever to adapt to the darkness.

In the RSOI, when the earth shook and the sirens sounded from attacks, I didn't even notice. I actually slept through at least three separate rocket attacks (that I knew about). With the culmination of the Ramadan holiday, we also all had to wear full body armor and helmets. This was mandated from 1930 until midnight from August 7th until the 10th. Although we'd gotten attacked at those specific times before, I really couldn't figure out how exactly that specific time window was selected. It was also comical to see everyone trying to get done and get back to their living quarters by 1930 so that they didn't have to put on all of their shit.

Also comical was our ability to just keep getting hit by wave after wave of bad news. Everything from delays in our potentially earlier flights home, delays in replacements arriving, delays in replacement aircraft arriving, further restrictions on our flying which I could never even conceive were possible by that point, etc.

In tandem with that, I was recognizing that I suffered from a nearly total and true motivational burn out. I had been experiencing severe trouble giving much of a damn about anything at all. I knew that I had to get a little sleep, and enlist the help of a study buddy or two if I was to be successful in my APART evaluation. Fortunately, a few decent people in my troop answered my call for help, and they assisted me in going over the particular parts of our material that I so hated to look at. Thanks to a little help from my friends, I managed to study both the useful and the useless enough to have a bit more confidence going into the evaluation.

The first flight I did was fast paced. The weather was dropping rapidly, and we knew that we'd only be able to get a portion of the flight done before being forced to return. While we were walking out to the aircraft, the instructor stopped and stared at the mountains, shaking his head and considering walking back to the troop before even starting the aircraft. We'd pushed the bounds of safety for every other reason before and at that point, I was so ready to get it all over that I convinced him to push on and just keep an eye on it. We could then agree to come back as soon as one or the other of us were uncomfortable. He reluctantly agreed, and conceded my point. From there, it was a mad rush to beat the weather. Fortunately, I breezed through maneuver after maneuver, keeping my promise to only have one go at each to standard or better so we wouldn't have to repeat anything. The flight progressed very quickly and before I knew it, we were refueling the bird and putting it away for the evening. The APART was finally complete, and I wasn't quite sure what to do with myself. I still had some residual anxiety that I couldn't shake for some reason, so I channeled that energy and helped a good guy from Bravo Troop that was preparing for not only his APART, but also his PC ride with our Squadron SP. I spent two nights at the USO bouncing questions that were fresh in my mind off him, and I was glad that it appeared to really help him out and do some good. I'd had people help me out, and it was just the right thing to do in my mind. I was not sure how he fared because we went on opposite shifts, but I really hoped for the best for him.

*

We began to be forced into multiple iterations of never-ending awards ceremonies. The event was conducted every few days so that the leadership may pass out the deployment awards and commendations to every single soldier in the task force. Everyone would get something, unless they really did something messed up. The pain-in-the-ass part was that they demanded maximum participation in the form of an "audience" for this. It took forever, and the ceremony was in no way exciting or fulfilling for those "awardees" having to stand out in the sun to get pinned. It was done for the cameras, and everyone stood miserably by for their participation award. I stood in the audience on the day that I should have been restructuring my sleep schedule. Other pilots were in the same situation, and we overzealously cheered, clapped, and became giant over-the-top and falsely motivated wiseasses.

On the morning of August 13th, I was assigned to an early morning of general recon in the security zone. I figured that it would probably be one of, or perhaps even my last flight. I was at least with a good guy. We moved around outside the wire, looking for any set ups for indirect fire aimed at KAF or any of the other FOBs or COPs out in the area we patrolled. I took a lot of pictures, and our team flew rather aggressively and ballsy. We weren't concerned with the hard deck restrictions that day, finding several causes to break the rules and fly low. We'd learned as long as we could justify, then there were workarounds. It was yet another bit of cover-your-ass lawyering we'd had to learn along the way in surviving our command climate with our ever-convoluted bag of tricks. I laughed hard at the fact that we were still developing schemes and tricks, right there until the bitter end in order to be able to do our jobs. I figured I was done, and when the mission ended and we put the birds to bed, I walked away rather emotionally unmoved.

My emotions changed once we walked into the back door of our troop from the deck, and I was shocked to find people swarming the building.

NEW FACES?! I saw a lot of people that I didn't recognize in our troop. Our replacements had finally arrived in full. Most of them were doing a few days of classes like we had, and then would be fully integrated into our operations. They'd each do a few training flights with a combination of our IPs and their own until they had a basic understanding of the area. Probably two or three flights later, each and every one of the pilots would be fully mission capable and ready to take our place. We were more than ready and willing to hand them that torch.

The flight line was busy. Forklifts and people were moving about, putting down containers and emptying their contents out to conduct inventories. Many, many people were around and sporting their "Big '1'" unit patch rather than "the broken TV" unit patch that we had. I was very happy to see all of this, and felt a little sorry for their poor sweaty asses as they worked. Soon, I remembered doing the exact same thing nine months prior myself, while Hawaii dudes grinned at us and looked on just as I was doing. I waved to all of the strangers as I passed, offering a smile and a cheerful, "Welcome to wonderful Kandahar!"

We endured ever-increasing craziness in a seemingly desperate attempt to see just how ridiculous things could get. We had finally all hardened ourselves and gotten so numb, I didn't think that we were defeatable any longer. Our replacements had arrived, we were obviously not giving too much of a damn about anything anymore, everyone wanted to kill each other, and all we talked about was home. Yep, it seemed like we were definitely a stereotypical unit ready to head back to the U.S. in the very near future.

As I sat and watched the world crumbling around me, I started writing a small list of things that I wanted to immediately do when I returned back home. It read:

Take a bath

Swim in water

Walk down Broughton St. in Savannah on a nice afternoon with Lindsey and Scout

Play fetch

Go to the beach

Get a massage

Eat great food

Watch a thunderstorm from the garage

Listen to wind in the trees

Listen to birds sing

Listen to children laugh

Enjoy peace and quiet

Experience contentment and love

A few more days passed and our squadron and task force were in extreme flux. Things were moving rapidly, and changing even quicker. On our calendar in the troop, I noted that we were less than a week away from being right in the middle of intermixing all of the replacement guys within our teams. The flights and missions were slowly but surely allowing them to gain the tools to take over our operations. As each day passed, we had less and less that we were responsible for. I was getting the feeling that even some of the new guys were as ready for us to leave and get out of the way as we were to stand aside and return home.

As I continued to scan all of our troop information boards, I was also surprised to learn that I was scheduled to fly one more time, on a mission flight on the 18th. That was it. I knew that the flight would almost certainly mark the last combat mission that I would ever fly. During my deployment in Bagram, my last flight had been an absolutely great day. We had enjoyed great weather and had what literally amounted to a fun joyride. We had the keys and unlimited time and gas, able to stay out as long and go wherever we wanted, thanks to the fortunate circumstances of near-zero aggressive enemy operations that day around BAF. I knew KAF would prove different.

It took me a bit to fall asleep once back in my bunk at the RSOI. A sickness had once again been ripping through our ranks, and a lot of people were coughing, sneezing, and cursing throughout our large bay of bunks. I absolutely refused to get sick. I was not going to let that happen, so I'd been taking the remainder of my NyQuil as a preventative measure which, fortunately, had the side benefit of assisting me with knocking out in time to get a little bit of sleep. Unfortunately, I awoke hours before I needed to be up, restlessly tossing and turning, unable to fall back asleep.

Coffee helped us all perk up. My buddy bought a dozen donuts and we began to get ready for the flight. From the brief with intel and weather, we knew the day would be a long one. The crew I was joining in with had flown way longer than normal the previous day. The three that I was flying with informed me to get ready, as we'd be going out to the same area and would definitely be busy. They couldn't have been more correct. My last flying day in KAF was by no means a screw-around day like my last flight in BAF had been. We stayed very busy and I most definitely flew a full featured six hours. We began by providing overwatch for both Afghan ground forces and police as they moved to search and clear out hostile villages. I furiously worked the MMS, the binoculars, the camera, and the radios.

"Viper, Wrath 62, you've got military aged males who appear armed on the north side of the village moving tactically. Tell the ANA to watch out for—shit! They're taking fire now, at least three shooters, AK-47s—"

"Wrath break, break, break! We're taking rounds from the west!" I watched through my binoculars as U.S. and Afghan forces ran about and dust kicked up off the earth and qalat walls from multiple rounds flying every which way. Unable to cover anyone due to ROE concerns, proximity to civilians, structures, and danger close skirmishes, we could only observe. We sent report after report, staying high and wide trying to make sure we didn't catch an errant round. As luck would have it, the enemy seemed a little more preoccupied fighting the Afghan forces in their backyard than worrying about the far away and combat ineffective American helicopters.

Once relatively under control in that village, we saw multiple explosions along roads and further firefights erupt nearby. I hadn't seen the AO go so nuts in quite some time, so I certainly got my wish for one last pure adrenaline kick. The U.S.-to-Afghan casualty ratio was luckily much in favor of the red, white, and blue. The U.S. forces and most ANA survived, and insurgents died.

Back near the airfield at the end of the flight, we were relieved. The guy flying with me was also on his last flight. He was on the passenger manifest for the next C-17 set to leave in just a few days, and it was also his birthday. We sang happy birthday while swooping around and looking for anyone setting up attacks against the airfield. Once back near KAF, we spent about 15 more minutes scanning the area for additional threats or anything out of the ordinary. I took a lot more pictures, capitalizing on the last opportunity to ever do so again.

Then, it was all over. The clock had struck the end of our final mission hour, and it was time to go home. We flew in on the final approach, and I sank a little in my seat. I was unsure of what I felt, as I suppose it would be best described as a mixed emotion between relief and a little twinge of sadness. Nearly two years of my life had been spent playing our dangerous game, and no matter how I felt about it or how it happened, I could not help but admit that it had an impact on me. I knew that this was it; never again would I hunt the enemy in his homeland.

Still, Lindsey was back home eagerly awaiting my arrival, so I smiled a bit as we approached our ramp. Another brief wave of emotions came over me, almost like that of what's known as survivor's guilt. I thought about the fact that barring anything nuts like a rocket attack or local national shooting me on KAF, I would survive. There were those out there still fighting each day to attain that status, and yet others who had not been able to make it. The weight of that heavy emotion hit me harder than expected. I tried to tell myself not to feel guilty for returning home from a war, and I was sure that those who had perished would certainly never want their brothers in arms to ever feel guilty for making it home to their families. I would always honor and never forget the sacrifices of those who had not been able to make it out of the stupid land that

I was presently in, looking out over the mountains and cursing it all.

I then returned to my thoughts of the future and to the positive. We refueled, de-armed, and commenced a slow hover back to our parking pads. As our Kiowa's skids settled on the earth, we both let out a sigh of relief. We shook hands and congratulated each other on our performance during one hell of a final flight. Matt strolled out to help us put everything away, and he snapped a photo of us during our shut down before we cheered and high five'd our crew chiefs.

Celebrating at the end of my final combat flight.

CHAPTER 35

T he evening after my last flight, we hung out at the USO and everyone was in good spirits. A crew chief offered, so I even tried smoking a hookah, of all things. The following morning a few of us went up to the troop. There wasn't anything that we could help with anymore, and we got the impression that we were just in the way. That was fine with me. We departed the flight line and plopped our happy asses back in the air-conditioned USO next to our RSOI fortress.

The dates for our homecoming had started to become a little more concrete, but I was not going to announce anything or even get excited myself until I was damn sure it was accurate. It did appear that there was an actual push to finally remove all of us from KAF soon, at least. Some of our guys were down to mere days before the first few of the flights went out, and I couldn't wait for my turn.

Before I knew it, another five days had elapsed. It was already late August. Some from our troop departed, and some were even already home. Half of us remained, and since the incoming unit had brought their own Kiowas, we had all been busy scrubbing down our beat-up aircraft. The birds had to be very clean and prepared for inspection by Customs in order to be approved for loading onto the Air Force cargo aircraft. This was a serious undertaking—our aircraft were as filthy as one would expect after an unholy amount of time serving in Kandahar. Cleaning each one of them inside and out took several hours and many personnel to accomplish. It was positively nasty work, and everyones' hands and arms were cut up and stained by oil and gunk. Many ruined their uniforms due to the chemicals.

Finally, we only had one of our Charlie Troop birds left on the line that needed to be pulled off, washed, scrubbed, and inspected. It was the one that was always used to do dust landing qualifications, so it was by far the worst to deal with. In the midst of all of this, we also had to attend more mandatory ceremonies in order to watch everyone get whatever award they were slated for across the entire task force. It remained the dumbest dog-and-pony show, ever. There were so many awards that had been given to the undeserving, while so many more were passed over that should've gotten something better.

It was the way that the entire Army had gotten, though. I hated to see a real turd of a person get a bronze star simply because of the position that they held. A once highly regarded award was now handed out without regard to whether or not that person was worth a damn in that position. Awards were based on entitlement, not merit, but this was nothing new. My brother had been put in for a bronze star for valor while fighting in Baghdad. During the Battle of Adhamiyah on November 20, 2004, he had run between alleyways and streets to link up separated forces and platoons in the midst of intensive fire fights. He dodged barrages of both enemy and friendly rounds, with his sole purpose being to save a pinned down platoon and re-establish communications between squads and platoons all caught in the intense mayhem. His write ups from others who witnessed the account were so insane that one day I asked him how in the hell he wasn't dead. A friend of mine from college who had become a Marine officer read it, and subsequently had it hung in their leadership class area as an example of true gallantry and heroism under fire by a former Marine-turned-Army-Ranger. Despite all of that, the award that my brother received was downgraded from the bronze star to the lower and more common Army Commendation Medal (ARCOM), with a little "V" for valor. People also could get ARCOMs for correctly filing paperwork.

Meanwhile, several peanut brittle-munching, worthless morons who did nothing but exist our entire deployment, posed for smiling photos taken with an even higher award, minus the small "V" for valor part. This was for their position, not their merit or anything near a job well done.

The past few days had demonstrated that tempers and stress levels were both running abnormally high. Guys were getting onto each other about anything and everything, regardless if it was trivial and small nonsense or serious and large issues. Although animosity was building here and there, at least no one knocked each other out physically. I went with the flow and laughed at it all, to the annoyance of some of the more high-strung people. The Army practices chaos on a daily basis, and the more chaotic and disorganized it becomes, the more I laughed at what a crock of shit everything turned into so unnecessarily. Surprisingly, I was one of the more moderates of our group when it came to freaking the hell out. Back home in Savannah, we had a sign prominently displayed over our troop's coffee pot that stated: "The only difference between the Army and a circus is the number of tents." That quote never ceased to be a universal truth.

Just a few more days remained until I may board my STRAT-AIR flight, which was essentially a cargo plane transporting mostly equipment and a few accompanying personnel. No more rocket attacks, no more engagements with Hadji, no more funeral ceremonies. I knew that this time around, I, along with everyone else, would need to take some extra time to readjust to home. After returning home last time, I had spent many long nights sitting at my bar alone, sipping scotch. For hours, I sat processing it all, decompressing while staring unknown distances out into space. It was going to be nice to have some loving company for a change.

*

The road home from the deployment was not a smooth one. We were told that we would depart Afghanistan on August 20th, then it became the 27th. Next, I was told it would be the 26th, and then, the 28th. On the 28th, we waited several hours for an airplane that never came, and were told that it would be another 12 hours. That 12 hours turned into another 12 hours. We slept on the concrete atop our bags and under the stars, in a forever waiting game.

Our last day was one of confusion and mixed information. We played a lot of video games at the USO to pass the time. Four of us sat hacking like mad on the controllers in a *Super Mario Brothers* battle, cussing each other out for killing each other's player by accident. We all wore smiles and laughed. It had been a very long time since that had happened. Later, we waited at the bus stop, ready to get to our plane and finally go home. A pilot walked up, grinning and said, "Hey, dumbasses, where do you think you're going?"

"We're going to the ramp of course, load-out is in an hour," one man replied. We were mirthlessly laughed at and informed that our flight wasn't going to arrive until about 0300 the following morning. That time-table was even a giant "maybe." I looked at my watch; it wasn't even 1030 in the morning on our current day. Accustomed to disappointment and numb to everything, we sighed and walked back to the RSOI to drop bags and wander back to the USO.

Later, we made our round two on the bus out to the airfield, but understandably, were a little bit more jaded and untrusting than our previous bus rides. We'd had our departure time changed on us four times, and had even endured one last rocket attack from Hadji in his best efforts to properly say goodbye. Luckily, no one was injured and our moods changed once we pulled onto the flight line and saw a large, C-17 Air Force cargo plane with "Charleston" written across the tail complete with a palm and moon emblem. South Carolina Air Guard. Our ride was a beautiful sight.

While we waited on them to prepare to receive our cargo and refuel, a few of us decided to try our luck to tour a National Air Cargo company 747 jet parked next to our C-17. We walked to the stairs and a man led us up after a brief and friendly exchange. We walked around the massive cargo bay, and we then met the pilots. Up in the cockpit, we got a small tutorial on how the systems worked along with a few interesting things about the plane. It was not the oldest, and not the newest, general purpose cargo 747—simple and effective. I liked it a lot, and it was motivating for us to discuss potential futures in the airlines or cargo world. The pilots had a lot of good input and advice, and it was cool to hear each pilot's story about how they got to where they were today. I was convinced that there were as many paths taken that led to flying large cargo or passenger jets as there were pilots. Hell, the First Officer was delivering Chinese food when he got the call to come sit in on a flight with National for his first time. He was in-between flight jobs and got lucky someone called in sick. Both pilots also proved that it was not all about what you knew, but also who you knew in the airline industry. That same thing could be said about the civilian helicopter world, as well. We led them out to our Kiowas to tour and ask questions in return, and it was an interesting and informational exchange.

We said our goodbyes once the crew chiefs signaled to us that it was load out time. We shuffled bags around, sweated profusely, and heaved heavy equipment and helicopters onto the C-17. Once finally complete, we were told to take our seats and prepare for liftoff. Tired but extremely content, I unfolded one of the seats on the side of the cargo bay and plopped down heavily. We had one final delay as they dickered with who-knows-what on our temperamental C-17, but then it finally decided that it had no more issues to throw at us and it was time to fly to Germany.

Once at cruise altitude, we were free to get up and move about wherever or however we saw fit. The plane was massive and there was lots of room for the 10 of us to sprawl out under the Kiowas. I moved about my nook in the plane, setting up my little nest under the tail boom of a Kiowa and soon fell fast asleep. I was barely awake for any of the ride from Afghanistan to Germany.

I awoke to someone kicking my foot, saying that it was time for me to get off the floor from under the Kiowa and back to my seat. We touched down in the afternoon in Germany and were put on a bus headed over to the terminal. We had weapons with us, and German Customs officials stored them in an armory cage. We were then sent away to our sleeping area for the night. The Air Force guys asked if we were coming to stay at their nice hotel nearby and if we wanted to go out to eat with them. I informed them that the Army doesn't quite roll like the Air Force, and that we'd probably be sleeping on cots somewhere. I actually wasn't too far off.

On the next morning flight out of Germany, all of the previous days of missed or broken sleep finally caught up to me. I woke up from my slumber under a Kiowa fuselage with about two hours left in the flight to go before reaching our fuel stop in Bangor, Maine. My watch was subsequently and finally set to U.S. Eastern Standard Time and before I knew it, we were on the ground refueling.

We de-planed and an Air Force school bus offered to take us off base for a quick lunch if we wanted. We were in a hurry, but I was extremely vocal and insistent that I was not about to go to McDonald's in Maine. I wanted delicious, world-renowned Maine seafood. Most of the others berated me and told me that we didn't have time, but somehow, I won half of the guys over. We went to Captain Nick's, a local seafood joint where we ordered to-go meals (which they were not prepared to deal with, but diligently and thankfully obliged). We made it back to the plane, where the remaining people cussed us for taking so long. I got the last laugh though because once we showed up, we were still delayed another 30 minutes for maintenance reasons and I got to slowly enjoy every delicious bite of my seafood while some of the others ate their soggy, lukewarm, crappy fast food. Suckers!

With the plane fixed and our bellies full and content, we took back off for the last three hours of our journey directly to Hunter Army Airfield. Still a bit tired, I slept almost the entire way again under a Kiowa like everyone else.

When we landed at Hunter, it felt like a giant weight was lifted off of my body. I slumped slightly in my seat, listening to a nice, calm piece of classical music. No one cheered; we 10 Kiowa pilots from Charlie and Bravo Troops only wore tired smiles and nodded knowingly and happily to one another. When we deplaned, many soldiers who stood by awaiting our arrival rapidly set about offloading our bags and unloading the aircraft. We were told to not worry about a thing; just drop off our weapons and go inside the terminal. Our previous commander and senior maintenance pilot that had to leave Afghanistan early due to medical issues were waiting on us. They welcomed us home with warm smiles and firm handshakes, and it was great to see them. They both helped get us through the admin stations that were set up, which was amazingly fast and efficient.

We were quickly shuttled over to our hanger, where the families were waiting. We got into our small formation, and the hangar doors were immediately opened and we were marched inside. Families cheered and began to take pictures. Being only 10 of us, I was relieved at the generally small size of the reception crowd rather than the giant spectacle I'd experienced before. We stood for the national anthem, Army song, and 3rd ID "Dog Face Soldier" song.

The damn Army song was the one that had actually changed at some point, and we were all still stifling laughs as we screwed it all up in an attempt to lip sync it. The lieutenant colonel that stood before us was also suppressing a laugh and grinned himself, as the soldiers before him in formation were obviously delirious. We made it through the songs, and he spared us a long speech. We were given a vocal four-day pass, and told, "See you at 0630 on Wednesday. Fallout!"

Lindsey looked beautiful in her Georgia peach-colored dress and high heels. I almost didn't recognize her being so tall at first. We hugged for a long time, and it was so great to finally see her and hold her close again.

Just like that, it was all over. Lindsey and I got into her car, and we stared at each other. Her eyes welled with tears and she wore a permanent, beautiful smile. An ice cold Midas Touch beer from Dogfish Head Brewery sat in the cup holder for me. We got home and I snuck into the backyard through the fence while Lindsey let our dog out the back door. Scout immediately ran to me, jumping high and wagging her tail so hard that her whole body was one writhing ball of excitement.

It was nice to be back in my house and in my bed, next to my wife and our dog laying close by. I cannot describe the feelings of contentment and happiness that I had since getting off of that plane. The following day was low-key while she quietly and patiently allowed me to readjust.

Soon, the smallest things hit me like a brick. The smell, feel, and sight of grass! Listen, wind in the trees! Wow, carpet. A shower that doesn't require shoes, usable internet, and solid air conditioning. Kids outside playing. Not just rain, but a real thunderstorm. We have a car and can go places, anywhere we want! Water! I jumped into a pool. Hugs and kisses, human interaction.

These were some of the things that I had spent so long without that became the most amazing sensations for me. It would take a bit for me to get used to everything again, and I did get frustrated by small things like not remembering where the water glasses were, or feeling lost in my own house sometimes. It also took a conscious effort to obey traffic laws while driving.

There was no easy way for me to finally close out the writing that I had been sending to my friends and family. It was almost with a degree of sadness that I ended my last and final update. Writing home had been a great outlet for me. I thought that I may one day look back upon it all with a high degree of mixed emotions. Some of the things that happened to us on the KAF deployment were absolutely terrible, and would bring painful memories forever. Some of the other memories that we made while successfully saving lives would be experiences that I would always take humble pride in and never forget. I closed with what my grandmother and I had talked about, prior to her passing away while I was in KAF. I could just hear her beckoning me, "Do it, Ryan. Publish your words, and let everyone know what was really happening over there." I had promised her that one day, when I was ready, I would.

After finishing my final journal, I sat staring off into space for a few moments. Lindsey came in, put her hands lightly on my shoulders, and leaned over to kiss me on the cheek.

"Sweetheart, are you ready to go downtown?" Lindsey asked. I reached up and held tightly onto her hands and closed my eyes. No haunting images came. There were no frantic radio transmissions, and no firefights to deal with. The stress and anxiety had already begun to melt away.

"Yes, I want nothing more in the world."

EPILOGUE

Not long after returning home, Lindsey and I spent 25 days backpacking across England, Belgium, Germany, and the Czech Republic. The trip was everything that we had hoped it would be and was also the perfect way to celebrate moving on. In a true testament to the "small world" concept, I had even run into my previous Fox Troop commander in Germany while ordering a beer. Once I returned from that epic fun, my last year in the Army began and was indeed an interesting one to behold. Dede Murawsky and I had the same timeline for our exit from the Army—to the day, in fact. Somehow, she and I had been joined at the hip from our initial small Kiowa class until the present. Since we graduated together, our contracts were up on the same day, as well.

We both set about obtaining the formal paperwork to begin our process. The biggest and most telling sign of the hostility we would face was the name of the main packet that we would have to complete successfully. The Un-Qualified Resignation (UQR) had all of the connotations of setting a soldier up to admit to being a quitter. Statements had to be made, and many signatures had to be obtained. Like any major Army packet, the process was a murky and uncertain one, with many pitfalls and "gotchas" that could delay a soldier from separating upon the expiration of their contract.

Dede and I worked diligently to get the properly formatted paperwork in order, and we were met with about the expected amount of indignation and difficulty that we had expected. Our standing in the squadron, despite anything that we may have contributed or given our all for in the many previous years and two deployments, meant next to nothing. We were the most recent pair of "quitters," and essentially written off. Even so, we tried hard to still do our jobs and let the comments and stigma not affect us as best we could.

Not long after returning from Kandahar and reintegrating into the non-deployed world, Lindsey and I discussed our future family plans. We talked about where we may want to go, and what we may want to do. I rented a twin-engine airplane and got my skills back up so that I would be better prepared for the eventuality of an airplane job, rather than a helicopter job. Hopefully, it would be one with an airline. A friend from Charlie Troop asked when we were going to have children, and we listed the reasons why we intended to wait until after I had left the Army. We cited reasons such as moving, career uncertainty, and all of the stresses that we had ahead as we moved closer to my separation date. He laughed, called us idiots, and reminded us that as long as I was still in the Army, everything would be paid for. We couldn't believe it—he was right. After he left, we talked about the smartest thing to do for our family.

A few weeks later, I returned home from the troop, sweaty and discouraged. Lindsey told me that she had made something for me to eat, and that it was in the oven. I walked across the kitchen, opened the oven (which was not on), and pulled out a pan that had a small set of baby clothes in it. Confused and still hungry, I asked if she was trying to tell me that she was pregnant, effectively having "a bun in the oven."

Teary-eyed and excited, she held up the positive pregnancy test and said, "Yes! We're gonna have a baby!"

I was incredibly happy and we hugged tight. I pulled away from her with a grin on my face and said, "But seriously, you didn't cook anything? I'm starving." She then punched me in the arm.

Everyone continued forward with their respective duties in the squadron, flying and training for the next war even while rumors circulated. The OH-58D Kiowa was the horse, but the Warriors were the ones up in the saddle. It was becoming clear that the Army had plans for the Kiowa's ultimate demise, yet the fate for the Warriors was full of uncertainty. A general unease about the future grew, like a dark cloud looming on the horizon.

Despite our continued training and acting as though another deployment may occur, those who had initially doubted my decisions and intentions regarding separating from the Army began asking for information about the airline path that I was pursuing. The shift from tactical to commercial aviation thinking amongst our pilots became increasingly evident. Our mission planning room had the pictures for threat identification of vehicles and weapons systems torn down and replaced by civil aviation maps detailing most of the contiguous United States. The writing was literally on the wall for everyone, whether they liked it or not.

By late Summer 2014, the new plan everyone was afraid to hear became a confirmed reality—the Kiowa Warrior fleet across the entire Army would be officially scrapped. We were informed that Kiowa pilots with more than 15 years of service would be retired, and the other pilots would be transitioned to a new aircraft. Since the Army was standing up several new UAV units, the hope was that some of our pilots may be welcomed with open arms into that community.

In late Fall 2014, it was announced that 3-17 Cavalry itself was also officially being disbanded. The only orders for the foreseeable future were to begin completely shutting down the squadron. I was then informed that my next flight would probably be my last. Our mission was to fly to the Fort Stewart range complex and support ground forces conducting a training exercise. The soldiers were located in a mock village, and we would provide overhead cover and training in the form of talking guys onto targets within the village. This also served to help their newest unit members learn how to communicate with and utilize aircraft. Believing it may be my last flight, I absolutely and positively flew the Kiowa like I stole it. Banking, climbing, and descending hard as if I were possessed, the left seater at one point told me that he may actually throw up and asked me to tone it down a notch.

Once we returned to HAAF, I requested that I may be given a proper last flight. Surprisingly, it was briefed and approved to take place the following week. Another pilot in our troop who had joined us after our deployment was also separating, so our "retirement" flight would be flying on our agreed-upon plan as a pair. We were each provided a left seater and would essentially be given the keys to two Kiowas for the day.

On September 11, 2014, we took off and flew towards Tybee Island. I inquired with the fire department about the ownership of a helicopter pad that sat empty next to the lighthouse. They said that as far as the local government of that island was concerned, it was all ours. We approached low and circled the lighthouse, to the surprise of tourists and a pack of Cub Scouts that were visiting. A giant, beautiful American flag gently waved from the lighthouse to remember those who had been lost in the attacks which had spurred me to join the military in the first place.

My now very-pregnant and very-beautiful wife was out there with Dede to greet us and take pictures. I landed at the helipad by the lighthouse, taking a snapshot with Lindsey and giving her a big kiss while the small crowd of tourists at the lighthouse cheered. I then jumped back into my Kiowa and we took off to the north after a few more orbits around the area.

We stopped to refuel in Charleston, SC, and we ate an epically filling seafood lunch, complete with locally made key lime pie. Our bellies were stuffed and we contentedly flew rather slowly back toward HAAF. As I entered the airfield on our final approach, a knot developed in my chest. It occurred to me that it may even be my last time to ever fly a helicopter.

We rounded the corner at a hover and approached our hangers and helipads. I noticed a bunch of men and women in Stetsons attempting to hide in the hangar and it made me smile. I set my Kiowa down gently onto our parking pad after a brief 10 more precious seconds of flight, telling her goodbye and thanking her for all of the battles that she had borne. As we completed our shut down sequence, a fire truck rounded the corner. I jumped out, in the tradition of trying to run and not get sprayed by the water cannon. Matt Vaccaro sprinted out of the hangar and intercepted me, and we both locked in mock combat as the fire truck sprayed us both down. He and I embraced and he congratulated me, while other members of Charlie Troop and our squadron-mates emerged to shake my soaking-wet hand. I felt very fortunate and honored to have at least gotten a nice last flight in, as well as a great send-off.

In October 2014, I successfully interviewed and was hired by a regional carrier owned by American Airlines. My training date was set to begin only a few weeks from my official exit from the Army. Along with the great news of being hired by an airline, I was also blessed with the greatest thing of all: Our healthy and happy little baby girl was born. Robin May Robicheaux looked into mine and Lindsey's eyes, and we couldn't have been happier. She was, and still is, the most beautiful thing that I had ever seen in the whole world.

My troop only lightly tasked me after Robin's birth. On my last day in the unit before terminal leave, my father and Lindsey brought our new baby girl up to the troop. Everyone said their goodbyes, and I proudly wore my unit patch on my uniform, a practice which had been outlawed years ago. The commander for Alpha Troop laughed and congratulated me for going out with that last symbolic bang.

I wore my Stetson with pride and we proceeded out to the hangar, where I sat for my last time in a Kiowa cockpit with my new baby. I talked to her quietly, telling her that I loved her, and showed her the interior of the cockpit which I had survived so many missions in while trying to help and save our ground forces. Her little hands touched the controls and I flipped through the glowing display screens to her wide-eyed amazement. I knew that she would never remember it, but at least I also knew that she had seen what had been such a big part of my life and of those that I served with. It was the best possible way to spend my final moments and say goodbye to the beloved Kiowa.

Dede and I went into our respective terminal leave periods in December 2014, finally separating completely from the Army one month later. As winter proceeded, 3-17 Cavalry continued to transfer people to other units and schools that would allow them to transition to new aircraft or career fields. During this time, the newest Charlie Troop commander became very ill. By the end of February 2015, she could no longer be physically present. One of our pilots, CW2 Andy Wilson, was chosen to take command of the troop. Over the next few weeks, all of Charlie Troop's aircraft and the majority of the remaining pilots and crew chiefs were transferred to Alpha and Bravo Troops. Within two months, only five pilots and one crew chief remained in Charlie Troop.

In a formation of 20-plus aircraft, the ceremonial last flight of 3-17 Cavalry was conducted over Savannah and Tybee Island on May 17, 2015. I made it a point to travel back to Savannah so that we could meet up downtown with Dede and watch from the rooftop of a hotel. Shortly afterwards, the remaining Kiowa pilots were hit with further bad news.

Despite the assurances of well-intentioned and honest people, the criteria for who would be forcibly retired or transitioned to new positions had changed. Not everyone would be provided a future career path in the Army—very-senior and very-junior warrant officers may be given transitions or retired, but the mid-grade warrant officers were on their own. A list of merit was made up to decide who would be transitioned to a new aircraft, but the criteria and the list were unfortunately kept secret.

Some were able to revert back to the career fields that they held previously as enlisted soldiers. A good fit for any scout pilot who was interested would be a transfer into the newly expanding Army UAV community, but unfortunately, by the time the UAV branch revised their requirements, many pilots that may have transferred had already resigned from the Army.

For those few that remained after the squadron's ceremonial last flight, and before going their separate ways, they had one final flying task. The *true* final flight of 3-17 Cavalry's Kiowas was the cross country journey from Savannah to Davis-Monthan Air Force Base in Tucson, Arizona—the home of the infamous aircraft boneyard. Some of the retired Kiowas would be placed in long-term storage, a small contingent were sent to allied nations overseas, and others became museum pieces, were destroyed, or would end up on firing ranges as targets.

For several days and in small groups, 3-17's few remaining pilots flew the long and lonely journey from Savannah to their aircraft's final resting place in Arizona. When they arrived, and even before the blades could finish their final spin down, contractors tasked with receiving the aircraft were already swarming over them, like vultures picking at a carcass.

On September 1, 2015, the 3-17 Cavalry Squadron was officially deactivated. Andy reported that it was one of the most miserable days of his life. A few months later, on his final day of active duty, he signed the last piece of paper required and drove out of the gate. No one saw him off, and he never even received a thank you. Andy's account of the fate of 3-17 Cavalry after I'd left is much appreciated and, in fact, he seems to be the only one who even bothered to record the final days of our Kiowa Warrior squadron.

*

My transition from flying a small and agile helicopter to a civilian regional jet was a bit tougher than I had anticipated. It goes without saying that they were about as different as an aircraft can be from one another. Training was held for months and far away from family, which was difficult in itself. It was all worth it, however, and I was awarded my civilian airline pilot's wings after my final checkride. For two years in Knoxville, Tennessee, I built my flight hours, and was eventually hired by a major airline and moved to Florida.

Andy introduced me to podcast host Vincent Aiello, and I was both humbled and honored to spend over an hour on *The Fighter Pilot Podcast's* feature OH-58D Kiowa Warrior episode, speaking all about our beloved aircraft and our fierce devotion to the ground forces. I was also extremely grateful for the many veteran service organizations that existed to help those like myself adjust to normal life. Project Healing Waters Fly Fishing, Inc., as well as Fish With a Hero, taught me how to fly fish and took me on calming and rewarding trips, all for free. The lengths such groups went for veterans was wonderful, and I further discovered more organizations doing great work—Pets for Patriots, Wounded Warrior Project, Veterans of Foreign Wars, Rescue 22 Foundation, Team RWB (Red, White, and Blue), Rotary To Airline Group, and hundreds more, big and small, that I wish I had the space to individually list and thank. As I further settled into civilian life, I continued to support as many veteran-owned businesses as I could by doing things like chugging Black Rifle Coffee, using Grill Your Ass Off seasonings, and watching VetTV in order to experience much-needed comedic relief.

I kept up with prior squadron-mates, and it amazed me how many directions those from mine and the other troops had gone in. Some like Nick,

Erik, Dede, and Jay still flew, having jobs with MEDEVAC outfits or police departments. Some had managed to stay in the Army, several of which had naturally migrated over to the Apache community. The UAV community had absorbed a few, but not nearly as many Kiowa pilots as many had initially hoped. The same went for the other airframes and jobs across the military. A small and talented compliment migrated over to the more clandestine and special services within the military and DoD. Others had left the military and flying altogether, finding the most uncharacteristic or unexpected of paths. Matt Vaccaro moved back to his home state of New Hampshire, growing a beard and living with his huge family in a nice log house in the woods and working for a construction company. Another bought a big rig, and was a semi-truck driver out of the Port of Savannah. One announced plans to stock the shelves of gas stations for a distributing company, while another began a Chik-Fil-A franchise in Tennessee. Our Kiowa pilot brothers had truly scattered to the winds.

My desire to finish the book took a while to finally come to fruition, mostly because the accounts and experiences were just too fresh and emotionally jarring. I'd made a promise however, so I embarked to complete the last mission, the last thing that I needed to do related to the military before I could truly leave it all behind me. I reached out and found Brian Fullen almost immediately. He had become an SP in the Apache world and was stationed in Hawaii, having risen in their ranks substantially since he and I had last talked. The real kicker was that he was still in the Cavalry, and they still wore their Stetsons and called themselves troops and squadrons. I couldn't believe it!

The Apache Attack community had split, and a new wing had been created with their aircraft. The Air Cavalry had survived like a phoenix from the ashes, only it had morphed into a different form. Several prior Kiowa pilots were among these ranks, and they were doing their damnedest to do what they had always done. The mission remained loosely the same, and the Kiowa had been fully replaced by the originally planned pairing of an Apache and a Predator UAV. This idea looked good on paper. From what I understood however, the actual implementation and reality turned out to be what many in the Kiowa community had expected.

Despite the "bigger and better" toys concept, it just wasn't the same. I hoped that the ground guys would get quality coverage with the replacement plan, and hopefully, to the level they had once enjoyed with a Kiowa Warrior SWT overhead. Even if the replacement platforms were not the best suited for the task, I knew that the survival of the Air Cavalry meant that those charged with protecting our ground forces would still find a way.

After another short search, Dede and I were *very* surprised to learn that 3-17 Cavalry had also been reborn. I stared in disbelief at a photo of Alpha Troop's prior Kiowa SP proudly standing next to an Apache, right there on HAAF. In the picture, he wore not only the Cavalry colors on a *unit baseball cap(!)*, but he also wore our Charlie Troop "Crazyhorse" patch, which remained unchanged.

3-17 Cavalry had resumed operations as an Apache Cavalry unit only a few months after the unit had been closed, and they had already deployed two times since. The Kiowa-turned-Apache-pilot had become Charlie Troop's SP, and he was happy to report that his guys had a tremendous amount of pride. They were very passionate about being in the Cavalry and had embraced the culture that surrounds a hard-charging CAV unit.

Where I had stepped back, others were picking up and running with the ball. I did not feel as though I had been strong enough in my constitution or resiliency to continue my military service, and that feeling of failure had eaten at me like a silent, insidious psychological cancer. My bitterness and discontented feelings were born of everything which I had been involved in, witnessed, and/or failed to effect change in. To suddenly know that 3-17 Cavalry had been reborn, and that the pilot we spoke with offered determined resolve, hope, and pride in their continuing accomplishments was an indescribable relief.

*

I sat on the beach near my home in Florida. Closing my eyes, the constant memories and pictures dredged up from years of reliving every single event while writing and editing had almost all subsided.

I looked out over the ocean, relishing the feel of the gentle breeze and the warm sun upon my skin. I closed my eyes again, sitting still, and smelling the sea air. I listened to the distant sounds of the waves, palm trees swaying, birds calling, and my five-year-old girl playing in the sand.

A little wet hand was on my knee suddenly and my daughter asked, "Daddy, why are your eyes closed?" I smiled at her.

"I was just thinking, baby."

"What are you thinking about?" She asked innocently, her wide blue eyes staring intently into mine. I choked up a bit, thinking of all of those whom we had served with and lost that would never get to have such a conversation.

"I am thinking about how lucky, and how very fortunate I am, to have such a loving and happy family. I'm also thinking about how much I love you," I told her.

Robin smiled wide and said, "I love you too, Daddy! Will you come play with me?"

I nodded and held her hand tight as Lindsey smiled. Robin and I walked towards the ocean, which I had longed for during all of those difficult times, now being able to laugh and play in the waves with the most beautiful little girl in the world.

And to finally be at peace.

ACKNOWLEDGEMENTS

The writing in this book could not have been possible without the support of all of those family and friends that I mentioned countless times within. Without their support, both during and after the events, the entire book would have never even happened.

I thank the members of TF Knighthawk, especially Fox Troop 3-17 and Bravo Company 1-3, that I fought alongside during the Bagram deployment. They helped shape and support my development as an Army aviator. The Red-Headed Black Sheep is where I grew up, and I'll always have a special place in my mind for those people and experiences.

I thank the members of TF Lighthorse, especially Charlie Troop, that I fought alongside during the Kandahar deployment, along with the members of our other line and support troops and companies who supported us, the list goes on. We took what we were given and gave all that we could.

Individually, a special thanks goes to the following individuals who stepped up to ensure that I could fact-check my work and ensure that everything was as accurate a representation of the events could be. Many listed also took time from their lives to go back and relive their own events in order to contribute, which I am also extremely grateful and humbled to have been able to include.

My wife, Lindsey, for her support and encouragement over the years. She was there when I needed her and helped me to give this work my all.

My immediate family and in-laws, for reading through revisions and giving positive and critical feedback.

My editor, Leigh Corbell, for her attention and dedication to my manuscript. Without her, this book would have been vastly different (and probably terrible).

My proofreader, Jackie Dawn, for giving the manuscript the final polish and critique that it required.

CW2 Dede Murawsky, for her friendship, diligent manuscript reviewing, and encouragement, beginning back in the early days of when she discovered that I was writing things down. She also helped me pass ALSE school, because I suck at sewing.

CW2 Jay Amarillo, for his contributed account of his crash in aircraft 569, and the harrowing escape and rescue that they endured.

CW2 Andy Wilson, for ensuring that a record was available regarding how everything ended on the Kiowa side before 3-17 Cavalry was later reborn an Apache unit.

CW2 Nikia "Nick" Payne, for his mentorship and assistance in recounting events regarding the Black Sheep. Nick made that deployment bearable, and kept me sane with his antics and positive attitude.

CW3 Erik Newhouse, for his mentorship and assistance, as well as keeping me going with comedic relief on Team Pigeon.

CW3 Pete Higgs-Coultard, for helping me recount and accurately portray events from the Bagram deployment.

CW3 Matt Vaccaro, for his mentorship, guidance, and friendship both during and outside of the deployments and helping me remember and correctly portray our stories.

CW2 Brian Fullen, for his years of continued friendship and for keeping me in the loop with the new Apache Cavalry and their impressive exploits.

Last, but certainly not least, I thank those military men and women who came before and after me. They answered the call of their country, and I will always be in awe of their stories and sacrifices. I also thank those currently volunteering to serve, as they continue to answer the demands put upon them, despite what even their own personal beliefs or convictions may be.

It takes true courage, and I genuinely salute you.

GLOSSARY

AFN: Armed Forces Network (cable television with cheesy commercials and propaganda, but decent movies and many live football and other events from the states).

AK-47: Automatic 7.62x39 chambered rifle, typically used with a 30-round magazine. Very simple, rugged, powerful, and used in conflict zones the world over.

AK-74: Automatic 5.45x39 chambered rifle, typically used with a 30-round magazine. As rugged and simple as its predecessor, it is an improved version now fielded by the Russian Federation and has found its way into many global conflict zones.

ALSE: Aviation Life Support Equipment, which entails issuing and servicing all of the flight and survival gear that a pilot uses.

AMC: Air Mission Commander.

ANA: Afghan National Army.

ANP: Afghan National Police.

AO: Area of Operations.

APACHE (AH-64): Armed Attack helicopter. Typically carries Hellfire missiles, two 14-shot rocket pods, and a nose mounted 30mm cannon. Heavily armed and armored, sky tank.

APFT: Army Physical Fitness Test.

B-HUT: A wooden shack, subdivided into eight separate 6'x 8' rooms.

BAF: Bagram Airfield (Parwan Province, Afghanistan).

BHO: Battle Handover. One battlefield asset relieves another upon receiving this report.

BINGO FUEL: A situationally-based and predetermined fuel level that, upon reaching, an aircraft must break station to get more gas.

BLACKHAWK (UH-60): Utility helicopter, multi-purpose roles to include MEDEVAC.

BONGING: Your Kiowa is far below bingo fuel and has reached a critically low fuel point of less than 100lbs. All Kiowa pilots worth their salt have experienced this more than once.

THE BOWL: Large flat area where Bagram airfield lies surrounded by large mountains.

CAS: Close Air Support.

CAVALRY / CAV: Steeped in bad-ass, long and storied tradition, the U.S. Cavalry traces its roots to horseback mounted warriors and scouts. The Air Cavalry began utilizing helicopters in Vietnam to serve the multiple roles of reconnaissance, protection, and transportation of ground forces.

CCA: Close Combat Attack.

CHINOOK (CH-47): Giant, twin-rotor transport and cargo helicopter. It's a beast.

CHU: Container Housing Unit.

COMMISSIONED OFFICER: The rank that houses all of the "Sirs." From lieutenant to general, these are the commanders and administrators of the Army.

COP: Combat Outpost; smaller than an FOB.

CP: Command Post. Each troop has one to conduct unit related business and planning.

CREW DOG: Crew Chief. They work on the helicopters and support the pilots. Take care of the Crew Dogs, and they take care of you. We couldn't operate without them and appreciated the hell out of their efforts and support.

DANGER CLOSE: An extremely Close Combat Attack in proximity to friendlies.

DoD: Department of Defense.

ENLISTED: Everyone that is not an officer. This would be the rank "Grades" of E-1 through E-9. The lower enlisted grades of E-1 through E-3 are three levels of privates, and an E-4 is a specialist or corporal. The NCO "Grades" of E-5 to E-9 are also listed in this Glossary.

EXFIL: Exfiltrate, or to withdraw surreptitiously, especially from a dangerous place.

FADEC: Full Authority Digital Electronic Control. The fuel metering control for our engine, ensuring whatever power demand we placed received enough gas to do it.

FARP: Forward Arming and Refueling Point. Oftentimes located on a remote base, this is where gas and munitions were located.

FARPIES: The crews that would rearm and refuel us at the FARPs. They were as instrumental as a NASCAR pit crew in ensuring that we could keep the fight going, and we appreciated the hell out of them.

FLECHETTES: 2.75 Hydra Rocket variant that dispenses 1,179 dart-like projectiles at a target, affectionately called a "cone of nails." Very deadly and effective, creates pretty sparkles on the rocks as they destroy things.

FOB: Forward Operating Base; larger than a simple outpost but often remotely located.

GARRISON: Non-Combat or Field environment. Where uniform standards and staff concerns happen. This is the catch-all term for back home at the unit while not involved directly in combat operations or field training.

GIRoA: Government of the Islamic Republic of Afghanistan.

GREEN WORLD: The world as viewed through Night Vision equipment.

GRID: Said in reference to a map location identifier; we used the Military Grid Reference System (MGRS) instead of Latitude / Longitude. I still prefer MGRS to this day.

HAAF: Hunter Army Airfield (Savannah, GA).

HADJI: Blanket, non-politically correct term for Middle Eastern folks used by our Armed Forces.

HAQQANI NETWORK: A Taliban group trained, supported, and funded by Pakistan's spy agency, the Inter-Services Intelligence directorate. We give

Pakistan untold riches to fight extremists, and they play both sides.

HE ROCKETS: High Explosive 2.75 Hydra rocket variant with a 10lb warhead. A larger (less encountered) variant was also available with a 17lb warhead.

HELLFIRE: Large, extremely accurate and destructive missile. Multiple missile warhead types available for use depending upon the type of target intended.

HIT THE RACK: Go to sleep.

HVT: High Value Target; an individual that warrants particular attention and may need to be captured for interrogation and securing valuable intel, or simply killed and removed from the battlefield.

HYDRA ROCKETS: Standard rocket carried by Kiowas and Apaches. The 2.75 Hydra Rocket family has several variants available, such as high explosive, phosphorus, flechettes, etc.

IED: Improvised Explosive Device.

IMC: Instrument Meteorological Conditions, bad weather in the form of poor visibility, low or lots of clouds/fog, thunderstorms, etc.

IIMC: Inadvertent Instrument Meteorological Conditions, accidentally flying into the above.

INS: Insurgents.

IP: Instructor Pilot.

IR LIGHT: An infrared spectrum light that is filtered to only be seen with NVDs.

ISAF: International Security Assistance Force.

"K's": Kilometers, used in a sentence such as, "Move a few Ks to the west."

KAF: Kandahar Airfield (Kandahar Province, Afghanistan).

KIA: Killed in Action.

KINETIC ACTIVITY: Lots of shooting and/or bad stuff going down.

KIOWA (OH-58): Observation/Recon and close air support aircraft. One of the coolest things that ever existed in the air, ever (just ask any ground guy(s) ever supported by one).

LAO: Local Area Orientation.

LEAVE: Paid vacation accrued every month. A soldier can amass as many as 60 days of leave, but cannot usually apply more than 45 days at a time.

LZ: Landing Zone.

M3P: Standard helicopter-mounted, .50 caliber machine gun always situated on the left side of the Kiowa when installed. Carried a 500rd magazine of .50 cal belt-linked rounds.

M4: Shortened, 14.5 inch barreled version of the U.S. standard issue M-16 battle rifle, chambered in 5.56x45 NATO and typically used with a 30-round magazine.

M9: Standard issue Beretta 9mm handgun. Carries a high capacity magazine, generally issued to Officers, NCOs, and select support/other personnel. Pilots were issued both the M9 and the M4.

MAM: Military-Aged-Male.

MATV: Officially spelled out; Mine-resistant, ambush-protected, all-terrain vehicle. Armored truck built to thrive in the rough Afghan terrain. I watched one roll down a hillside, get hooked up, righted, and drive away. Beast of a vehicle.

MEDEVAC: Medical Evacuation. Usually conducted by a Blackhawk purpose configured and staffed (which was known as a "DUSTOFF").

MFD: Multi-Function Display. Almost all information we required of the helicopter and its systems could be called up on this central screen, one in front of each pilot.

Mi-17: Russian utility aircraft, serves in very similar roles to that of a Blackhawk.

MIA: Missing In Action.

MMS: Mast Mounted Sight, the giant camera ball on top of our rotor disc that housed thermal and other optics/capabilities.

MORALES-FRASIER: French-controlled base with a FARP that serviced several coalition and contractor aircraft. Situated on the north-western edge of the Tagab Valley.

MRAP: Officially spelled out; Mine-resistant, ambush-protected vehicle. It's an armored truck. Very resistant to IED attacks, RPGs, and small arms ambushes by the enemy. Responsible for taking the hit and saving a lot of our soldiers' lives.

MTP: Maintenance Test Pilot.

MWR: Morale, Wellness, and Recreation. These facilities and centers sprinkled across the globe provide everything from small scale comforts and services to much larger resorts and vacation opportunities.

NCO: Non-Commissioned Officer; higher enlisted ranks of E-5 to E-9. In other words, an ascending ladder of sergeant types. An E-4 is sometimes made an NCO and called a corporal.

NO ILLUM: When the moon is not at its peak proficiency to aid us in seeing stuff. Basically a New Moon, Darkened Moon, or early/late Crescent Moon. These evenings would also sometimes be referred to as "Asshole Dark."

NVD / NVG: Night Vision Device / Night Vision Goggles.

ODA: Operational Detachment Alpha. An SF "A-Team" which operates independently and is comprised of approximately 13 men, each with a specific specialty.

OER: Officer Evaluation Report, completed annually, overviewing an individual officer's performance and professional development. Too many focus on their personal OER, wilfully causing misery to their soldiers in pursuit of personal gain to show how great they are as a leader.

OGA: Other Government Agency.

ON NIGHTS: A pilot or crew chief on a completely nocturnal schedule, akin to working a graveyard shift.

PASS: Paid vacation that is not deducted from your leave dates.

PASAB: U.S. FOB with FARP that we typically used in the Kandahar area.

PC: Pilot in Command.

PI: Pilot.

PINK TEAM: Team composed of one Kiowa and one Apache. Sometimes referred to as a "Hunter-Killer" team.

PKM: Large belt-fed machine gun, chambered in 7.62x54R.

POP SHOTS: Used erroneously by those who are ignorant to the real term for this action against forces, correctly called "Pot Shots," or sporadic/harassing fire.

POW: Prisoner of War.

PT: Physical Training.

PX: Post Exchange (read "Army Walmart").

PZ: Pickup Zone. This is where aircraft land and pick up passengers or wounded.

QRF: Quick Reaction Force. Moment's notice, sprinting to the aircraft while still donning gear, on-call 24/7 status that we rotated out through daily with for the entire BAF deployment. Long 12+hr shifts split respectively into day and night.

QALAT: Mud hut or squarish building that the residents live in.

RED PHOS: Red Phosphorous variant of the 2.75 Hydra rocket. 72 wedges burning at over 900°C to light the area up.

REMF / POGUE: An individual whose job precludes them from encountering most or all of the dangers and rigors of actual combat. Obviously a mostly derogatory term.

RETROGRADE: A better sounding word than "Retreat."

REVERSE OUT: Switching your sleep and work schedule from days to nights or nights to days. Takes 48hrs minimum officially, but the effects are still felt for a few days thereafter.

ROE: Rules of Engagement. A convoluted web to protect higher-level careers and add undue risk of injury or death to warfighters (in my not-so-solitary opinion).

RPG: Rocket Propelled Grenade. Shot from a special shoulder fired launcher, accuracy and effectiveness depends upon the training of the shooter.

RPK: Automatic 7.62x39 chambered rifle, often used with a 75 round drum magazine. Essentially a longer barreled, beefed up AK-47 on steroids.

RSOI: Reception, Staging, Onward-Movement, and Integration. No wonder I had to look that up.

SAW: Squad Automatic Weapon. Belt-fed machine gun that carries 200+ rds and has an extremely high rate of fire, using the same 5.56 NATO ammunition as the M4 / M-16 rifles.

SCOUTS: We find stuff, then let others know it's there. We then decide whether or not it's worth searching or destroying and if so, how to do so.

SECRET SQUIRREL/SWOOPY: SOF Operations, or actions like those they did.

SECURITY ZONE: Blanket term used to entirely reference the Kandahar AO.

SF/SOF: Special Forces/Special Operations Forces.

SHEMAGH: Middle Eastern scarf. They're actually quite comfortable and useful.

SOCOM: Special Operations Command.

SP: Standardization Pilot. The instructor in charge of the other instructors within a troop or squadron.

SPEED-BALL: Air drop of combat critical supplies, often amidst heavy fighting.

SQUADRON: The Cavalry term for a Brigade, which is composed of several subordinate units known as Troops.

SWT: Scout Weapons Team, pair of Kiowas.

TAGAB VALLEY: Vast, primarily north-south running valley in the troubled Kapisa Province, mostly under control by the French. Extremely dangerous hotbed of enemy activity and where much of our action occurred.

TDY: Temporary Duty assignment.

TERPS: Interpreters.

TIC: Troops in Contact, forces in an active fight with the enemy.

TOC: Tactical Operations Center. This is the location in which most decisions concerning the conduct of operations and ongoing missions are made. It's a dark, sad, hate-filled room that no pilot ever likes to enter.

TROOP: The Cavalry term for a Company unit that serves under the umbrella of a Squadron. Not to be confused with the blanket term for soldiers from the U.S. or other nations, who are occasionally referred to en masse as "troops" sometimes.

USO: United Service Organizations. A non-profit that provides wide-ranging support and entertainment to military personnel.

VMC: Visual Meteorological Conditions. Another way to denote a relatively decent day to fly without any immediate threat(s) due to weather.

WOJG: Warrant Officer Junior Grade. Generally a playful or not-so-playful derogatory term.

WADI: River-bed or watercourse area, usually dry until periods of rainfall.

WARRANT OFFICER: Less than five percent of the Army, a rank that lies above Enlisted and Non-Commissioned Officer, and below Commissioned Officer. A warrant is a specialty officer in their field, commonly referred to as a "subject matter expert." Formally, warrants are addressed as "Mister" or "Miss," and more commonly, just via first names or nicknames.

WX: Weather.

YELLOW DUCK: A warning issued via radio to your crew that an imminent pants-pissing will take place unless a proper relief point is found soon.

ABOUT THE AUTHOR

Right out of high school, 9/11 spurred Ryan to join the Army National Guard as a medic. Upon graduating from college, he transferred into the active duty component of the Army, becoming a warrant officer and attending flight school. He deployed twice to Afghanistan as an OH-58D Kiowa Warrior pilot assigned to 3-17 Cavalry—One year out of Bagram Airbase, and nearly a year out of Kandahar. After returning from Kandahar, Ryan separated from the Army and became an airline pilot. Time served in Afghanistan has resulted in a slightly busted verbal filter, a bent yet vibrant sense of humor, and a drive to stay involved with and support fellow veterans. He wishes to simply appreciate and enjoy life, and his wife Lindsey, daughter Robin, and dog Scout are his world. Additionally, in expected fashion, he loves: the outdoors, the smell of gunpowder and jet exhaust, single malt scotch, smoked jerky, strong coffee, and freedom.

You can connect with Ryan via his website:

www.scoutsoutbook.com

or social media:

www.instagram.com/scoutsoutbook

Printed in Great Britain
by Amazon

55926482R00245